by

LeRoy G. Pratt

Iowa Department of Public Instruction

1975

American Revolution Bicentennial Edition

IOWA

76

BICENTENNIAL USA

Published under authority of Sections 17.23, 17.27, 257.18(16) and 257.18(20), *Code of Iowa*

State of Iowa
DEPARTMENT OF PUBLIC INSTRUCTION
Des Moines, Iowa 50319

STATE BOARD OF PUBLIC INSTRUCTION

Muriel I. Shepard, President, Allison
T. J. Heronimus, Vice-President, Grundy Center
Robert J. Beecher, Creston
Jolly Ann Davidson, Clarinda
Ronald P. Hallock, West Des Moines
Virginia Harper, Fort Madison
Robert G. Koons, Clinton
Georgia A. Sievers, Avoca
John E. van der Linden, Sibley

ADMINISTRATION

Robert D. Benton, State Superintendent, and Executive Officer
of the State Board of Public Instruction
David H. Bechtel, Administrative Assistant
Richard N. Smith, Deputy State Superintendent

Information and Publications Services

R. E. Schallert, Chief
LeRoy G. Pratt, Publications Editor

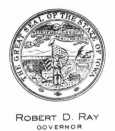

ROBERT D. RAY
GOVERNOR

Office of the Governor

**STATE CAPITOL
DES MOINES, IOWA 50319**

GREETINGS:

It has been wisely said that a society ignorant of its own past is doomed to repeat the mistakes of the past. It is equally true that knowledge of the heritage which has been transmitted to us from the past provides us with strength and inspiration to meet the challenges of our own time, just as our forebears came to grips with the different -- but no less formidable -- problems by which they were confronted.

Therefore, all efforts to increase our understanding of the past -- and to put the past to work for the improvement of the present and future -- deserve encouragement.

I particularly welcome every effort to bring Iowa's colorful, vigorous history alive for the Iowans of today and for those who visit us from elsewhere. It is a dramatic story which is forever revealing new dimensions and providing fresh illumination of present-day Iowa living.

As we approach our nation's 200th birthday and enter the last quarter of this century, we increasingly prize the partnership of land and people which has made Iowa such a good place in which to live. By the same token, we know that continued change will be necessary in the future to preserve the fundamentals of the way of life we prize.

Through deeper understanding of the past, we shall better be able to take stock of where we are as Iowans and to chart a rewarding course for the years that stretch ahead.

Sincerely,

Robert D. Ray
Governor

PREFACE

In this Bicentennial period, Iowans, as all Americans, turn to the past more than ever. The approach of the 200th anniversary of our country brings an added awareness of our heritage and a greater appreciation of our historic past.

The Bicentennial Edition of *Discovering Historic Iowa* should be invaluable to teachers of Iowa history, librarians, students, historical groups, and other educational and lay organizations, as well as tourists, for information about the Hawkeye State.

By requiring that the history of Iowa be taught in our schools, the people of this state have recognized the importance of Iowa's heritage. This serves to instill in our young people the perspective needed to properly understand local, regional, state, and national history and show how these are interrelated.

Anyone having a desire to learn more about Iowa--its historic sites, landmarks, natural areas, archeological sites, outdoor classrooms, wildlife exhibits, and cultural institutions--will find this book extremely useful and interesting.

Robert D. Benton, Ed. D.
State Superintendent of Public Instruction

ACKNOWLEDGMENTS

The invaluable assistance of countless individuals, organizations, societies, and agencies of government is gratefully acknowledged. It is not possible to name all of these, but special recognition is due the staff members of the Division of Historical Museum and Archives of the State Historical Department for assistance in providing and in checking factual information; the State Historical Society for assistance in obtaining the names of officers of local and county historical societies; the Iowa State Conservation Commission for supplying and verifying information about state and county parks, preserves, and historic areas; the Iowa Development Commission for providing information on Iowa's celebrations, festivals, and historic events; and the Des Moines Public Library.

The Iowa American Revolution Bicentennial Commission officially endorsed this publication and generously provided funds to permit a larger printing, making possible a much wider distribution of the book.

Once again, the Iowa Local Historical and Museum Association (ILHMA), in addition to giving its enthusiastic support to the publication, was helpful in encouraging its member societies to submit current information for inclusion in the book. The support of the Iowa Society for the Preservation of Historic Landmarks (Iowa Landmarks Society) and its members and of the Iowa Chapter of The Nature Conservancy are also acknowledged.

Some of the information included was originally obtained by the author in 1968 from questionnaires completed and returned by historical societies, museums, conservation boards, chambers of commerce, and other organizations and included in the publication, *A Guide to Historic Iowa.* The information contained in the earlier publications has been rechecked and verified by correspondence, telephone calls, and personal visits.

The cover design, line drawings, and art work appearing throughout the book are by various artists, including Eloise Anderson, Frances Lenan Dean, Monte Hammond, Richard Lewis, Jeff Lockwood, Dennis Schrage, and William J. Wagner.

Grateful recognition is also given to all persons who helped in typing the manuscript and checking proofs, and to personnel in the DPI Word Processing Center for typesetting and running the final printout.

INTRODUCTION

The State Department of Public Instruction published the *Directory of County and Local Historical Societies and Museums in Iowa* early in 1966. Two years later, *A Guide to Historic Iowa* was issued by the DPI. In 1972 this became *Discovering Historic Iowa*, which expanded and brought up-to-date the information on historical societies, museums, archeological sites, geological areas, botanical preserves, wildlife exhibits, outdoor classrooms, zoos, art centers, scientific facilities, and places of historical or cultural interest. Since the supply of the 1972 edition was soon exhausted, the present revision was planned.

Until comparatively recent years there has been an apparent lack of concern about our heritage and an attitude that Iowa has nothing much of historic interest to offer. But there is evidence that we are awakening to the importance of local history and its relationship to state and national events. This change is indicated by the significant increase in the number of county and local historical societies, the creation of county and regional tourism councils, the establishment of county conservation boards, the erection of historical markers along our highways, legislation designed to give financial assistance to county or local historical societies, the observance of centennials and anniversaries of historic importance, the requirement (passed by the 61st General Assembly) that Iowa history be included in the course of study and taught in Iowa schools, and the many projects endorsed by the Iowa American Revolution Bicentennial Commission.

Our heritage is important to the youth of Iowa. A knowledge of history helps in understanding how we have become what we are. Local history has special merit in that it supplies illustrative material, which is often closely related to national history.

Typically, as communities get older, there is an increasing interest in the past. Iowa celebrated its centennial as a state in 1946. Since then, more and more centennial celebrations have been held in our cities and towns.

There is a growing awareness of the need for open space and recreation—a greater sense of appreciation of our heritage——an opportunity for more leisure time out-of-doors——and greater mobility of people. The increased number of outdoor classrooms and the preservation of natural areas are indications of this renewed interest in nature and the world about us.

Museums, historic places, and natural areas can provide educational activities and stimulate our cultural interests and values. They offer meaningful ways for us to use our leisure time. As Aristotle observed, "The goal of education is the wise use of leisure."

This publication does not list all recreational areas, but does include many areas of this type if they are also of historical, geological, archeological, or botanical interest, or are used as outdoor classrooms by schools, colleges, universities, or ecology study groups. For information about recreational facilities, readers may wish to contact the Iowa State Conservation Commission or the Iowa Development Commission. In addition, all but 2 of Iowa's 99 counties have county conservation boards operating more than 825 areas, ranging from rest stops and athletic fields to parks, botanical preserves, and historic sites.

The Iowa State Department of Public Instruction is interested in filling the need of teachers for curriculum and instructional materials. This guide is intended to supplement materials prepared by the Curriculum Division. It provides information, not previously available in one convenient reference, for use of teachers, students, tourists, and all others interested in Iowa's history. It is hoped readers will find the book interesting and useful. Perhaps it will provide further evidence that Iowa is a good place in which to live and grow. As an emigrant from an eastern state expressed it, "Coming to Iowa is like taking off tight shoes."

Discovering Historic Iowa is arranged in alphabetical and numerical order by name and number of county. In alphabetical order under each county will be found the names of all known societies, museums, landmarks, sites, natural areas, and facilities used for educational purposes within that county.

The location map will be of help in locating counties or areas geographically, and may be used in planning tours or field trips. The index will aid in identifying and determining the location of these points of interest. Names of persons who may be contacted locally are given whenever available. However, it should be kept in kind that officers of organizations are constantly changing, and new attractions are continually coming into existence. A calendar of celebrations, festivals, and historic events regularly observed in Iowa begins on page 294. This is followed by a map showing Iowa's many nationality and religious groups, and a map of Iowa's rivers. An alphabetical index will be found on page 299.

Information has been obtained from a variety of sources, some of which are relatively inaccessible to most readers. It is hoped that many of the little events and sidelights on Iowa history will be new and interesting to readers. An attempt has been made to make the guide as inclusive and accurate as possible. Names, dates, and events have been checked and cross-checked. Even so, inaccuracies have a way of creeping in. Any additions or corrections should be brought to the attention of the author at 317 S.W. 42nd Street, Des Moines, Iowa 50312, or Information and Publications Services, Department of Public Instruction, Des Moines, Iowa 50319, for possible future revisions or editions of this publication.

IOWA COUNTIES

LOCATION MAP AND COUNTY NUMBERS

1 2 3 4 5 6 7 8 9 10 11 12 13

A
LYON 60 — OSCEOLA 72 — DICKINSON 30 — EMMET 32 — KOSSUTH 55 — WINNEBAGO 95 — WORTH 98 — MITCHELL 66 — HOWARD 45 — WINNESHIEK 96 — ALLAMAKEE 3

B
SIOUX 84 — O'BRIEN 71 — CLAY 21 — PALO ALTO 74 — HANCOCK 41 — CERRO GORDO 17 — FLOYD 34 — CHICKASAW 19 — FAYETTE 33 — CLAYTON 22

C
PLYMOUTH 75 — CHEROKEE 18 — BUENA VISTA 11 — POCAHONTAS 76 — HUMBOLDT 46 — WRIGHT 99 — FRANKLIN 35 — BUTLER 12 — BREMER 9 — WEBSTER 94 — BLACK HAWK 7 — BUCHANAN 10 — DELAWARE 28 — DUBUQUE 31

D
WOODBURY 97 — IDA 47 — SAC 81 — CALHOUN 13 — HAMILTON 40 — HARDIN 42 — GRUNDY 38 — TAMA 86 — BENTON 6 — LINN 57 — JONES 53 — JACKSON 49

E
MONONA 67 — CRAWFORD 24 — CARROLL 14 — GREENE 37 — BOONE 8 — STORY 85 — MARSHALL 64 — CEDAR 16 — CLINTON 23

F
HARRISON 43 — SHELBY 83 — AUDUBON 5 — GUTHRIE 39 — DALLAS 25 — POLK 77 — JASPER 50 — POWESHIEK 79 — IOWA 48 — JOHNSON 52 — SCOTT 82 — MUSCATINE 70

G
POTTAWATTAMIE 78 — CASS 15 — ADAIR 1 — MADISON 61 — WARREN 91 — MARION 63 — MAHASKA 62 — KEOKUK 54 — WASHINGTON 92 — LOUISA 58

H
MILLS 65 — MONTGOMERY 69 — ADAMS 2 — UNION 88 — CLARKE 20 — LUCAS 59 — MONROE 68 — WAPELLO 90 — JEFFERSON 51 — HENRY 44 — DES MOINES 29

I
FREMONT 36 — PAGE 73 — TAYLOR 87 — RINGGOLD 80 — DECATUR 27 — WAYNE 93 — APPANOOSE 4 — DAVIS 26 — VAN BUREN 89 — LEE 56

1 2 3 4 5 6 7 8 9 10 11 12 13

1 - ADAIR

Greenfield
G-4

● **Adair County Anquestors**
Greenfield, Iowa

Mrs. Ethel Handley,
Corresponding Secretary
R. R. 2, Box 113
Greenfield, Iowa 50849

● **Adair County Historical Society**
Greenfield, Iowa

Mrs. Elmer (Hazel) Raasch, President
Bridgewater, Iowa 50837
or
Mrs. Ralph Jensen, Secretary
Greenfield, Iowa 50849

Organized: 1975
Meetings: Last Thursday of month, 7:30 p.m.
Number of Members: 40

A chapter of the Iowa Genealogical Society (see Polk County).

Incorporated: 1967
Meetings: First Monday of each month
Number of Members: 650
Dues: $1.00 annual; $2.00 contributing; $50.00 life; over $50.00 benefactor

Historic sites and landmarks are being identified and marked. An old country schoolhouse, Grand River No. 3, was moved in 1967 to the Adair County Fairgrounds, and is open in late July, during the week of the fair. For 14 days in the fall this one-room country schoolhouse is used for an "Experiment in Local History." Children from different schools in Adair County attend classes taught by former rural school teachers in the environment of the early days of education. A big bell in the school's belfry calls pupils to classes in ciphering, penmanship, and reading. There is a recitation bench, spelldowns are conducted, and at recess the children take part in group play.

A collection of old books, diaries, pictures, and papers on Adair County history is owned by the Society. Other projects include the reprinting of the 1884 *History of Guthrie and Adair County*, a history map of Adair County, commemorative plates, and a Newsletter, published periodically.

The Bank of Memories, a museum located in an old bank building acquired in April 1971, is in Fontanelle, and may be visited during the summer, on weekends, or by appointment.

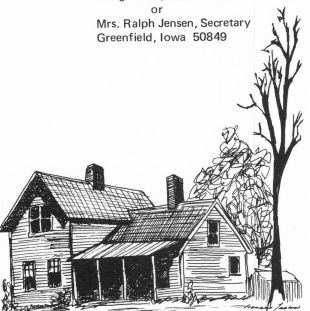

● **Henry A. Wallace Birthplace**
3 miles east, 2 miles north, and ½ mile west of Orient, Iowa. May be reached from Greenfield, Iowa by going 5 miles south on Iowa 25, then 4½ miles east.

Iowa's only U. S. Vice President, Henry Agard Wallace (1888-1965) was born here on October 7. At various times during his political career, Wallace was a Republican, a Democrat, and a Progressive. He served as Vice President under President Franklin D. Roosevelt from 1941-45. He also served as Secretary of Agriculture from 1933-40 and as Secretary of Commerce from 1945-46. He was a noted publisher and editor and an authority and experimentalist in agriculture--breeding chickens, strawberries, and hybrid corn. The birthplace farm, named Catalpa by the Wallace family, is privately owned, but a boulder marker has been placed along the roadside by Adair County Historical Society. In 1974, the farm was placed on the National Register of Historic Places.

The Henry A. Wallace Birthplace Memorial Committee was established to preserve the Wallace homestead, birthplace of Iowa's only U.S. Vice President, near Orient, Iowa.

COUNTY AND
COUNTY SEAT;
LOCATION ON MAP
    NAME AND LOCATION
    DESCRIPTION

1 - ADAIR
(continued)

● **Iowa Watershed Divide**
Adair, Iowa

The highest point on the Iowa Watershed Divide in southern Iowa is in the town of Adair, near the Adair-Guthrie County border. The Divide runs through the main business district. Water draining to the west eventually reaches the Missouri River, and to the east, water flows to the Mississippi River.

● **Ken Sidey Nature Area**
2½ miles southwest of Greenfield, Iowa, on gravel road. Go west 1½ miles on Iowa 92, then 1 mile south.

Adair County Conservation Board
Arthur L. Cannon, Recording Secretary
409 North 1st Street
Greenfield, Iowa 50849

A 107-acre tract, mostly covered with timber, set aside for nature study. The area lies just south of Nodaway Lake, which is the water reservoir for Greenfield, Iowa. Marked nature trails have identifying posts giving the names of plants and trees. The area is used extensively as an outdoor classroom. Some winter sports are permitted. The preserve was named for Ken Sidey, local newspaper publisher, whose regular column describes the plant and animal life observed there.

● **Mormon Trail Marker**
Along Iowa 25
Orient, Iowa

A tablet placed by the Daughters of the American Revolution on the local high school grounds, in memory of the pioneers who followed the Mormon Trail and its tributaries. This spot would have been at the western boundary of Iowa had the Constitution of 1844 been adopted. However, this Constitution was twice submitted to the voters and twice rejected largely because of dissatisfaction with the boundaries proposed for the new State. The Constitution finally adopted placed the western boundary at the Missouri River.

● **Mormon Trail Park**
1½ miles southeast of Bridgewater, Iowa

Adair County Conservation Board
Arthur L. Cannon, Recording Secretary
409 North 1st Street
Greenfield, Iowa 50849

In this 160-acre tract may be seen old wagon trails worn in the prairie sod by the Mormons in their trek across Iowa to the West. The park contains hiking trails and complete recreational facilities, with a 35-acre artificial lake.

● **Site of Jesse James Train Robbery**
Along U. S. 6, west of Adair, Iowa

A locomotive wheel marks the site of the first robbery of a moving train in the West. On July 21, 1873, Jesse James and his gang derailed the Chicago, Rock Island and Pacific train, killing the engineer, John Rafferty. The outlaws stole an amount variously reported from $1,700 to $4,000 from the train safe, and robbed the passengers of their money and valuables. Patrols and search parties traced the outlaws—— Jesse James, Frank James, Cole Younger, Jim Younger, Bob Younger, Bill Chadwell, and Clell Miller——into Missouri. Rewards were offered by the railroad and the State of Iowa for their capture, but the gang escaped. It

1 - ADAIR
(continued)

Site of Jesse James Train Robbery
(continued)

was the Adair train robbery that helped boost Jesse James and his brother Frank into national notoriety. Jesse James was finally murdered by a member of his own gang, Bob Ford.

● **Woodside Prairie**
Southeast of Bridgewater, or southwest of Orient, Iowa, in Washington Township

Miss Ethyl Woodside
Orient, Iowa 50858

A 9-acre tract of virgin Iowa prairie. The rolling land was purchased by M. W. Woodside in 1881, and has never been grazed or plowed. The prairie is mowed and burned off to keep down woody plants. From spring until fall the area is ever-changing, splashed with the color of wild flowers and native grasses. Some of the plants to be seen are New Jersey tea, rattlesnake master, butterfly weed, partridge pea, yellow coneflower, gayfeather, blazing star, Jerusalem artichoke, wild petunia, wood betony, pink and white beardtongue, Culver's root, blue vervain, blue-eyed grass, sweet William, wood lily, violets, puccoon, and wild rye.

ADAMS

rning
H-4

● **Adams County Historical Society**
Corning, Iowa

Mrs. Harry B. Sickler, President
907 Nodaway Street
Corning, Iowa 50841

Incorporated: 1957
Meetings: Irregular
Number of Members: 98 (life)
Dues: $2.00 annual; $25.00 life.

The Society has been inactive at times, but in 1957 the former Icarian Schoolhouse was relocated on West Sixth Street in Corning. It contains pioneer artifacts, books, and old school furnishings, and may be visited. The old Corning jail, built in 1877, has been purchased and restored as a county museum.

The farm of Howard Townsend, located 4 miles east and ¼ mile north of Corning on U. S. 34 is one part of the historic Icarian Colony. The farm home was originally the dining hall of the communistic society.

ALLAMAKEE

ukon
A-11

● **Allamakee County Historical Museum**
Allamakee Street
Waukon, Iowa 52172

Len Hansmeier, Custodian
23 East Main
Waukon, Iowa 52172

Admission: $0.50
Open: 2:00-4:00 p.m. Saturday and Sunday, June through August, and during "Fall Color Days" in late September and early October. Special tours by appointment. Closed in winter as building is not heated.

The century-old former Allamakee County Courthouse is maintained as a county museum. The exterior and interior have been preserved in a manner typical of the early period. The courtroom on the second floor is furnished with old law books, judge's chair and bench, witness chair, and the jury box. Other exhibits include a Victorian parlor, kitchen, and bedroom; old-time school furnishings; early-day medical equipment; and military articles. The original cupola contains a working bell.

3 - ALLAMAKEE
(continued)

● **Allamakee County Historical Society**
Waukon, Iowa

Miss Sarah K. Smerud, President
New Albin, Iowa 52160

Organized: 1964
Meetings: Fourth Monday of each month
Number of Members: 150
Dues: $2.00 annual

Maintains Allamakee County Historical Museum in old courthouse (see above). The Society also locates and identifies historic sites and old cemeteries in the county and sponsored the reprinting (in 1974) of the E. M. Hancock *History of Allamakee County*.

● **Effigy Mounds National Monument**
P. O. Box K, McGregor, Iowa 52157

See Clayton County for information.

● **Fish Farm Mounds State Preserve**
3 miles south of New Albin,
off Iowa 26

Three-acre wooded terrace containing 30 conical Indian burial mounds of archeological and historic interest. The mounds of various sizes date from around 200-500 A.D. They are located on what was once a farm owned by the Fish family.

● **Hartley Fort**
7 miles southwest of
New Albin, Iowa

A 2-acre preserve containing the remains of a stockaded fort built about 1200 A.D. by Woodland Indians as protection from invading Indians of the Oneota culture. The ancient fort is located at the mouth of French Creek, which empties into the Upper Iowa River.

● **John R. Mott Boyhood Home**
200 block, West Williams Street
Postville, Iowa

A bronze plaque on a granite boulder identifies the boyhood home of the international religious leader John Raleigh Mott (1865-1955), who was awarded the Nobel peace prize (with Emily Greene Balch) in 1946 for his work in international church and missionary movements. Mott spent much of his early life in Iowa. The large wooden frame house has been converted to apartments and is known as Mott Manor. The new high school building in Postville is called the John R. Mott High School.

● **State Boundary Marker**
Near New Albin, Iowa

In extreme northeast Iowa, near the mouth of the Upper Iowa (Oneota) River, is a cast-iron post marking the boundary between Iowa and Minnesota. In letters, one below the other, are the words "Iowa" on the south side of the marker and "Minnesota" on the north side. The other two sides of the marker bear the date "1849" and the latitude "43-30" (43 degrees and 30 minutes north latitude). Captain Thomas J. Lee, of the U. S. Topographic Engineers established the site for the boundary marker by astronomical observation. The monument was later used as a base point by the border survey party in 1852. The 600-pound post itself was brought to Victory, Wisconsin by steamboat, then hauled on an ox-drawn sled to be placed in its present location. Records indicate that Captain Lee paid A. Dowling $57.00 for the cast-iron monument on October 19, 1849. During the boundary dispute, Iowans suggested that the state line be extended as far north as the Minnesota River. At another time, Minnesotans urged the adoption of the 42nd parallel of latitude as the boundary which would have put Dubuque, Iowa in Minnesota. The iron post is the only original marker remaining on the northern boundary line of the State of Iowa.

- ALLAMAKEE
(continued)

● **Stone School**
3 blocks west of Mississippi
River, in Lansing, Iowa

Eastern Allamakee Community
School District
Lansing, Iowa 52151

An old stone school building in continuous use for 109 years. Built in 1864 of locally quarried limestone, the school is believed to be the oldest independent school district building in continuous use as a school building in Iowa. The first high school graduation was held in 1882, with one student graduating. At that time, the high school course was for two years. Additions were made to the stone building in 1867 and 1892 to accommodate more students, but the town's population decreased after 1875. The last classes (elementary) were held in the school on May 30, 1973. The 8-classroom building has walls 2 feet thick, and ceilings are 12 feet high. Much of the oak and white pine used in constructing the 2-story schoolhouse was cut locally. The Stone School has been placed on the National Register of Historic Places in Iowa. It is used for community meetings and has been proposed as a museum to display a record of pioneer life in the area.

Mt. Hosmer towers over the town of Lansing, affording a panoramic view of the Mississippi River and 3 states.

● **Yellow River State Forest**
Scattered areas near Waukon
Junction, off Iowa 76 and 364
P. O. Box 115, McGregor, Iowa 52157

A multiple-use recreation area of 5,610 acres. Trout streams, wildlife, state-owned sawmill, pioneer farm buildings, and unusual plant life, including a low-growing type of Yew uncommon in this climate, are of interest. Beginning in 1960, the forest in the Harper's Ferry area has been stocked with wild turkeys.

● **APPANOOSE**

terville
-8

● **Appanoose County Historical Society**
527 North Main
Centerville, Iowa 52544

Mrs. Beulah Mitchell, President
P. O. Box 157
Cincinnati, Iowa 52549

Organized: 1928; reorganized October 27, 1967
Number of Members: 600
Dues: $1.00; $25.00 life

A museum and county historical markers help to preserve the history and lore of Appanoose County. The Norfolk and Western Railroad Depot in Moravia and a 1½-story log cabin are being preserved.

● **Little Flock Chapel**
2 miles west of Plano, Iowa
on Iowa 2

Appanoose County Conservation Board
Waldo Imus, Secretary-Treasurer
415 East Wall Street
Centerville, Iowa 52544

A 9' x 18' reconstruction of Little Flock Baptist Church, organized November 4, 1859. The congregation held its last meeting on July 17, 1966, and voted the following year to dispose of the property. It was deeded to Appanoose County Conservation Board and, since the original building had been torn down, a replica of the church was built in 1969 on the 1-acre tract. Inside the chapel are 6 tiny pews where one can sit and meditate while soft gospel music fills the air. Picnic facilities are on the grounds.

● **Moulton Historical Society**
Moulton, Iowa

Mrs. Ormand Stevenson, President
Moulton, Iowa 52572

Organized: 1965
Number of Members: 100
Dues: $2.00 annual; $25.00 life
Museum Open: Weekends

Participated in centennial celebration at Moulton and provided historical articles for the newspaper. A museum building was acquired in 1975. Articles from Moulton and the surrounding area are on display.

COUNTY AND
COUNTY SEAT;
LOCATION ON MAP
     NAME AND LOCATION
     DESCRIPTION

4 - APPANOOSE
(continued)

● **Rathbun Lake**
Dam located 6 miles
north of Centerville, Iowa

Gate Closing Ceremony: November 21, 1969

An 11,200-acre lake (when filled) formed by a 2-mile long dam on the Chariton River. The $26.5 million dam was 5 years in the making. The flood control project regulates the runoff from a drainage area of 549 square miles. Located in an area once noted for coal mining, until the mines played out in the 1940's, the largest body of water in Iowa stretches upriver for 11 miles, spreading over the river valley into Appanoose, Monroe, Wayne, and Lucas Counties. Many little communities with colorful names are in the once-booming coal mining region--Mystic, Confidence, Sunshine, Bethlehem, Darby, Iconium, and Moravia.

Honey Creek State Park is being developed as a part of the Rathbun Lake complex. Located on a peninsula on the north side of the lake, the 800-acre recreational area will include an interpretive center and trails leading to numerous Indian mounds and other points of interest.

5 - AUDUBON

Audubon
F-3

● **Audubon County Genealogical Society**
Audubon, Iowa

Mrs. Francis Ballou,
Corresponding Secretary
Audubon, Iowa 50025

A local chapter of the Iowa Genealogical Society (see Polk County).

● **Audubon County Historical Museum**
115 W. Washington Street
Exira, Iowa 50076

Dedicated: September 5, 1966
Admission: Freewill offering
Open: Sundays, 1:30-4:30 p.m., May 30 to October 1;
     other times by appointment

A museum, located in the former Exchange State Bank Building, is operated by Audubon County Historical Society. Displays of fossils, rocks, early tools, antiques, and furniture are featured. There are also special loan exhibits of dolls, bells, fans, and articles associated with pioneer life.

● **Audubon County Historical Society**
115 W. Washington Street
Exira, Iowa 50076

Claire McAninch, President
Exira, Iowa 50076
     or
Leon Milliman
Exira, Iowa 50076

Organized: January 1960
Incorporated: July 23, 1965
Meetings: Third Thursday of each month, in Exira
Number of Members: 600
Dues: $1.00 annual; $10.00 lifetime

Local history, and data on schools, churches, and old stagecoach routes being collected. Audubon County Historical Museum (see above) is maintained at Exira, Iowa. The former Audubon County Home (built in 1890) is to be restored as a county museum.

AUDUBON
(continued)

- **Littlefield Wilderness**
  4 miles east and 2 miles south of Exira, Iowa

  Audubon County Conservation Board
  Wayne Hansen, Chairman
  R. R.
  Audubon, Iowa 50025

A 60-acre tract which includes a stand of native Iowa hardwood timber (white and red oak, walnut, hackberry, black cherry, and elm), wild flowers, and shrubs, and is a sanctuary for many native song birds. The wilderness is rather hilly, with narrow ridges separated by deep ravines. Maintained as a forest preserve, it is adjacent to Littlefield Park, a recreational area offering modern camping facilities, shelters, and picnic tables.

- **Plow in Oak Park**
  1 mile south of Exira on U.S. 71

A 5—acre roadside park containing an ancient oak tree with an old iron plow embedded in its heart. The plow was leaned against the young oak by the son of a pioneer farmer and left undisturbed. It is said to have been rediscovered in 1880 when the railroad was built through this area. As the tree grows, less and less of the plow is visible and it no longer rests on the ground. The oak now measures over 104 inches in circumference.

BENTON

nton
D-9

- **Benton City Park**
  9 miles east of Vinton on County Road V

  Benton County Conservation Board
  Alfred A. Happel, Chairman
  703 West 17th Street
  Vinton, Iowa 52349

A 39-acre historic site along the Cedar River, where the first settlement in Benton County took place. Preserved as a natural and scenic area.

- **Benton County Historical Society**
  P. O. Box 266
  Vinton, Iowa 52349

  Mrs. Dale (Dee) Hensing, President
  R. R. 2
  Vinton, Iowa 52349
         or
  Mrs. Glen (Helen) Mayhew,
  Secretary-Treasurer
  210 Riverview Drive
  Vinton, Iowa 52349
         or
  Mrs. Harold (Marietta) Miller, Museum
  311 East 5th Street
  Vinton, Iowa 52349

Organized: September 1971
Meetings: Annual meeting first Saturday in November; genealogy section, monthly; other meetings as called.
Number of Members: 150
Dues: $2.50 annual

A society, which includes a genealogical section, organized to promote interest in local history. Historic sites are being marked and all cemeteries in Benton County are being cataloged.

The George Horridge home (c. 1870's), located at 612 First Avenue in Vinton, was acquired in 1972 and is being restored and furnished for a museum and library to be named for Buren R. Sherman (1836-1904), Governor of Iowa 1882-1886. About a block away is the former Rock Island Depot, built before the turn of the century. The 1-story brick building was presented to the Society by Keith Elwick, and will become a part of the museum complex. The museum is open by appointment.

The Iowa Braille and Sight Saving School was founded in 1852 at Vinton by Samuel Bacon.

6 - BENTON
(continued)

- **Minne Estema Park**
  6 miles north of Vinton on
  Iowa 101 and old Brandon Road

  Benton County Conservation Board
  Alfred A. Happel, Chairman
  703 West 17th Street
  Vinton, Iowa 52349

Remains of historic old resort hotel on 60-acre site along the east bank of the Cedar River. The foundations of the once popular and fashionable hotel may still be seen. There are linear and conical Indian mounds on a bluff overlooking the river. A natural area includes timber and grassy slopes. Picnicking and camping facilities are available.

- **Old Jumbo Well**
  Eighth Avenue and Eighth Street
  Belle Plaine, Iowa

A granite marker identifies the spot where Old Jumbo Well broke out on August 26, 1886. The gusher of artesian water was not brought under control until October 6, 1887. A new well was being drilled for fire protection by William Weir and Sons, who were hired for $175. They struck water at 195 feet and soon had more than they could cope with. Water flooded the streets and great quantities of sand were thrown out of the hole. Originally only 2 inches in diameter, the hole was 3 feet across by the following day, and a fountain of water 5 feet high was gushing out. In the months that followed, all sorts of schemes were tried to cut off the water. The flow was later estimated at 5 to 9 million gallons per day. From 500 to 1,000 carloads of sand were thrown out of the well, in addition to large boulders and pieces of petrified wood. The well was hailed as the 8th wonder of the world, and European papers ran exaggerated accounts of water running 100 feet deep through the streets of Belle Plaine, with people reportedly being rescued from rooftops. By the time Jumbo was finally brought under control, it had consumed 40 carloads of stone, 130 barrels of cement, uncounted carloads of sand and clay, 77 feet of 16-inch pipe, 60 feet of 5-inch pipe, 162 feet of 18-inch pipe, and an iron cone 3 feet in diameter and 25 feet long. Today, all of this lies beneath the pavement at the intersection. The marker was erected in 1954 by Artesia Chapter of the Daughters of the American Revolution at Belle Plaine.

- **Wild Cat Bluff**
  2 miles south of Urbana, Iowa

  Benton County Conservation Board
  Alfred A. Happel, Chairman
  703 West 17th Street
  Vinton, Iowa 52349

A high limestone bluff and many varieties of trees and shrubs are included in this 119-acre tract along Brown's Branch as it flows into the Cedar River. The general recreational area provides an opportunity for nature study, with facilities for boating, fishing, picnicking, and camping.

7 - BLACK HAWK

Waterloo
C-9

- **Ag Museum**
  First and Chestnut Streets
  LaPorte City, Iowa

  LaPorte City FFA Chapter
  Ronald Borton, Advisor
  21 Bruce Lane
  LaPorte City, Iowa 50651

Founded: July 1970
Admission: Free; donations welcome
Open: First weekend in April through last weekend in October, 1:00-5:00 p.m., Saturday and Sunday; other times by appointment

The first FFA (Future Farmers of America) sponsored museum in the United States, and the only one in Iowa. Over 3,000 articles are housed in the old LaPorte City fire station (1876) and jail (1911). The exterior of the 2-story building is being restored to its original appearance. On

- BLACK HAWK
(continued)

Ag Museum
(continued)

display on the first floor are tools and farm equipment. A changing art exhibit is in the reception room. Upstairs are homemaking articles, a kitchen, a general store, a doctor's office, and a church interior.

● **Antique Acres**
North of Cedar Falls, Iowa, along U.S. 218

Black Hawk Thresherman's Club, Owners

Exhibits of threshing equipment and displays of antique farm machinery. A blacksmith shop dating back to about 1880 has been brought in from New Hartford. Included are the forge, anvils, and other equipment and tools.

● **Bennington Township Cemetery and Prairie**
7 miles northeast of Waterloo, Iowa on the Black Hawk-Butler County Line

Myrle M. Burk
1511 East Gresham Road
Waterloo, Iowa 50701

An old burial ground including about 2½ acres of native prairie with many wild flowers, including bird's-foot violet, shooting star, prairie phlox, prairie clover, rattlesnake master, false wild indigo, and blazing star, and native grasses. There have been no burials in the cemetery for about 75 years.

● **Black Hawk Park**
1 mile north and 1 mile west of Cedar Falls, Iowa, along the Cedar River

Black Hawk County Conservation Board
Leo E. Hansen, Executive Officer
2410 West Lone Tree Road
Cedar Falls, Iowa 50613

The first and the largest park in Black Hawk County under the jurisdiction of the Black Hawk County Conservation Board, providing the nucleus for the Cedar River Green Belt. The headquarters building is located just inside the entrance to the 1,121-acre park. Acquiring this land involved purchases from over 20 owners. The Cedar River runs through the entire length of the heavily wooded area and there are several ponds in the park. Wild flowers to be seen, in season, include hepatica, spring beauties, rue anemone, and trillium. Facilities are provided for picnicking, camping, hiking, horseback riding, boating, fishing, target practice, and winter sports. The park is adjacent to Washington Union Access (on the east side of the Cedar River), Railroad Lakes (a waterfowl area), and Beaver Creek Access. Indians have roved through the timbered stretches along the river and many artifacts and remains of campsites have been found. In 1968, the old rural 1-room school from Bennington Township, Section 15, was acquired. It has been moved to the park, restored, and furnished to preserve our educational heritage.

● **Bruggeman Park**
2 miles north and 2 miles east of Dunkerton, Iowa

Black Hawk County Conservation Board
Leo E. Hansen, Executive Officer
2410 West Lone Tree Road
Cedar Falls, Iowa 50613

A 210-acre area, largely undeveloped, along the banks of the Wapsipinicon River. The "white potato water" was one of the favorite hunting and fishing spots of the Indians. Red or river birch grows to great heights here, together with oaks and hickory trees. Bird watchers have observed rose-breasted grosbeaks and pileated woodpeckers in the deep woods. The park is used for nature study, canoeing, picnicking, fishing, and hunting. While the land for the park was obtained from several owners, it was named for Waterloo dentist and realtor, C. R. Bruggeman.

7 - BLACK HAWK
(continued)

● **Cedar Falls Historical Society**
303 Clay Street
Cedar Falls, Iowa 50613

Douglas Hieber, President
33 Timber Ledge Place
Cedar Falls, Iowa 50613

Organized: March 22, 1964
Meetings: Monthly
Number of Members: 205
Dues: $2.00 annual
Admission to House: Free

Century-old house, acquired March 1, 1966 from Mr. and Mrs. J. F. Dempster, (owners of the property since 1945) has been restored, remodeled, and furnished to serve as a research center and home for the Society. The home, opened to the public May 30, 1968, was originally built by A. D. Barnum in 1862. He also built the Civil War Orphans Home on the University of Northern Iowa campus, which later became the first Iowa Normal School. Barnum's home was built in classic style with a cupola to serve as a lookout for Indians. The Gothic rounded windows were hand-molded, with terra cotta trim from the early Cedar Falls pottery works. The Society home includes a gallery for traveling art exhibits pertaining to Cedar Falls, library, workroom, offices, period room, displays of items of local historical interest, and the J. B. (Joe) Clay Room containing artifacts collected during his world travels.

● **Cedar Valley Historical Society**
Waterloo, Iowa

Mrs. Paul R. Hayes, President
246 Western
Waterloo, Iowa 50704

Incorporated: March 1, 1974

● **Hickory Hills Park**
7 miles north of
Dysart, Iowa

Black Hawk County Conservation
  Board
Leo E. Hansen, Executive Officer
2410 West Lone Tree Road
Cedar Falls, Iowa 50613

A 500-acre recreation area offering opportunity for picnicking, camping, fishing, boating, hiking, horseback riding, swimming, winter sports, and nature study. The area south of the 60-acre artificial lake is used as a wildlife habitat. There are large stands of hickory, oak, walnut, butternut, and locust trees on the high ground. A wildlife display and observation area is also in the park. In the spring the ravines are covered with bluebells, columbine, Dutchman's breeches, violets, and wild crabapples. Morel mushrooms, wild grapes, raspberries, and gooseberries are also found here.

● **Jacob Hoffman Cabin Replica**
Overman Park, located between
West Second and Third Streets
and Clay and Franklin Streets
Cedar Falls, Iowa

Cedar Falls Parks and
Arborist Department
City Hall
220 Clay Street
Cedar Falls, Iowa 50613

Ground-breaking Ceremonies: October 26, 1971

A replica of the pioneer cabin built in the 1850's by Jacob Hoffman. The original 12-by 20-foot slab cabin was located northeast of Waterloo in Bennington Township. Hoffman walked more than 100 miles to Dubuque in 1854 to file a claim for the land. Cedar Falls author Bess Streeter Aldrich used Hoffman as the prototype for the character Wayne Lockwood in her novel "Song of Years." The book is a historical account of the early settlement of Black Hawk County, particularly Cedar Falls and Waterloo. The cabin replica contains some of the original furnishings.

- BLACK HAWK
  (continued)

● **Museum of History and Science**
(Grout Historical Museum)
Park Avenue at South Street
Waterloo, Iowa 50701

Phillip M. Pollock, Director

Founded: 1933 by Henry C. Grout
Opened to Public: August 30, 1956
Admission: Free
Open: Tuesday through Friday, 1:00-4:30 p.m.; Saturday, 10:00 a.m.-4:00 p.m.; closed Sunday, Monday, and holidays.

A brick and stone museum building situated on the site of the old Leavitt home. Permanent exhibits may be seen on the earth sciences, Iowa and local history, pioneer life, Indians of Iowa, and early American arts and crafts (spinning, weaving, dyeing, and woodworking). Pioneer exhibits include log cabin (1850), tool shed (1850-1860), carpenter shop (1860-1900), country store (1880-1910), and drug store (1880-1910), all appropriately furnished. There are also collections of musical instruments, period costumes (1850-1920), Civil War items, early day toys, spectacles, and lighting equipment, and changing exhibits.

The historical reference library contains maps and other materials on Iowa and early Waterloo.

A Planetarium (capacity of 65), offers lectures every Saturday at 2:30 p.m.

Guided tours are available Tuesday through Friday, for groups of 20 or more, by advance appointment.

● **Northeast Iowa Genealogical Society**
Waterloo, Iowa

Mrs. Walter (Gerry) Figi,
  Corresponding Secretary
415 Home Park Boulevard
Waterloo, Iowa 50701

Incorporated: April 12, 1974
Meetings: Third Tuesday of month, except June, July, and August
Number of Members: 35
Dues: $5.00 annual; $8.00 husband and wife

A local chapter of the Iowa Genealogical Society (see Polk County). Research is done on family records, cemetery records, and churches in Black Hawk County. A library is maintained in the Museum of History and Science (see above). The *Cedar Tree* is printed twice a year.

7 - BLACK HAWK
(continued)

● **Rensselaer Russell House**
West Third and South Streets,
facing Washington Park
Waterloo, Iowa

The Association for the Preservation
of the Rensselaer Russell House
P.O. Box 843
Waterloo, Iowa 50701

or

Mrs. Craig Clark
1151 Meadow Lane
Waterloo, Iowa 50701

● **River Birch Bottoms**
2 miles east of
Dunkerton, Iowa

Black Hawk County Conservation
 Board
Leo E. Hansen, Executive Officer
2410 West Lone Tree Road
Cedar Falls, Iowa 50613

Completed: 1861
Restored: 1963
Admission: $0.50
Open: Wednesday and Sunday, 1:30-4:00 p.m., except
 January through March; tours scheduled any time by
 special request.

A fine example of mid-Victorian architecture (1861).
Originally costing $5,878.83, the house is one of the three
oldest still standing in Black Hawk County. It has been
restored and furnished in typical Victorian decor. Some of
the original furnishings in the house are the Steinway grand
piano, the hall grandfather clock, and two floor-to-ceiling
mirrors in the downstairs rooms.

The property was purchased by the Peoples Mutual Savings
and Loan Association in 1962 and leased to the Junior
Service League which was responsible for the restoration of
the home. A permanent board of civic volunteers, the
Association for the Preservation of the Rensselaer Russell
House, continues to maintain and operate the house.

Rensselaer Russell (1828-1896) was born in New York and
moved with his wife and daughter to Waterloo in 1858,
when the town had a population of about 400.
Construction on the house was begun in 1858.
Bricks--85,000 of them--and other building materials were
brought from Dubuque by wagon. Russell also had
downtown commercial properties, and he donated the land
(Russell Square) to Waterloo in 1872 for Washington Park,
the scene of early-day 4th of July celebrations and other
holiday festivities. Today, an oriental pagoda and gardens
are located in the park.

Following the death of Rensselaer Russell in 1896, his
daughter, Lillian, who had been born in 1869, married
Clyde Orrin Lamson. Lillian had kept house for her father
following her mother's death in 1887, so the newlyweds
lived in the Russell House. Lillian continued in her father's
business activities, and her husband was also active in
banking, real estate, and manufacturing. Lamson and his
wife jointly erected the Russell-Lamson Building in
Waterloo. The Lamsons had two children, Russell Orrin
Lamson and Maxine Russell Lamson (Mrs. D. E. Gerow).
The son resided in the family home until 1964.

An 80-acre nature preserve being kept in its natural state.

- BLACK HAWK
(continued)

- **Sandy Prairie**
8 miles northwest of
Cedar Falls, Iowa

Wayne Mark, owner
R.R. 3
Cedar Falls, Iowa 50613

A privately owned 40-acre dry sandy upland prairie with wet swale and marshy areas. This is one of very few places left in Iowa where sphagnum moss may be seen. Wild flowers bloom in abundance--blazing star, goldenrod, prairie smoke, prairie phlox, browned-eyed Susan, and coneflowers.

- **Siggelkov Park**
5 miles north of
Dunkerton, Iowa

Black Hawk County Conservation
Board
Leo E. Hansen, Executive Officer
2410 West Lone Tree Road
Cedar Falls, Iowa 50613

A 64-acre tract, within the Wapsie Green Belt, which includes the site of the early village of Frogtown. This land was originally purchased in 1853 from the United States Government by an early settler. A natural rock bottom in the Wapsipinicon River at one point made this an ideal place for a ford. A dam was later built at the same location and a grist mill and a sawmill were put into operation. The little village of Frogtown came into existence around 1870, and included a blacksmith shop, general store and saloon, and several houses. Construction was begun on a railroad from Anamosa to the Minnesota border, but a lack of funds prevented its completion. (A portion of the old railroad bed may be seen from Siggelkov Park.) Frogtown began to decline in the late 1890's and there is little left today to indicate that such a place ever existed. The town is said to have been named for the frogs that used to fill the entire valley with their song on summer nights. The park was named for Emory and Mabel Siggelkov, the previous owners of the land. The virgin timber within the park has been kept intact, and consists mainly of the shaggy-barked red or river birch, a tree common to the Wapsie Valley, hickory, and oak. The park is used for picnicking, camping, and fishing.

- **Stone Barn**
Along Iowa 57 west of
Cedar Falls, Iowa

A large stone barn built in 1875 by the Fields family, who came to this country from England. They kept large English Shire work horses in the barn, which has a root cellar where beets were stored to feed the horses. A square silo was also built inside the barn.

- **Sullivan Park**
Webster and East 4th Street
Waterloo, Iowa

An 8-acre park established in the neighborhood where the five Sullivan brothers of World War II formerly lived and played. Five sons--George, Francis, Matt, Joe, and Al--of Thomas F. Sullivan, a Waterloo railroad conductor, enlisted in the U.S. Navy and, at their request, were all assigned to the same ship, the USS *Juneau*, a light cruiser. A Japanese torpedo sank the ship in late November of 1942, at Guadalcanal, and all five brothers perished. A shamrock-shaped bronze plaque has been placed in the center of the park as a memorial.

The United States Navy commissioned a destroyer, *The Sullivans*, the first ship to be named for more than one person. The 376-foot-long destroyer, launched April 4, 1943, saw action in the Pacific before the end of World War II, and engaged in duty during the Korean conflict. She was put in mothballs in the early 1960's. In 1974, the Navy presented a replica of the ship to the City of Waterloo. To further honor the five sailor Sullivans, Congress established

7 - BLACK HAWK
(continued)

Sullivan Park
(continued)

a living memorial by planting a cluster of apple trees on the grounds of the national Capitol.

● **Thunder Woman Park**
North edge of Finchford, Iowa

Black Hawk County Conservation Board
Leo E. Hansen, Executive Officer
2410 West Lone Tree Road
Cedar Falls, Iowa 50613

A 96-acre park including a nature trail and a 7-acre pine plantation. Hiking, camping, picnicking, fishing, and nature study are popular. A 125-foot suspension bridge connects the north and south sections of the park. Thunder Woman, a Winnebago squaw, lies buried in Newell Cemetery, about 2 miles from the park.

● **University of Northern Iowa Museum**
Hudson Road
Cedar Falls, Iowa 50613

Dr. Pauline Sauer, Director

Founded: 1893
Admission: Free
Open: Monday through Friday, 1:00-5:00 p.m. during academic year; closed during vacations

Outstanding geology collection; displays on U.S. and Iowa history, American Indians, and non-Western cultures; exhibits of mammals, birds, reptiles, fish, and world-wide collection of shells, corals, and sponges. Special programs available to school groups by advance appointment.

Iowa State Normal School opened on September 6, 1876. The institution was first housed in a building used as a state-supported orphanage for children of Civil War veterans. The old building was equipped with wood-burning stoves and kerosene lamps. In 1909, the name of the school was changed to Iowa State Teachers College, and on July 1, 1967 it was accorded university status and the name changed to University of Northern Iowa.

8 - BOONE

Boone
E-5

● **Boone County Genealogical Society**
Boone, Iowa

Larry Adams, Corresponding Secretary
969 Park Circle
Boone, Iowa 50036

Organized: December 1974
Number of Members: 40

A chapter of the Iowa Genealogical Society (see Polk County).

● **Boone County Historical Society**
Boone, Iowa

Edward H. Meyers, President
1521 Carroll Street
Boone, Iowa 50036

Organized: November 8, 1966
Meetings: As announced
Number of Members: 1,172
Dues: $4.00 annual

Hickory Grove School, a typical small country school in Boone County, has been moved to the Don Williams Recreation Area, and furnished as it was in the 1920's. The wooden frame Mineral Ridge Methodist Church has been acquired and preserved. A Kate Shelley Memorial Museum and Park is being developed at Moingona.

Other activities include the marking of historic sites, preserving public records and materials on local history, displaying historic relics, and reprinting the 1880 *Boone County History* and the 1910 supplement to the *Boone News Republican*.

BOONE
(continued)

● **Kate Shelley Marker**
Ogden, Iowa

A marker dedicated on September 5, 1941 to the memory of Kate Shelley (September 25, 1865-January 21, 1912), who was presented a gold medal by the State of Iowa on this site, in recognition of an act of heroism. On the night of July 6, 1881 she crawled across the wooden ties of the Des Moines River bridge at Moingona, Iowa during a raging storm and flood to warn an approaching passenger train that a bridge across Honey Creek was washed out. The lantern she used to flag down the train and prevent it from plunging into the rain-swollen creek is on display in the State Historical Building in Des Moines. Many lives were saved and Kate, who was only 15, became a national heroine. A Chicago newspaper raised a fund to pay off the mortgage on the home of her family, and temperance leader Frances Willard arranged for her to enroll in college. After attending Simpson College, Kate secured a teacher's certificate and taught in Boone County schools for several years. Kate Shelley (an aunt of Jack Shelley, formerly news director at WHO, now an associate professor of technical journalism at Iowa State University) was station agent for the Chicago and North Western Railway Co. at Moingona from 1903 until 1911, prior to her death the following year. She is buried in the family plot at Sacred Heart Cemetery in Boone.

Mayme Shelley, a younger sister of Kate, died July 9, 1973 at the age of 101. Mayme was 9 when Kate performed her heroic deed, and for much of her lifetime she served as an unofficial historian of the event. Neither of the sisters married. Mayme, who also taught school, was employed at other periods in her life as a bank teller and as a practical nurse.

Mike Shelley came here from Ireland with his wife and daughter Kate in 1866. Starting out as a section hand for the C & NW Railroad in 1867, he later became section foreman. Their home across the Des Moines River from Moingona is no longer standing.

The old bridge across Honey Creek is now gone except for the stone piers. The present railroad bridge, located on the main line of the Milwaukee Railroad running west out of Madrid, replaced what was claimed to be "the longest double-tracked bridge in the United States" when it was completed in 1913 and named in honor of Kate Shelley. This bridge, together with the piers of the so-called High Bridge across the Des Moines River south of Madrid in Dallas County, was removed as part of the Saylorville Reservoir project.

● **Ledges State Park**
Madrid, Iowa 50156
6 miles south of Boone, on Iowa 164

State Conservation Commission
State Office Building
300 Fourth Street
Des Moines, Iowa 50319

Dedicated: November 9, 1924

One of Iowa's first state parks, named for its unusual rock formations. High sandstone cliffs and ledges border Pease Creek which flows into the Des Moines River at the west edge of the park. Nature trails lead through areas of natural beauty to such scenic spots as Table Rock, Crow's Nest, Inspiration Point, and Hutton Memorial. Indian Council

8 - BOONE
(continued)

Ledges State Park
(continued)

Ledge was once a popular place for pow-wows of the Sioux, Sac and Fox. A wide variety of birds and animals may be seen, while shrubs, trees, and wild flowers, including some rare species, grow abundantly in the 940-acre park. Within hiking distance, just south of the park, are some interesting Indian mounds. Camping, picnicking, fishing, and boating facilities are available. The State Conservation Commission's Wildlife Research and Exhibit Station (see below) adjoins the park.

● **Mamie Doud Eisenhower Birthplace**
718 Carroll Street
Boone, Iowa

A bronze plaque marks the site of the birthplace of Mamie Doud Eisenhower, wife of Dwight David Eisenhower (1890-1969), President of the United States (1953-1961). The home is being moved to another location and restored to its original state.

● **Railroad Prairie**
1 mile east of Boone, Iowa
between old U.S. 30 and
Chicago and North Western
Railroad right-of-way

A 15-acre strip of railroad right-of-way which parallels the highway. This remaining bit of prairie provides a typical wild flower display from spring through fall and serves as a teaching area for schools and Iowa State University.

● **Wildlife Research and Exhibit Station**
South edge of Ledges State Park

State Conservation Commission
State Office Building
300 Fourth Street
Des Moines, Iowa 50319

Dedicated: 1962
Admission: Free
Open: Daily, 10:00 a.m.-7:00 p.m., from first Sunday in May until last Sunday in October

Habits of birds and animals native to Iowa may be observed under the supervision of competent guides. Animals are brought to the exhibits from the wild by conservation officers. Over 80 species of waterfowl and wild game may be seen, including shore birds, eagles, swans, game birds, squirrels, raccoons, beavers, otters, opossums, mink, skunks, prairie dogs, and deer. Research is conducted on deer, pheasants, and quail, and birds are raised at the station to be released.

9 - BREMER

Waverly
C-9

● **Bremer County Historical Society**
402 West Bremer Avenue
Waverly, Iowa 50677

J. W. (Bill) Lynes, President
Plainfield, Iowa 50666
or
Mrs. Delbert Shepard, Museum Director
211 Second Street, S. W.
Waverly, Iowa 50677

Organized: November 1958
Meetings: Annual meeting first Tuesday in May
Number of Members: 650
Dues: $1.00 annual

Maintains a county museum in Waverly House (see below).

| COUNTY AND COUNTY SEAT; LOCATION ON MAP | NAME AND LOCATION | DESCRIPTION |

BREMER
(continued)

● **North Woods Park**
1 mile north of
Sumner, Iowa

Bremer County Conservation Board
Dale Pothast, Executive Officer
R. R. 1, Waverly, Iowa 50677

An area of 81 acres, with access to the Little Wapsipinicon River, covered with upland timber (oak, hickory, maple, wild cherry, and cottonwood), and a stand of hazelnut underbrush. The multiple use area has facilities for picnicking and camping.

● **Schield International Museum**
Bremer Avenue on U.S. 218 and
Iowa 3, across from campus of
Wartburg College
Waverly, Iowa 50677

Admission: $0.50; children 6-14, $0.25; under 6, free

Collection of unusual objects from far away places, acquired by a self-made millionaire machinery manufacturer. On display are the first Bantam (a dragline mounted on a truck chassis) built in 1942 at the Schield Lime Quarry, huge elephant tusks, giant clam shells, Russian crawler tractor, 1956 Russian Pobeda 4-door sedan, 1912 Model T Ford, horsedrawn steam engine, and Persian rugs.

● **Waverly House**
402 West Bremer Avenue
Waverly, Iowa 50677

Admission: $0.50; children under 14, $0.25
Open: Tuesday through Saturday, 1:30-4:00 p.m., and Sunday, 2:00-4:00 p.m., May through October. Tours by appointment.

County museum maintained by Bremer County Historical Society in Waverly House, which was the first hotel and stagecoach stop in Waverly. Built in 1856 of native timber and brick, it is the last of its kind in northeast Iowa. Over 1,900 pioneer items on display including a 334 year-old violin, antique telephones, Civil War items, a chair once used by the 27th President of the United States (1909-1913) William Howard Taft (1857-1930), toys, quilts, a rare folding bathtub, pictures, clocks, books, newspapers, and clothing. Exhibits of old country store; schoolroom; Victorian living room, kitchen, and bedrooms; ghost towns of county; and original Buck Creek post office.

BUCHANAN

ependence
C-10

● **Amish Settlement**
Near Hazelton, Iowa

Some of the Old Order Amish moved to this area in 1914 from Kalona (see Washington County), because they believed that the Kalona group was becoming too worldly.

● **Buchanan County Historical Society**
Independence, Iowa

Clarence Snyder, President
Golf Course Road
Independence, Iowa 50644

Organized: 1961
Meetings: Third Tuesday of each month except June, July, and August
Number of Members: 125
Dues: $2.00 annual

10 - BUCHANAN
(continued)

Buchanan County Historical Society
(continued)

Maintains museum located in Buchanan County Courthouse, containing materials and exhibits of local historical interest. The old horse barn on the Buchanan County Fairgrounds is also used as a museum to display farm machinery, engines, an old printing press, and other equipment. The Society also inventories cemeteries in the county.

● **Rush Park**
West edge of Independence, Iowa
on U.S. 20

Remains of kite-shaped track and amphitheater, dating back to the time when Independence was the center of the harness racing world. The C. W. Williams home and carriage barn are now a cafe and tavern. Axtell's barn is located at the rear of the lot at 500-4th Street S.W., and is now a garage.

● **Wapsie Mill**
On U.S. 20
Independence, Iowa

Wapsie Mill was erected in 1867-1868 on the west side of the Wapsipinicon River. Originally a flour mill, it is still in operation. Privately owned.

● **Westburg No. 7 Community Center and Museum**
2 miles west of Independence, Iowa on U.S. 20, then 4 miles south, 1½ miles west, and 1 mile south

Harry J. Circus, Owner
Route 3, Independence, Iowa
50644

Dedicated: June 10, 1965
Admission: Free
Open: Sunday, 2:00-4:00 p.m., June through October
　　　　other times upon request

Restoration of Westburg No. 7 rural schoolhouse, built in 1883 and used as school until May 21, 1965. Text books, school records and equipment, including maps, globes, pictures, flags, bell, pump organ, and desks. Building used for community meetings.

11 - BUENA VISTA

Storm Lake
C-3

● **Buena Vista County Historical Society**
Storm Lake, Iowa

Max E. Ireland, President
503 Lake Avenue
Storm Lake, Iowa 50588
or
Inez Young, Treasurer
Storm Lake Public Library
Storm Lake, Iowa 50588

Organized: August 11, 1960
Meetings: Third Thursday of month
Number of Members: 175
Dues: $1.00 annual; $100.00 life membership
Cabin open: Sunday, 2:00-5:00 p.m., from Memorial Day to Labor Day, and by special appointment; voluntary contributions accepted

Collects and preserves information and articles related to the county's early growth and development.

Prairie log house, built by Halvor Ellerton Dahl prior to 1871, near Rembrandt, is now located on East Lakeshore Drive, along U.S. 71, Storm Lake. Constructed of oak logs cut from timber along the Little Sioux River, the structure is a good example of Scandinavian type construction of a homesteader's cabin. The logs were squared by the "striking off and splitting" method to make a tight wall, and dovetailed at the corners. The log house has been restored and furnished in pioneer style.

- BUTLER

llison
C-8

- **Butler County Historical Association**
  Allison, Iowa

  Ben B. Westendorf, President
  303 Sixth Street
  Allison, Iowa 50602
  or
  Mrs. W. C. Shepard, Historian
  Allison, Iowa 50602

Organized: 1957
Meetings: March, May, and September
Number of Members: 140
Dues: $1.00 annual

Summer tours and picnics sponsored. Little Yellow Country Schoolhouse (see below) is maintained as a museum.

- **Fort Sumter Rock**
  6 miles southwest of
  Allison, Iowa, on the
  Kelsey blacktop road
  1½ miles south of
  Iowa 3

  Mrs. Harold (Helen) Folkerts
  R. R. 2
  Allison, Iowa

A large, partially buried glacial granite boulder. The rock, about 5 feet above ground, is located along the edge of the county road (blacktop). The words "Fort Sumter" have been painted on the rock. According to legend, a pioneer was on his way back home from the mill at Cedar Falls where he had heard the news of the firing on Fort Sumter, in the harbor of Charleston, S.C., signalling the start of the Civil War, on April 12, 1861. He wrote on the rock with axle grease from his wagon, "Fort Sumter was taken." A small flag is flown on the rock.

- **Heery Woods State Park**
  ½ mile south of
  Clarksville, Iowa

  State Conservation Commission
  State Office Building
  300 Fourth Street
  Des Moines, Iowa 50319

A pleasant spot along the Shell Rock River, named to commemorate John Heery, who took out the first land warrant in Butler County in 1853. There is a low dam in a bend of the river. The park is used for picnicking, fishing, and hiking.

The nearby town of Clarksville was settled in 1853 and was named for 2 brothers, Thomas and Jeremiah Clark.

- **Joseph B. Clay Prairie**
  North of Parkersburg or
  3 miles south of Allison on
  Highway 14 to intersection
  with blacktop county road to
  Shell Rock, Iowa, then east
  1 mile to Butler Center Cemetery

A 2.64-acre tract of unbroken Iowa prairie adjacent to the old cemetery, which is still maintained and used for burials. Clay Prairie was originally part of the cemetery for the early-day settlement of Butler Center. When the railroad was built through Allison, Butler Center died out and nothing but the cemetery and prairie remain today. The view of the surrounding countryside to the north and east gives an idea of what the original Iowa prairie looked like. This patch of unturned prairie is owned by the University of Northern Iowa Foundation (Formerly the State College of Iowa Foundation) and is protected under the Iowa State Preserves System. The prairie was named for Joseph B. Clay, a graduate and long-time friend of the University, who was the prime mover in preserving this small part of Iowa's heritage. Here, many kinds of prairie wild flowers bloom in profusion. These include shooting star, prairie smoke, prairie willow, and pussywillow. This is a favorite nature study spot, and is used by the University as a field laboratory by biology students.

BUTLER COUNTY
(continued)

● **Little Yellow Country Schoolhouse**
Court House Square

Mrs. Ethel Parks
Allison, Iowa 50602
or
W. C. Polderboer
409 Pine Street
Allison, Iowa 50602

Admission: Donations accepted
Open: By appointment

A rural school, preserved as a museum, contains exhibits of bird eggs, moths, butterflies, and antiques. In the schoolhouse are a 100-year old teacher's desk and records of country schools. The school was originally located about 2 miles south of Ardale, Iowa.

● **Parkersburg Historical Society**
Parkersburg, Iowa

Peter Olthoff
904 Wemple Street
Parkersburg, Iowa 50665

or

Gladys Meyers,
Secretary and Historian
404 Lincoln Street
Parkersburg, Iowa 50665

Incorporated: June 16, 1970
Meetings: Board, first Wednesday of month; Annual meeting in June
Dues: $2.00
Open: Special occasions and by appointment

The 19th-century C. C. Wolf 3-story, brick home (1895), located in the west-central part of Parkersburg (Fifth and Bethel Streets) has been restored and is maintained as a museum. The Parkersburg Historical Home displays antiques and memorabilia associated with the community. Included are pieces of furniture, a kitchen range, slate sink, ice box, loom, collection of spectacles, calendars, pictures, and railroad depot agent's equipment from the Illinois Central Railroad depot, closed in 1971 when passenger service was discontinued. The living room, music room, kitchen, and turret bedroom are appropriately furnished. The interior of the house has 14 different kinds or combinations of carved woodwork, and stained glass windows were imported from France. The home had been used as a school, church, library, and community house before it was acquired by the Society.

● **Pilot Rock**
3½ miles northwest of
Allison, Iowa

Pioneer landmark, located in Section 22 of West Point Township. This is one of the largest boulders in Iowa, measuring 38 feet long, 26 feet wide, and 12 feet in height above the ground. Pilot Rock is composed of very hard gray granite, similar to other glacial boulders in this area.

● **Shell Rock Mills**
Shell Rock, Iowa

In 1857, the first grist mill was built on the west side of the Shell Rock River at Shell Rock. The original 30' x 40', 3-story building cost $10,000 and was built by George W. Adair, the town's founder, who arrived there in 1853. This mill has been torn down. Still standing is the Shell Rock Grain and Milling Company mill, on the opposite side of the river. It was built in 1858, of solid walnut, and an addition went up in 1888. A 14" x 14" walnut beam goes across the roof of the structure, and wooden pegs were used rather than nails.

Horse drawn wagons and bobsleds, tractors, and trucks have been used through the years to haul grain to the mill. Ground cereal was sold and delivered to Butler County grocery stores as recently as 1944. In addition to breakfast food, corn meal, pure buckwheat and pancake flour was also ground at the mill. Although use of water power has

BUTLER COUNTY
(Continued)

Shell Rock Mills
(continued)

long since ceased, the mill still grinds livestock feed, using electric power, and the grinding room smells of corn and the sweetness of the additives used today.

The Shell Rock River, which flows out of Albert Lea Lake, in Minnesota, is a tributary of the Cedar River. It has furnished water power for many of the early Iowa mills in Butler, Floyd, Cerro Gordo, and Worth Counties.

· CALHOUN

ckwell City
D-4

● **Calhoun County Historical Society**
626 8th Street
Rockwell City, Iowa 50579

Mrs. Roy Hoyt, President
500 East Lake
Rockwell City, Iowa 50579
or
Mrs. Clarence Webb, Secretary
R. R. 2
Rockwell City, Iowa 50579

Organized: October 1956
Incorporated: 1962
Meetings: Third Tuesday of each month, 7:30 p.m.
Number of Members: 150
Dues: $1.00 annual

Early in 1968, the old West School in Rockwell City was purchased by the society. This 2-story brick building has been converted to house the Calhoun County Museum (see below), and provide rooms for workshops and public meetings.

● **Calhoun County Museum**
626 8th Street
Rockwell City, Iowa 50579

Acquired: 1968
Admission: Free
Open: Sunday, 2:00-4:00 p.m., May to October; other times by appointment

The former West School has been remodeled to house a county museum, owned and operated by Calhoun County Historical Society. Displays include pioneer home furnishings and farm machinery; study files of photographs; old manuscripts; maps; and genealogies.

CARROLL

·oll
·-3

● **Carroll County Historical Society**
Carroll, Iowa

Mrs. Virgil Baumhover, President
Carroll, Iowa 51401

Organized: April 1967
Dues: $2.00 annual

Farmstead museum planned near Swan Lake Park.

● **Dickson Timber**
5 miles northeast of
Glidden, Iowa

Carroll County Conservation Board
Russell White, Executive Officer
Swan Lake Park
Carroll, Iowa 51401

An area of 155 acres of hardwood timber, with oak, ash, and hickory the predominant species. There are many varieties of wild flowers, and squirrels, deer, and song birds are plentiful. Primarily intended for nature study and use as an outdoor classroom, with seasonal sports and picnicking permitted.

● **Grave of Merle D. Hay**
Westlawn Cemetery
Glidden, Iowa

A monument of Carolina granite erected to the memory of Private Merle D. Hay, one of the first three American soldiers and the first from Iowa to be killed in World War I. His death occurred on November 3, 1917, near Artois, France. On the central part of the monument is a reproduction of a cartoon by J. N. (Ding) Darling, showing Uncle Sam holding a dead soldier in his arms.

14 - CARROLL
(continued)

● **Holstein-Friesian Museum**
507 Main (on Iowa 141)
Manning, Iowa

Opened: January 1, 1968
Admission: Free; donations appreciated
Open: Wednesday, Friday, and Sunday, 1:00-5:00 p.m.; other times by appointment

The only Holstein museum in America features antiques and memorabilia donated by breeders of the black and white cows, the most popular dairy animal in the world. Items include historical records, pictures, sale catalogs, trophies, and the milk stool and neck chain of the late College Ormsby Burke (Mama), holder of the lifetime record for milk production-- 334,219 pounds. Registration papers for many of the other prominent members of the breed may be seen, as well as a copy of the cancelled check for $42,000 written by Rowntree Farms Ltd. of Woodbridge, Ontario, Canada, for Glenafton Nettie Benheur Maude, the second highest-selling Holstein cow.

The pictorial history of the Holstein breed, which originated in the lowlands of Holland and North Friesland, is depicted chronologically on panels around the walls of the museum. A special feature is an original oil painting by J. Grant Steele, done about 1908, of Pietertje Maid Ormsby, "Mother of the Breed."

15 - CASS

Atlantic
G-3

● **Cass County Historical Society**
Griswold, Iowa

Mrs. E.C. Fry, President
Griswold, Iowa 51535

Organized: 1963
Number of Members: 280
Museums Open: Monday, Wednesday, and Saturday, 12:30-9:00 p.m., June through August

Cass County Museum, located in old bank building on south side of Main in Griswold. A Schoolhouse Museum, in Sunnyside Park at Atlantic, is owned and maintained by the city.

● **Frank Chapman Pellett Memorial Woods**
Atlantic, Iowa

Mr. & Mrs. Melvin Pellett, owners
Atlantic, Iowa 50022

A 5-acre tract set aside in 1907 as a wild flower preserve by Frank Chapman Pellet (1879-1951), a well-known naturalist, author, and beekeeper. Two large, red granite boulders with bronze plaques mark the entrance to the largely undisturbed woodland. An abundance of spring flowers, common to Iowa, may be seen. The woods also shelter many varieties of birds. A foot path from the rail

- CASS
(continued)

Frank Chapman Pellett Memorial Woods
(continued)

gate leads through the area, and appropriate signs identify the flowers and trees. The sanctuary serves as a living laboratory for nature study.

● **Lewis Town and Country Boosters**
Lewis, Iowa

J. Frank Berry, Lewis, Iowa 51544
or
R.K. Breckerbaumer, Lewis, Iowa 51544

Organized: January 1, 1966
Meetings: Fourth Monday of month, 8:00 p.m.
Number of Members: 45
Dues: $12.00 annual

Organized to identify, mark, and promote interest in historic sites in the area.

The 1856-1860 Mormon Trails across the county are still visible. A Mormon Handcart Trail marker and replica of a wooden handcart is in Lewis City Park. These sturdy carts were made of native wood, shaped with a hand axe. The owner's possessions were loaded on the carts and, in some cases, those too feeble to walk rode in the carts as they were pushed by the Mormons from Illinois to Utah.

Other local historic landmarks include the Old Stone House built before the Civil War by Reverend George Hitchcock and used as a station on the Underground Railroad, the Civil War Army Barracks, old Ferry House, the original Cass County Courthouse, and Lewis Congregational Church.

CEDAR

ton
-12

● **Cedar County Historical Society**
Tipton, Iowa

William Hartz, President
Durant, Iowa 52747
or
Mrs. Ina Barewald,
Corresponding Secretary
Tipton, Iowa 52772

Organized: October 10, 1957
Meetings: Annual meeting second Thursday in January: annual picnic, last Sunday in July; Board meets fourth Thursday evening of each month
Number of Members: 500
Dues: $2.00 annual

Cedar County Historical Review published annually since 1958. Past issues have contained articles and pictures on rural churches, early country schools, pioneer life, early transportation, pioneer firearms, limestone quarries, and early settlers in Cedar County. Meetings feature historical programs.

Landmarks and historic sites in Cedar County include the former Tipton Union School, constructed in 1853 at 121 East Second Street and opened as the first free graded school, including a high school, west of the Mississippi River; the Henry Hardman Home, southeast of Tipton, site of the first court, the first school, and the first church services (marked by boulder erected by the Society); and the William Maxon Home (see below), located northeast of Springdale.

● **Grave of Elliott Parr**
About 3 miles southwest of Lowden, Iowa

The final resting place of Elliott Parr, a Civil War veteran and member of a pioneer Lowden family. The lone grave is in a ¼-acre cemetery carved from the land settled by Billy Parr, the veteran's father, who came here from Ohio in 1848. Elliott Parr served in the Civil War with 4 of his brothers, and returned safely home, only to be struck down

16 - CEDAR
(continued)

Grave of Elliott Parr
(continued)

during the 1867 smallpox epidemic in Cedar County. Residents in the area, terrified of the dread disease, refused to allow smallpox victims to be buried in Lowden's Van Horn Cemetery, the only burial ground in the vicinity. So it was that the victim's father deeded the tiny cemetery to Cedar County and buried his son there. A simple headstone with the inscription "Elliott Parr, Company K, 35th Iowa Infantry" marks the grave. No date of birth or death are shown. The small plot is enclosed with a high wire fence.

● **Herbert Hoover National Historic Site**
West Branch, Iowa 52358

Mrs. Lorraine Mintzmyer, Superintendent

Dedicated: 1962; Herbert Hoover National Historic Site designated August 12, 1965
Admission: Adults $0.50; children under 15, free; school groups, free
Open: Monday-Saturday, 9:00 a.m.-6:00 p.m., and Sunday, 10:00 a.m.-6:00 p.m., May-Labor Day; 9:00 a.m.-5:00 p.m., Labor Day-April

Herbert Hoover Presidential Library and Museum (operated by National Archives and Records Service) includes public papers, personal correspondence, books, manuscripts, audiovisual materials, and memorabilia of former President Herbert Clark Hoover (1874-1964), first U.S. President born west of the Mississippi River. The Research Library has a book collection of 8,000 volumes dealing with the economic, political, and social history of 20th-Century America, and student and staff research work areas. In the 200-seat auditorium, films are shown to the public twice daily during the summer and by appointment during the winter.

The 2-room Hoover Birthplace Cottage, restored in 1938 to its original appearance, is maintained by the National Park Service, and contains many possessions of the Hoover family. The cottage, built about 1870 by Jesse Clark Hoover, stands on its original site, near Wapsinonoc Creek's west branch. A replica of the Blacksmith Shop, operated by the President's father, stands to the rear of the cottage, and is equipped with the tools of the trade. Across the street is the old Quaker Meeting House which Herbert Hoover attended as a boy. His mother, Hulda, often spoke

CEDAR
(continued)

Herbert Hoover National Historic Site
(continued)

before the Quaker congregation. The building had been moved and altered many times before it was moved to the present site in 1964 and restored. A plot of former agricultural land was planted to prairie grasses in 1971. The graves of President and Mrs. Hoover are located on a hillside about ¼ mile southwest of the birthplace cottage, within the 33-acre park which surrounds these points of interest.

● **Lowden Historical Society**
Lowden, Iowa

Rev. Paul C. Jordan, President
Box K
Lowden, Iowa 52255
or
Mrs. LeRoy Boettger, Secretary
R. R.
Lowden, Iowa 52255

Incorporated: November 6, 1973
Meetings: Every fifth Tuesday of each month (about 4 times per year)
Number of Members: 53
Dues: $2.00 annual

Conducts research on local businesses and the history of the town from earliest days, and collects items of historic interest for display.

● **West Branch Heritage Foundation**
P.O. Box 66
West Branch, Iowa 52358

Organized: August 22, 1963
Meetings: At call of president
Number of Members: 200
Dues: $3.00 individual; $5.00 couple; $10.00 sustaining; $25.00 sponsor; $50.00 patron

Operates West Branch Heritage Museum (see below). Two blocks of "old town" have been restored to their original appearance and preserved. The organization also participates in the observance of Herbert Hoover's birthday and other historic events.

● **West Branch Heritage Museum**
109 West Main Street
West Branch, Iowa 52358

Dedicated: August 10, 1964-
Admission: Free
Open: Weekdays, 9:30 a.m.-4:30 p.m., Sundays, 12:00-5:00 p.m. during summer; by appointment anytime

Maintained by members of West Branch Heritage Foundation (see above). The building, erected in 1884, was originally a grocery store, but also served as a harness and shoe store, music store, and variety store.

Museum exhibits include articles brought to West Branch by the first Quaker pioneers from Ohio and Pennsylvania, such as hand tools, tinware, glass, china, silverware, clothing, and toys. Relics from the William Maxon Home (see below), used by John Brown, and Indian artifacts, including Clovis points and a buffalo robe, may also be seen. One room is furnished as a pioneer home, with fireplace, rope bed, dough tray, pie cupboard, and dining table. Souvenirs and home made items are sold.

16 - CEDAR
(continued)

● **William Maxon Home**
3 miles northeast of Springdale, Iowa

A 2-ton glacial boulder, with a bronze plaque erected by the D A R in 1924, has been placed at the home of William Maxon. The house was used as winter quarters by anti-slavery agitator John Brown and his men in 1857-1858.

The Quakers, many of whom settled at Springdale, were determined Abolitionists. One of the escape routes for the slaves led from Tabor through Des Moines, Grinnell, Iowa City, West Branch, Springdale, and Tipton, to Clinton, Iowa. While in Springdale, John Brown planned and prepared for the attack on the United States arsenal at Harper's Ferry, Virginia. Two Springdale brothers, Edwin and Barclay Coppoc, were among the six Iowans who took part in the raid on Sunday, October 16, 1859. Edwin (only 24 years old) was captured and hanged with John Brown on December 16, 1859. Barclay (age 20) escaped and returned home to Springdale on December 17, the day after his brother was executed. With the outbreak of the Civil War, Barclay Coppoc joined the Union Army and was commissioned a lieutenant in the 3rd Kansas Volunteer Infantry. He was later killed in a train wreck, caused by guerrillas, near St. Joseph, Missouri.

17 - CERRO GORDO

Mason City
B-7

● **Charles H. MacNider Museum**
303 Second Street South East
Mason City, Iowa 50401

Richard E. Leet, Director and Resident Artist
(address as shown above)

Established: January 9, 1966
Admission: Free
Open: Tuesday and Friday, 10:00 a.m.-9:00 p.m.; Wednesday, Thursday, and Saturday, 10:00 a.m.-5:00 p.m.; Sunday, 2:00-5:00 p.m.; closed Monday

Contains permanent art collection and traveling exhibits. Lectures and demonstrations on art, a film series, music series, and art classes are offered.

The Hanford MacNider Room is being added to the museum as a tribute to General MacNider, who died February 17, 1968.

General Hanford MacNider, a son of Charles H. MacNider, built Indianhead, a 50-room mansion southeast of Mason City in 1929 on the highest point in Cerro Gordo County. Indianhead was named from the shoulder patch worn by General MacNider's World War I division, the Second Division. The stone home was donated by the MacNider family estate to North Iowa Community College in August 1970.

● **Clay Banks Forest**
2 miles south and 6 miles
east of Mason City, Iowa

Cerro Gordo County Conservation Board
Thomas Stehn, Executive Officer
220 North Washington
Mason City, Iowa 50401

A 56-acre area, adjacent to the Winnebago River, named for its clay banks which contain shells, fossils, and Indian artifacts. There is a flowing spring, a stand of hardwood timber, and abundant wildlife.

- CERRO GORDO
(continued)

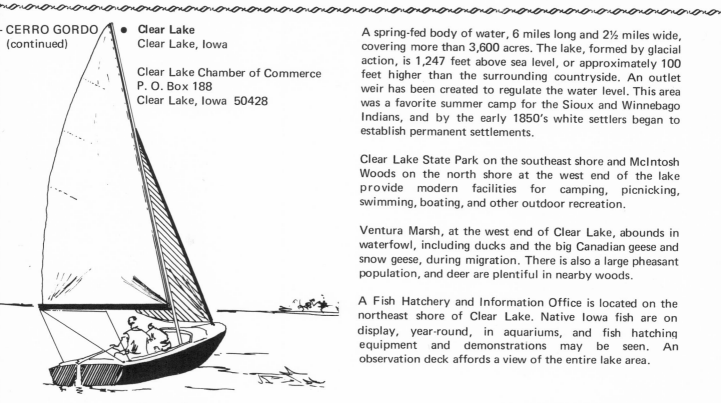

● **Clear Lake**
Clear Lake, Iowa

Clear Lake Chamber of Commerce
P. O. Box 188
Clear Lake, Iowa 50428

A spring-fed body of water, 6 miles long and 2½ miles wide, covering more than 3,600 acres. The lake, formed by glacial action, is 1,247 feet above sea level, or approximately 100 feet higher than the surrounding countryside. An outlet weir has been created to regulate the water level. This area was a favorite summer camp for the Sioux and Winnebago Indians, and by the early 1850's white settlers began to establish permanent settlements.

Clear Lake State Park on the southeast shore and McIntosh Woods on the north shore at the west end of the lake provide modern facilities for camping, picnicking, swimming, boating, and other outdoor recreation.

Ventura Marsh, at the west end of Clear Lake, abounds in waterfowl, including ducks and the big Canadian geese and snow geese, during migration. There is also a large pheasant population, and deer are plentiful in nearby woods.

A Fish Hatchery and Information Office is located on the northeast shore of Clear Lake. Native Iowa fish are on display, year-round, in aquariums, and fish hatching equipment and demonstrations may be seen. An observation deck affords a view of the entire lake area.

● **Lincoln Statue**
Clear Lake Cemetery
Clear Lake, Iowa

A replica of the world famous Augustus Saint-Gaudens statue of Lincoln, standing, is said to be one of less than 100 of this type in existence. The monument, dedicated in 1919, is constructed of 10 pieces of Barre and Monticello granite, and weighs over 40 tons. It cost $5,290.00. Annual Memorial Day services are conducted at the monument.

● **North Central Iowa Genealogical Society**
Mason City, Iowa

Mrs. Dorothy Bitker,
Corresponding Secretary
1712 South Taft
Mason City, Iowa 50401

Meetings: First Saturday of month except June, July, August, and December, 2:00 p.m.
Number of Members: 37

Members publish a newsletter, *The Genie Bug*, and are copying Cerro Gordo County records of births, deaths, and marriages, wills and probate records, and tax lists. The Society is a chapter of the Iowa Genealogical Society (see Polk County).

● **Pioneer Museum and Historical Society of North Iowa**
P. O. Box 421, Mason City, Iowa 50401. Located between Mason City and Clear Lake on U.S. 18, at the entrance to Mason City Airport

David M. Murphy, President
1600 12th Street N.E.
Mason City, Iowa 50401
or

Incorporated: October 7, 1964

Kinney Pioneer Museum, a brick and masonry building located on a 7-acre tract, contains exhibits to memorialize and preserve the heritage of North Central Iowa. Included are a fossil collection; Indian artifacts; agricultural tools and machinery; handmade farm implements; furniture, utensils, old dolls, toys, and clothing used by early residents; and a pioneer hand pump fire truck.

The museum, opened to the public on May 15, 1966, was made possible by a gift of $100,000 from the Kinney-

17 - CERRO GORDO
(continued)

Pioneer Museum and Historical Society of North Iowa
(continued)

Enoch A. Norem, Chairman
Executive Committee
East State Street
Mason City, Iowa 50401

Lindstrom Foundation. The land was deeded to the Society by the Mason City Airport Commission and the City of Mason City.

● **Shell Rock River Green Belt**
2 miles south and 1½ miles east of Rock Falls, Iowa

Cerro Gordo County Conservation Board
Thomas Stehn, Executive Officer
220 North Washington
Mason City, Iowa 50401

Several parcels of timber, pasture, and meadow land, totalling 590 acres, adjacent to the Shell Rock River, extending from Rock Falls to Nora Springs, 12 miles downstream. The green belt includes shoreline on slopes above the river, forested with native hardwood trees; pasture land with native cedar trees; limestone bluffs lining the river banks; small lakes; a lagoon, just off the river; and a rock quarry. This is a favorite stream for canoeing, providing swiftwater, with little riffles and rapids, and scenic views. There are limited facilities for camping and picnicking, and the clear-water stream provides fishing. An archery range, nature and bridle trails, and a scenic parkway along the river are proposed.

● **Wilkinson Pioneer Park**
South edge of Rock Falls, Iowa

About 61 acres on the Shell Rock River, north of Shell Rock River Green Belt (see above). A wooden covered bridge, the newest in Iowa, was built in 1969 across a small pond excavated for it. The bridge is a copy of the old Cutler or Donahue covered bridge, located in Winterset City Park. In building the replica, native lumber was used, sawed 3 miles south of the bridge site at a local sawmill. Cottonwood was used for the lattice trusses. The bridge is 16 feet wide with a 10-foot clearance. The approaches to the bridge are each 40 feet long. There are excellent facilities for camping (including rest rooms with showers), picnicking, and recreation.

18 - CHEROKEE

Cherokee
C-2

● **Cherokee County Historical Society**
P.O. Box 1067
Cherokee, Iowa 51012

Robert Perry, President
Cherokee, Iowa 51012
or
Darleen Cummins, Secretary
221 Euclid Avenue
Cherokee, Iowa 51012

Organized: August 1963
Meetings: Fourth Monday of each month except June, July, and December, 8:00 p.m.
Number of Members: 86
Dues: $3.00 annual

Activities include a pioneer supper, lectures, workshops, field trips, film showings, exhibits, and maintenance of a restored historic cabin. The Society publishes a newsletter for members.

8 - CHEROKEE
(continued)

● **Fort Cherokee**
Near Little Sioux River
on Old Highway 21
Cherokee, Iowa

A commemorative marker placed near the location of the main gate of old Fort Cherokee. Erected in 1862-63, the fort was one of a series of defensive fortifications built to protect the northwest frontier. At the south corner of the log stockade was a 2-story blockhouse built of huge squared logs. The officers' quarters also projected outside the stockade walls. Inside the stockade were the guardhouse and storeroom, stable, and granary.

● **Iowa Archeological Society**
Duane C. Anderson, President
1923 California Avenue
Iowa City, Iowa 52240

Meetings: Annual meeting in spring, at different location each year
Number of Members: 284
Dues: $5.00 annual; $15.00 sustaining; $50.00 life

Patricia M. Williams, Secretary
117 East Willow
Cherokee, Iowa 51012

A non-profit, scientific society of amateur and professional archeologists whose purpose is to study, expand, preserve, and record the prehistoric heritage of Iowa. Publications include a *Newsletter,* issued periodically, which reports archeological finds and activities of members, and the *Journal of the Iowa Archeological Society,* containing reports of permanent scientific value describing archeological camps, villages, mounds, and tools left by the prehistoric Indians of Iowa. Field trips to archeological excavations may be arranged. Regional chapters have been organized as follows: Northwest (Cherokee), Northeast (Decorah), Quad City (Davenport), Southeast (Ottumwa), Central (Fort Dodge), and South Central (Mount Ayr).

● **Martin-Little Sioux Access**
4 miles east and 3/4 mile
south of Larrabee, Iowa

Cherokee County Conservation Board
Ronald L. Dudley, Executive Officer
1008 Rock Island Avenue
Cherokee, Iowa 51012

A 164-acre area devoted to picnicking, camping, hiking, horseback riding, fishing, and nature study. The rolling, hilly land is covered with hardwood timber (mainly burr and white oak, hickory, basswood, ironwood, wild plum, hackberry, wahoo, and maple), shrubs, native grasses, and a variety of wild flowers. There is an abundance of wildlife and of song birds, as well as a small spring in the area. Boat launching facilities are provided for float trips on the Little Sioux River.

● **Northwest Chapter,**
Iowa Archeological Society

Sanford Museum and Planetarium
117 East Willow
Cherokee, Iowa 51012

C. A. Brenner, President
Sheldon, Iowa

Established: 1951
Meetings: Third Sunday of each month except December, 2:00 p.m.
Number of Members: 50
Dues: $2.00 family; $1.00 student

A regional chapter of the Iowa Archeological Society (see above). Activities include lectures, film showings, workshops, supervised excavation of archeological sites, and field trips. The *NWIAS Newsletter* is published bimonthly.

● **Old White Mill**
Near junction of
Old Highway 21 and
Spruce Street
Cherokee, Iowa

A marker, erected in 1926, at the site of the Old White Mill built along the west bank of the Little Sioux River by J. W. Bliss, in the autumn of 1871. The old millstones were reclaimed and used as a base for the monument.

The mill was a 3-story frame structure, 40 x 60 feet. Its huge millstones--5 or 6 feet in diameter and 8 to 12 inches

18 - CHEROKEE
(continued)

Old White Mill
(continued)

thick--were hauled from Denison by oxteam. A large waterwheel, just outside the mill building, furnished the power for grinding. In 1887, the new owner of the mill, Charles Beckworth, changed to a full "rollery system," with a capacity of 50 barrels of flour a day. The grain was crushed between rollers and the old millstones were no longer used. The mill changed hands several times in later years. The great flood of 1891 swept away the old mill dam, after which the mill was converted to steam power. Operations later ceased, due to changing conditions, and the mill was finally torn down.

● **Phipps Site**
3 miles north of
Cherokee, Iowa

Paul Phipps, Owner
R. R. 1
Cherokee, Iowa 51012

A rich archeological site, adjacent to Mill Creek. This was the first of the Mill Creek sites to be excavated and the land has been returned to cultivation. There is no public access.

● **Pilot Rock**
South of Cherokee, Iowa

A huge glacial boulder (20' high, 40' wide, and 61' long) deeply embedded in the ground, has served as a landmark since pioneer days. The Sioux quartzite boulder was known to the Indians as Woven Stone. The trails of the countryside ran directly to this old landmark, and the spot was a favorite camping ground. The post office of Pilot Rock, which was in existence from October 5, 1865 until May 24, 1886, received its name from this rock.

● **Sanford Museum and Planetarium**
117 East Willow
Cherokee, Iowa 51012

Patricia M. Williams, Acting Director
(address as shown above)

Founded: 1941 (by Mr. and Mrs. W. A. Sanford as a memorial to their son, Tiel)
Opened to Public: April 22, 1951
Admission: Free
Open: Monday through Friday, 9:00 a.m.-noon and 1:00-5:00 p.m.; Saturday, 9:00 a.m.-noon; Sunday, 2:00-5:00 p.m.; closed on major holidays

A non-profit cultural and educational institution, accredited by the American Association of Museums. The Museum includes exhibits on local history, Indians, archeology, paleontology, geology, birds, ice age animals, art, and antique furniture. There are also loan and circulating exhibitions, guided tours, field trips, lectures, and films. A school-museum program, utilizing museum specimens and exhibits, has been developed to improve student learning and attitude, with the aid of a Title III ESEA grant. Various types of memberships in the Sanford Museum Association are available.

The first planetarium in Iowa (1950), has demonstrations

- CHEROKEE
(continued)

Sanford Museum and Planetarium
(continued)

(45 minutes) by appointment, in advance, for groups of 15-50 persons. The planetarium was dedicated by Armond Spitz, inventor of the Spitz Planetarium instrument.

Meeting place for Sanford Museum Association, Cherokee County Historical Society, Northwest Chapter of the Iowa Archeological Society, and Cherokee Arts Council.

- **Stiles School House Museum**
  Southwest corner of Silver Township, southeast of Quimby, Iowa

  Lester L. and Marguerite S. Whiting, Custodians
  338 Fountain Street
  Cherokee, Iowa 51012

Admission: Free; donations accepted
Open: Sunday, 2:00-5:00 p.m. during summer; other times by appointment, for groups

Old Number 9, a 1-room rural schoolhouse, furnished. A collection of pioneer items, antiques, farm tools and machinery, and Indian artifacts may be seen.

- CHICKASAW

w Hampton
B-9

- **Adolph Munson Park**
  3½ miles northwest of Lawler, Iowa; or 3½ miles north of New Hampton on U.S. 63, then 4½ miles east.

  Chicsaw County Conservation Board
  Vincent C. Gebel, Executive Officer
  P.O. Box 311
  New Hampton, Iowa 50659

Old ghost town, Jacksonville, Iowa, which was located on the old Dragoon (Military) Trail, is preserved in a 3-acre park. The settlement was first called Greenville in honor of the man who built the first house, a log hotel, in Jacksonville Township. When the town was surveyed and platted, its name was changed. The first newspaper to be published in Chickasaw County, the *Chickasaw Republican*, was started here in May 1857. A post office was established January 29, 1856, and discontinued August 5, 1887. An old cemetery contains gravestones dating back to 1854. A log cabin, furnished with articles out of the historic past, a 1-room rural schoolhouse, and an old country store are enclosed by a rail fence. Picnic facilities are available on the site.

- **Chickasaw County Historical Society**
  New Hampton, Iowa

  Mrs. Glen (Leota) Dudley, President
  R. R. 1
  Ionia, Iowa 50645

Organized: December 8, 1953; incorporated February 1954
Meetings: Annually in April; directors meet second Tuesday of month, 8:00 p.m.
Number of Members: 425
Dues: $1.00 annual; $2.00 associate; $10.00 life; $100.00 memorial
Admission to Old Bradford: $0.75
Open: Daily, 9:00 a.m.-5:30 p.m., May 1 to October 1, other times by appointment.

Sponsors historical pageants, annual wedding reunion dinner for Little Brown Church (Nashua), art exhibits, hobby exhibit, flower show, tours. Chickasaw Church (west of Ionia) and Deerfield Church (north of Bassett) have been restored. Beef stew dinner is held at Chickasaw Church in November, and an annual homecoming and dinner at Deerfield Church on the third Sunday in August.

19 - CHICKASAW
(continued)

Chickasaw County Historical Society
(continued)

A restored village is located at Old Bradford, one block from the Little Brown Church, built in 1864, (see below), inspiration for the famous hymn, "The Church in the Wildwood," by Dr. William S. Pitts. A number of old buildings are located on a 4-acre plot, making up the Chickasaw County Museum. These include log cabins, the office of Dr. Pitts, a blacksmith shop, an old rural schoolhouse, a country store, depot, Victorian cottage, museum, and a handicraft and gift shop. Also to be seen are an old wooden windmill, agricultural implements, antiques, and books.

Bradford was a thriving little village of about 1,000 inhabitants before the railroad bypassed it. All that remains of the original town is the old Bradford Academy building, now a residence, and the old stagecoach stop.

● **Devon Woods**
1 mile west, 3 miles north, and ½ mile west of New Hampton, Iowa; or 3 3/4 miles east of North Washington, Iowa

Chickasaw County Conservation Board
Vincent C. Gebel, Executive Officer
P. O. Box 311
New Hampton, Iowa 50659

An unimproved timber area used for nature study. Native hardwood trees, shrubs, and wild flowers are being preserved. A small slough provides a nesting area and cover for upland game birds and mammals.

● **Goodale Conservation Area**
4 miles west, ½ mile south, and 1¼ miles west of Alta Vista, Iowa

Chickasaw County Conservation Board
Vincent C. Gebel, Executive Officer
P. O. Box 311
New Hampton, Iowa 50659

A wildlife food and shelter area along both sides of the Wapsipinicon River. Tree plantings and reforestation are under way.

● **Howard Woods**
2 miles northwest of Nashua, Iowa

Chickasaw County Conservation Board
Vincent C. Gebel, Executive Officer
P. O. Box 311
New Hampton, Iowa 50659

A 20-acre area which runs to the Cedar River. Open for fishing, picnicking, camping, boating, and nature study.

● **Jenn Timber**
6 miles west of New Hampton, Iowa on U.S. 18, then ½ mile north

Chickasaw County Conservation Board
Vincent C. Gebel, Executive Officer
P. O. Box 311
New Hampton, Iowa 50659

A nature study area containing many varieties of wild flowers, ferns, shrubs, and native trees. The timber is under Forest Reserve management.

9 - CHICKASAW
(continued)

● **Little Brown Church in the Vale**
Bradford, Iowa
near Nashua, Iowa

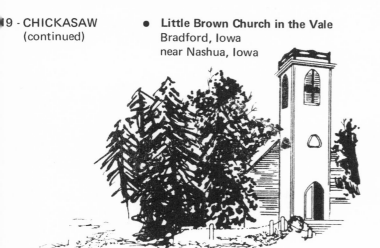

Dedicated: December 29, 1864

The church made popular by the hymn, "The Church in the Wildwood." The hymn was actually written before the church was erected. Dr. William S. Pitts, a dentist and teacher of singing, visited Bradford in 1857 and wrote the song after returning to his native state of Wisconsin, remembering an "attractive and lovely spot." The "little brown church" was added from his imagination. In 1863, Dr. Pitts moved to Iowa, locating in Fredericksburg, 20 miles from Bradford.

The church was originally organized in 1855. The simple frame building with its square tower without a spire was erected in 1864 and painted brown, as in the song. Its architect was Reverend J. K. Nutting, who also designed the Tabor Congregational Church.

● **Split Rock Park**
2½ miles south, 1½ miles west, and ½ mile south of Fredericksburg, Iowa; or 10 miles south, 4 miles east, and ½ mile north of New Hampton, Iowa

Chickasaw County Conservation Board
Vincent C. Gebel, Executive Officer
P. O. Box 311
New Hampton, Iowa 50659

Named for a large granite rock, split in half and embedded in the ground. The 80-acre park includes a 10-acre spring-fed lake, stocked with fish. A swimming beach and bathhouse are on the north shore of the lake. In addition, there are hiking trails, a picnic area, and a camping area. A damp, wooded section contains many of the wild flowers becoming scarce in Iowa, affording an opportunity for nature study.

● **Twin Ponds**
Southwest of New Hampton, Iowa; or 2 miles south and 3 miles east of Ionia, Iowa

Chickasaw County Conservation Board
Vincent C. Gebel, Executive Officer
P. O. Box 311
New Hampton, Iowa 50659

A 160-acre area bisected by the Wapsipinicon River. In the area subject to flooding are many kinds of aquatic plants. Throughout the flood plain are various high spots of land in the form of hummocks. Trees include oak, hickory, maple, cherry, elm, poplar, willow, and river birch. Many varieties of prairie wild flowers may be seen. Facilities include fishing ponds, an educational unit of outdoor classrooms for use of schools and nature study groups, nature trails, wilderness camping, and picnic tables.

● **Wapsie River Access**
1 mile south and 2½ miles west of North Washington, Iowa

Chickasaw County Conservation Board
Vincent C. Gebel, Executive Officer
P. O. Box 311
New Hampton, Iowa 50659

A 60-acre tract providing access to the Wapsipinicon River. It is utilized as a fishing and hunting area, outdoor classroom, and wildlife habitat. Some of the land is subject to flooding, and is covered with bottomland timber, with potholes and marshy areas.

20 - CLARKE

Osceola
H-6

● **Clarke County Historical Society**
Osceola, Iowa

Robert Diehl, President
R. R. 4
Osceola, Iowa 50213
or
Melvin H. Goeldner
209 East Pearl Street
Osceola, Iowa 50213

Organized: May 21, 1970
Meetings: Third Thursday of month, 7:30 p.m.
Number of Members: 175
Dues: $1.00 annual

Clarke County Historical Museum is located in downtown Osceola, at 117½ South Main Street. Articles and documents, including family histories for Clarke County, have been collected for the museum. There are displays of farm machinery and tools, harness, doctors' instruments, old kitchen equipment, dining room and parlor furnishings, old documents, clothing, old school desks and church pews, and other articles associated with the history of Clarke County.

A 100-year old log cabin was moved in 1970 to the Clarke County Fairgrounds and restored. The 12' x 14' cabin was built mainly of oak logs by George Harlan, who is buried in Union Chapel Cemetery. Near the Harlan cabin is a well house built by G. L. Terry, a skilled carpenter who lived at Weldon, Iowa.

The site of Lost Camp, a temporary settlement founded by the Mormons, is located in Section 17, Green Bay Township.

● **Mormon Trail**

Joseph Smith, Jr. established his first church in New York, later moving on into Ohio, Missouri, and Illinois, where he and his followers built the city of Nauvoo. After Smith and his brother were killed by a mob at Carthage, Illinois, the church broke into factions. Brigham Young became leader of the larger group and set out to establish a church in the west, finally locating at Salt Lake City, Utah. The Mormon Trail went through 12 counties across southern Iowa: Lee, Van Buren, Davis, Appanoose, Wayne, Decatur, Lucas, Clarke, Union, Adair, Cass, and Pottawattamie. In Clarke County, the trail or road meandered across Franklin, Green Bay, Knox, Ward, and Troy Townships.

21 - CLAY

Spencer
B-3

● **Fort Peterson**
Located on farm of
Mr. & Mrs. Duane Johnson
Peterson, Iowa 51047

Fort Peterson was one of a string of forts constructed and manned by troops known as the Northern Border Brigade, built after the Spirit Lake Massacre of 1857. These forts were established at five points along a line passing through Correctionville, Cherokee, Peterson, Estherville, and Chain Lake. In May 1856, Ambrose S. Mead and J. A. Kirchner, the first settlers in Clay County, broke the sod at a settlement first called Long Grove. The town was renamed Howard when a request was made for a post office, but the Post Office Department substituted the name Peterson. This was the first county seat, and the location of the first sawmill and the first newspaper in Clay County. Following the slaughter of over 1,000 white settlers in Minnesota in 1862, Lt. Col. James Sawyer sent a detail from his headquarters in Spirit Lake to protect the settlement and build the fort. It stood within the town of Peterson and was

1 - CLAY
(continued)

Fort Peterson
(continued)

constructed of hand-hewn, black walnut logs. Axe marks may still be seen on the logs. The building was constructed with wooden pins--no nails were used. The loopholes through the walls were larger on the inside so rifles could be swung around, permitting greater range. The original blockhouse had a second story, rotated 45 degrees. A stockade, triangular in shape (152' x 100' x 100'), surrounded the fort. The stockade was also made of black walnut logs, driven into the ground.

There are many stories about soldiers at the fort, and legends of buried gold, and of a pioneer said to have been buried in a sitting position because his frozen body could not be straightened out.

When the danger from Indians subsided, the stockade was torn down and burned for fuel. Pieces of the wood were saved and used to make a lamp. A gavel was also made for the Masonic Lodge. The fort itself was moved about a mile west of town and occupied as a farm home. In 1938, the old fort was moved again, about 100 yards northwest, to make room for a new residence. A tablet marks the original site.

Between the town of Peterson and the present location of the fort is a log cabin built about 1867. The cabin contains many tools and utensils used by the pioneers. Privately owned, it may be visited with permission.

● **Inkpaduta Trail**
From Peterson, Iowa to Arnolds Park, Iowa

Dr. F. V. Maytum
Spirit Lake, Iowa 51360

A 62-mile long hiking trail laid out by the Prairie Gold Area Council of the Boy Scouts of America, following the trail used by Inkpaduta and his band of hostile Sioux Indians during the Spirit Lake Massacre of 1857. The trail starts at the Heywood Cabin in Peterson and ends at the Gardner Log Cabin in Arnolds Park, crossing parts of Clay and Dickinson Counties. It has been approved for use of Boy Scouts for a hiking merit badge.

● **Kindlespire Park**
5 miles west and ½ mile south of Webb, Iowa

Clay County Conservation Board
Charles R. Swan, Chairman
R. R., Ruthven, Iowa 51358

A 160-acre, undeveloped area, divided by the Little Sioux River, including both bottomlands and high ground. Timber includes oak, elm, basswood, willow, box elder, and walnut. There are Indian mounds on the bluff along the south side of the river.

● **Parker Historical Society of Clay County**
East Third Street
Spencer, Iowa 51301

Paul Swaim, President
Webb, Iowa 51366
        or
Owen Cook
Spencer, Iowa 51301

Organized: January 13, 1960
Meetings: Four times each year
Number of Members: 183
Dues: $2.00 annual; $5.00 family; $30.00 life
Museum Open: Sundays during summer; other times by
                    appointment

Organized to identify and mark historic sites, and collect and preserve items associated with the history of Clay County.

21 - CLAY
(continued)

Parker Historical Society of Clay County
(continued)

The former home of Reverend and Mrs. Parker was donated to Society. The museum exhibits include farm machinery, tools, clothing, pictures, and other items from Iowa's past.

● **Peterson Heritage, Inc.**
Peterson, Iowa

James Hass, President
Peterson, Iowa 51047

Incorporated: July 14, 1971

● **Rock Forest School**
Peterson, Iowa

Willard Kracht
Peterson Lions Club
Peterson, Iowa 51047
or
C. B. Reed
Peterson, Iowa 51047

Open: Sunday, 2:00-5:00 p.m., or by appointment

Small, white, wooden rural schoolhouse, built about 1868 in extreme NW part of Section 20, Peterson Township, Clay County. Used as school and church until 1918, when it was moved to a farm to serve as a garage and tool shop. In January, 1963 the old school building was moved to swimming pool park in Peterson and restored by the Peterson Lions Club. The school is representative of hundreds of other rural schools that formerly dotted the countryside about 2 miles apart. It is furnished with items typical of Midwestern prairie schools of 100 years ago--old school desks, pot-bellied stove, teacher's desk, piano, blackboards, old school bells, rollup maps, and old pictures.

22 - CLAYTON

Elkader
B-11

● **Bixby State Park**
2 miles north of Iowa 3 at Edgewood, Iowa, on county road

State Conservation Commission
State Office Building
300 Fourth Street
Des Moines, Iowa 50319

Clayton County Conservation Board
Don R. Menken, Executive Officer
R. R. 2, Elkader, Iowa 52043

Phenomenal Ice Cave in beautiful, rugged, 69-acre area. This is one of the few such caves in the Middle West. The year-round temperature varies little from the freezing point. Bear Creek flows through the park, and there are several flowing springs, a profusion of wild flowers, hiking trails, and picnic facilities. Care and maintenance is provided by Clayton County under a management agreement with the State Conservation Commission.

● **Bloody Run**
2 miles west of
Marquette, Iowa

Clayton County Conservation Board
Don R. Menken, Executive Officer
R. R. 2, Elkader, Iowa 52043

Bloody Run, a spring-fed trout stream flows through a 135-acre forest preserve. High limestone bluffs covered with hardwood timber are included in the area. The Chicago, Milwaukee, St. Paul and Pacific Railroad crosses Bloody Run at 3 points within the property. There are facilities for fishing (special trout stamp on fishing license required), picnicking, and camping.

● **Buck Creek Area**
3 miles northeast of
Garnavillo, Iowa

Clayton County Conservation Board
Don R. Menken, Executive Officer
R. R. 2, Elkader, Iowa 52043

A 103-acre tract located near the headwaters of Buck Creek, a stocked trout stream. The area includes an excellent stand of hardwood timber, with plantings of coniferous trees. Fishing (special trout stamp on fishing license required), picnicking, and hunting are permitted.

22 - CLAYTON
(continued)

● **Chicken Ridge Scenic Overlook**
4 miles south of Elkader, along
east side of Iowa 13

Clayton County Conservation Board
Don R. Menken, Executive Officer
R. R. 2, Elkader, Iowa 52043

Scenic view from the reputed highest point in Clayton County. There are picnic tables on the 4-acre tract.

● **Effigy Mounds National Monument**
3 miles north of Marquette, on Iowa 76

Thomas Munson, Superintendent
P. O. Box K, McGregor, Iowa 52157

Established: October 25, 1949; Visitor Center opened 1960
Admission: Free
Open: Daily, 8:00 a.m.-5:00 p.m. (7:30 p.m. during summer);
closed Christmas Day

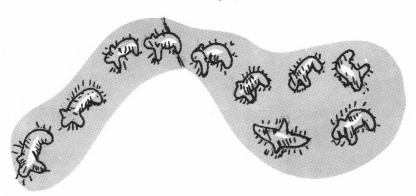

Within the monument's 2-square-mile area (in Allamakee and Clayton Counties) 191 known prehistoric mounds are preserved. These Indian burial mounds are of a type unique in North America, and are found only in southern Wisconsin and adjacent areas in Illinois, Minnesota, and Iowa. Twenty-nine mounds are in the form of bear and bird effigies, while the others are conical or linear shaped. The Visitor Center includes an archeological museum, with displays of local Woodland and Mississippian Cultures; artifacts; and herbarium. Audiovisual presentations are given in the auditorium. Self-guiding trails take visitors to the burial mounds, and to Fire Point for an excellent view of the Mississippi River. Conducted tours by appointment, and on a regular schedule during summer months.

● **First Gasoline Tractor Marker**
Along U.S. 18 and 52 at Froelich, Iowa

A granite marker and bronze plaque commemorate the building of the first gasoline-powered tractor, invented in 1892 by John Froelich, who operated a feed mill and elevator in the village of Froelich. During summers, Froelich, who worked with steam-powered threshing outfits in South Dakota's wheat fields, was annoyed with the problem of getting and hauling water for the steam engines. He conceived the idea of a gasoline-powered outfit and, after many months of effort in his shop at Froelich, he assembled a tractor that would move forward and backward under its own power. The invention was destined to have a far-reaching effect on modern agriculture. Froelich joined with others to organize the Waterloo Gasoline Tractor Engine Company, which later became John Deere and Company.

● **Garnavillo Historical Museum**
Garnavillo, Iowa 52049

Arnold D. Roggman, Curator
Garnavillo, Iowa 52049

Acquired: 1965
Open: Saturday and Sunday, 2:00-5:00 p.m. and 7:00-10:00 p.m., May 1 to October 15

22 - CLAYTON
(continued)

Garnavillo Historical Museum
(continued)

Located in a brick building erected in 1866 as a Congregational Church. The building was later purchased by James O. Crosby, early-day lawyer and surveyor, and was also used as a community building. The museum, opened to the public in July 1966 by Garnavillo Historical Society (see below), contains thousands of manuscripts, papers, letters, and magazines dating back to the 18th Century or earlier; old maps; hand tools; tintypes and photographs; bills of sale; posters and handbills; old wills and legal documents; displays of cameras and guns; model rooms of pioneer homes; and archeological exhibits; and 300 paintings by Althea Sherman (a noted Iowa ornithologist).

Althea Sherman (1853-1943) built a 22-foot wooden tower in 1914 at the former town of National, Iowa, located north of Garnavillo. The structure was built to include a 14-foot wooden chimney in the upper part of the tower to permit the study of the habits of the chimney swift. The Althea Sherman Swift Tower was moved in recent years to Andy Mountain Campground, ½ mile south of Harpers Ferry, Iowa, for preservation as a historic landmark. Chimney swifts still successfully nest in the tower.

● **Garnavillo Historical Society**
Garnavillo, Iowa 52049

Arnold Larson, President
Garnavillo, Iowa 52049

Incorporated: April 29, 1965

Owns and operates Garnavillo Historical Museum (see above).

● **Joy Springs Park**
2½ miles west and 1 mile south of Strawberry Point, Iowa

An 80-acre piece of timbered land, through which flow two trout streams--the Maquoketa River and Bruce Creek. Included in the area are 7 springs known as Joy Springs. There are facilities for picnicking and camping.

● **Lover's Leap Park**
North edge of Elkader, Iowa

Clayton County Conservation Board
Don R. Menken, Executive Officer
R. R. 2, Elkader, Iowa 52043

A 10-acre park located on the Turkey River bluff. Undeveloped at present, hiking trails and picnic facilities are planned for the park.

According to legend, the Indian sweetheart of an early settler jumped off the cliff into the Turkey River. Statues of the lovers are on the cliff, reached by trail.

- CLAYTON
(continued)

● **McGregor Historical Museum**
Second Street
McGregor, Iowa 52157

Mrs. Fred (Mae) Huebsch,
Curator

Opened: 1938
Admission: Donations accepted
Open: Wednesday, Saturday, and Sunday afternoons; other times by appointment

Located in the old Library Building and operated by McGregor Historical Society (see below). Displays include articles of historic interest from the McGregor area, including Civil War relics, household antiques, early school equipment and records, and the famous sand bottles by Andrew Clemens.

● **McGregor Historical Society**
Second Street
McGregor, Iowa 52157

Lynn Johnson, President
McGregor, Iowa 52157

Organized: 1941
Meetings: Quarterly
Number of Members: 150
Dues: $0.50 annual

Maintains McGregor Historical Museum (see above).

● **Merritt Forest**
4½ miles south and 2 miles
west of Guttenberg, Iowa
on county road

State Conservation Commission
State Office Building
300 Fourth Street
Des Moines, Iowa 50319

A 20-acre State Preserve containing a solid stand of virgin Iowa forest, never cut. The natural area is about 2 miles northwest of Millville, along the Turkey River.

● **Military Trail Marker**
North of Marquette, Iowa
on west side of highway

A marker erected by the Daughters of the American Revolution to commemorate the military trail from Fort Crawford (Prairie du Chien), Wisconsin to Fort Atkinson, Iowa. Supplies were transported over this road when Fort Atkinson was being constructed.

There are many ancient Indian mounds in the area.

● **Monona Historical Society**
Monona, Iowa

Mrs. Otmar H. Bruns, President
Box T
Monona, Iowa 52159

or

Miss Willa Helwig, Curator
Monona, Iowa 52159

Incorporated: February 2, 1968
Meetings: Quarterly and as called
Number of Members: 60
Dues: $1.00 annual

Maintains a museum in a 3-story, 12-room house built around 1909 at 302 South Egbert Street in Monona. Materials on hand include old plat books, cook books, doctor's books, the *Monona Leader* and other newspapers. The Society reprinted the 1882 history of Clayton County.

● **Moody's Musical Museum**
1111 West Main Street
McGregor, Iowa 52157

Founded: 1951
Admission: $0.50; children 5-12, $0.25; under 5, $0.10
Open: Daily, May through October

Features an extensive collection of old mechanical orchestrations, music boxes, and player pianos, in operating

22 - CLAYTON
(continued)

Moody's Musical Museum
(continued)

condition. Also to be seen are a Civil War display, country store and post office, Wells Fargo express office, whiskey still, Gay Nineties barber shop, steamboat lore, old automobiles, and life-size wax figures of colorful characters of the Old West. An interesting sand bottle collection includes the work of artists Andrew Clemens, Harvey Haltmeyer, and Robert Trayer.

Open: Privately owned, but may be seen at any time

● **Motor Mill**
Southeast of Elkader, Iowa
or 2 miles northeast of the
village of Communia, Iowa

An old 5-story stone mill on the Turkey River, where flour, corn meal, hominy, and feed were manufactured. Only a few scattered rocks remain of the 200-foot dam, which once stood 12 feet high. The waterwheel has long since disappeared.

The town of Motor was laid out in 1845. It had a bright future, but flourished only briefly because of a series of misfortunes. Floods, crop failures due to drought, grasshoppers, and chinch bugs brought an end to the boom. The mill, built at a cost of $90,000, ceased to operate in the late 1870's. Other stone buildings dating back to the existence of the town of Motor include the old livery stable (now used as a barn), the former tavern (now used as a farm home), and the 2-story cooperage.

● **National Fish Hatchery and Aquarium**
Guttenberg, Iowa

U. S. Department of the Interior
Fish and Wildlife Service
Bureau of Sport Fisheries and
Wildlife

Admission: Free
Open: Daily, 8:00 a.m.-5:00 p.m.

One of over 100 National Fish Hatcheries, strategically located throughout the country. The various tanks in the aquarium contain species of fish common to the area.

● **Osborne Conservation Education Center**
5 miles southwest of Elkader,
on Iowa 13, near Osborne, Iowa

Clayton County Conservation Board
Don R. Menken, Executive Officer
R. R. 2, Elkader, Iowa 52043

A tree plantation demonstration area for conservation, erosion control, and educational purposes. The 260-acre area, divided by the Volga River, is planted with various species of trees, and is used as an outdoor classroom by public and parochial schools. A visitor center, built in 1972, contains displays to help interpret the environment. A high bluff dips down sharply to the river, where a variety of trees and shrubs may be seen--black walnut, hickory, oak, maple, elm, poplar, ironwood, dogwood, cedar, prickly ash, and wild gooseberry. There are 3 marked, self-guiding trails--the Nature Trail (general ecology), the Conifer Trail,

- CLAYTON
(continued)

Osborne Conservation Education Center
(continued)

and the Soil Conservation Trail. A wildlife exhibit section includes buffalo (bison), Japanese Sika deer, whitetail deer, elk, raccoons, squirrels (2 species), skunks, wild turkeys, Canada geese, peafowl, quail, and several types of ducks, pheasants, and partridge.

A log cabin built around 1840, is the nucleus of a Pioneer Village, which will include a 1-room schoolhouse, railroad depot, and blacksmith shop. Recreational activities include fishing, hiking, picnicking, and camping.

● **Pikes Peak State Park**
2 miles southeast of McGregor, Iowa on Iowa 30

State Conservation Commission
State Office Building
300 Fourth Street
Des Moines, Iowa 50319

A unique combination of history and natural beauty, named for Zebulon M. Pike, who later discovered Colorado's Pikes Peak. This highest bluff on the Mississippi River has also been called Pikes Hill and Pikes Mountain.

The first white men to discover Iowa and the Upper Mississippi were Louis Joliet and Father Jacques Marquette. On June 17, 1673, the French explorers floated out from the mouth of the Wisconsin River into the mighty Mississippi opposite Pikes Peak-- exactly one month after their departure from St. Ignace Mission.

Two years after the Louisiana Purchase of 1803, the U. S. government sent Lieutenant Pike, then 26 years old, to explore the upper valley of the Mississippi River and select sites suitable for military posts. Although Pike recognized this hill as a strategic point and an excellent location for a fort, the War Department selected Prairie du Chien, Wisconsin (Fort Crawford) as the location of the fort.

Outstanding views of the confluence of the Wisconsin and Mississippi Rivers and the many bayous may be enjoyed from 500-foot bluffs. Other features include Indian mounds, famous colored sandstone, and trails over rugged terrain, one of which goes underneath Bridal Veil Falls, and on to Sand Cave and Picture Rock. Hikers can see sheer walls of Trenton limestone filled with fossils of brachiopods, gastropods, and cephalopods. Cliffs of St. Peter's sandstone contain banded, mottled, and figured patterns in shades of yellow, brown, red, white, black, and green. Fantastic pinnacles have been cut out of the rock by erosion of wind and water. Wild flowers may be seen in deep woods and on slopes of the cliffs and ridges in the area of over 500 acres. The Mississippi Valley is considered one of America's best areas for bird study, especially during migration.

Fireplaces and shelters are provided for picnickers, and the campground has modern rest rooms, with hot showers and laundry facilities.

22 - CLAYTON
(continued)

● **Pioneer Rock Church
or Ceres Church**

Located along U.S. 52 in the
ghost village of Ceres (pronounced
Sears), between Guttenberg and
Garnavillo, Iowa

Rocks quarried nearby were used by members of St. Peter's
German United Evangelical Lutheran Church to build this
2-story church in 1858. Regular services have not been
conducted for many years, but occasionally special services
or events take place at this enduring landmark. The interior
is equipped much as it was in pioneer times, with short-back
pews, a pulpit with winding stairs, the old organ, and a
heating stove.

● **Point Ann**
McGregor, Iowa

State-owned area containing Indian mounds; inaccessible by
car. From the Mississippi River the huge rock bluff is said
to resemble an Indian head.

● **Retz Memorial Forest**
Southeast of Elkader, Iowa
on dead end road, 1 mile
northeast of old stone mill
at Motor, Iowa

John Brayton
Treasurer, Iowa Chapter
The Nature Conservancy
R.R. 2, Sumner, Iowa 50674

A 49-acre area of natural beauty in the Turkey River
Valley, featuring a high woodland, a lush ravine, and
massive limestone boulders. The hardwood forest is
dominated by sugar maple and basswood, but includes red
oak, white oak, black walnut, white walnut, hickory, wild
cherry, ironwood, birch, and bigtooth aspen. Rocky, rugged
slopes are covered with mosses, lichens, liverworts, walking
ferns, maidenhair ferns, and an abundance of wild flowers.

One old-timer who grew up in the vicinity remembers it for
rattlesnakes, ginseng, and a lost lead mine. According to
legend, the Indians had a lead mine in this area along the
Turkey River during the Civil War. The lead ore was packed
to Dubuque where the Indians sold or exchanged it for
flour, sugar, bacon, tea, and cloth. White prospectors are
said to have tried to locate the mine, but were not able to
do so.

The property, formerly known as the Kopp Timber Tract,
was purchased by the Iowa Chapter of The Nature
Conservancy, a non-profit organization dedicated to the
preservation of natural areas for their aesthetic, scientific,
and educational values. The tract was renamed in memory
of Lyle Retz, former executive director of the Delaware
County Conservation Board and an avid conservationist.

● **Silica Mine**
South of Clayton, Iowa

Silica sand mining operations have been carried on in this
area since 1878. The pure silica mined here is one of the
few sources of the sand used mainly for foundry castings
and sandblasting. About 130,000 tons are removed yearly
from the 50-acre underground mine, located along the
banks of the Mississippi River, and Clayton sand has been
shipped all over the world. The present mine was started in
1916 by John Langworthy from Dubuque, but since 1959
it has been owned by the Martin-Marietta Corporation.
Previous operations were open pit, not underground. The
extremely pure sand is part of the St. Peter Sandstone
formation, which varies in thickness in Iowa from an
estimated 15 to 223 feet. Since the 1960's the Clayton
mine has been stocked with food, water, and medical
supplies for use as a civil defense shelter (capacity 44,000
persons).

- CLAYTON
(continued)

Silica Mine
(continued)

The town and the county were named for Congressman John M. Clayton of Delaware. The community was originally an important landing and shipping point for flour. Following a disastrous fire in 1901, which destroyed 23 buildings, the town of Clayton (founded in 1849) has declined in population from 1,000 to about 130 today. The Old Stone School was in continuous use for 103 years. The school area is now used for camping and picnicking. The town's water supply comes from springs, operated since 1881.

● **Spook Cave**
7 miles west of McGregor, and north on spur road near junction of U.S. 18 and U.S. 52

Gerald Mielke, Owner
McGregor, Iowa 52157

Opened: 1955
Admission: $1.50; rates for children and groups
Open: 8:00 a.m.-9:00 p.m., May 1-October 15

Natural underground river and cave with fascinating formations. A half-hour cruise, with guide, may be taken in 12-passenger electric- powered boats. Constant temperature of 47 degrees in cave. Water wheel, picnic area, campsite, and souvenir shop.

● **Table Rock**
2 miles northeast of Elkader, Iowa

Table Rock marks the place where one of the first celebrations in observance of the anniversary of American Independence was held in what is now Iowa. It took place on July 4, 1838, attended by the early settlers of Boardman Township. A bronze tablet was unveiled on July 4, 1931 to commemorate the event.

● **Turkey River Mounds**
3½ miles south and 1 mile east of Guttenberg, Iowa on county road

State Conservation Commission
State Office Building
300 Fourth Street
Des Moines, Iowa 50319

Acquired: 1939

A 62-acre archeological site, designated a State Preserve. The area includes a forested ridge with numerous conical and linear Indian mounds.

● **Turkey River Park**
1 mile south of Elkader, Iowa along Iowa 13

A multiple-use area of 2 acres. The triangular-shaped roadside park, bounded by the Turkey River on the east and Meisner Creek on the south, provides a picnic area, fishing access (said to be "the best catfish hole on the Turkey River"), and limited (overnight) camping for canoeists on the Turkey River. The spot, Reimer's Bend, is half way between the towns of Elgin and Elkport, a two-day trip by canoe.

● **Volga White Pine Forest Preserve**
North of Volga City, Iowa

Clayton County Conservation Board
Don R. Menken, Executive Officer
R.R. 2, Elkader, Iowa 52043

A natural white pine grove included in a 22-acre tract, the only such area in Clayton County. The rock-bottomed Volga River flows along one side of the property.

22 - CLAYTON
(continued)

● **Wilder Memorial Museum**
Strawberry Point, Iowa 52076

Alwin Zwanziger
Strawberry Point, Iowa 52076
or
Mrs. George (Ila Mae) Pattison
303 East Elm
Strawberry Point, Iowa 52076

Dedicated: April 11, 1970
Open: Daily, Memorial Day to Labor Day, 1:00-5;00 p.m.;
special groups at any time by appointment
Admission: $0.50; children $0.25

A project partially financed by a gift of $25,000 from the Wilder estate. The House of Dolls includes a collection of over 400 dolls, of all types and sizes, dating back to the 1700's. The collection was made over a period of 35 years by two sisters, Mrs. Blanche Baldridge and Mrs. Gladys Kenneally. Also on display are Indian artifacts, military items, geodes, wood carvings, art works, an 1847 working loom with a spinning wheel and wool winder, pioneer farm tools, antique clocks, furnished rooms (parlor, kitchen, bedroom, and child's room) of the 1890-1900 period, and articles from New Guinea.

23 - CLINTON

Clinton
E-13

● **Clinton County Historical Society**
Clinton, Iowa

Robert Soesbe, President
P. O. Box 3135
Clinton, Iowa 52732

Organized: February 26, 1965
Meetings: Quarterly; Board meets 6 times per year
Number of Members: 169
Dues: $2.00 annual; $10.00 life

The Society sponsors a museum on the showboat, Rhododendron, conducts historic tours in Clinton County, holds an Old Settlers Reunion, cooperates with Clinton County Conservation Board in locating and marking historic sites with descriptive signs, and maintains exhibits in Smithtown Church (1874). Located 2½ miles west and 2 miles north of Lost Nation, the church has been owned since 1970 by Clinton County Conservation Board, and contains the original pews and pulpit. The settlement of Smithtown dates back to 1865 and was named for David Smith, who is buried in the church cemetery with his wife.

● **Eagle Point Park**
End of North 3rd Street,
off of U.S. 67
Clinton, Iowa

City of Clinton Board
of Park Commissioners
1401 11th Avenue North
Clinton, Iowa 52732

Located on the Mississippi River bluffs overlooking Lake Clinton. This was once known as Joyce's Park for the donor of the land, David Joyce. Artifacts found here relate to a Woodland Indian culture dating back to around 200-600 A.D. Some of the vantage points are 200 feet above the river. In the park are stone viewing towers, woodland trails, ponds, live animal and bird exhibits, flower displays, and recreational facilities.

The Eagle Point Nature Society was organized in 1970, and a community nature center designed to pursue programs of educational, scientific, cultural, and recreational value. Slide and motion picture presentations are available for group showings.

Through the efforts of the One Room School Committee, organized in 1972, a 1935 rural schoolhouse was moved from its original site on Humeston Road, about 4 miles north of De Witt, to Eagle Point Park in June 1974. The school is to be a museum, with a Teacher Hall of Fame, and will be furnished as a typical schoolroom of the period.

| COUNTY AND COUNTY SEAT; LOCATION ON MAP | NAME AND LOCATION | DESCRIPTION |

3 - CLINTON
(continued)

● **Follett Park**
Along U.S. 67
Folletts, Iowa

Clinton County Conservation Board
Ben Martinsen, Secretary-Treasurer
758 South Bluff Boulevard
Clinton, Iowa 52732

A 7-acre tract preserved in memory of William D. Follett, the first white settler in the area. The historic site on the Great River Road includes picnic facilities.

● **Rhododendron Showboat Museum**
Riverview Park
Sixth Avenue North and River
Clinton, Iowa

City of Clinton Board of
Park Commissioners
1401-11th Avenue North
Clinton, Iowa 52732

Charles Creely, Custodian

Admission: $0.50; children under 6 free
Open: Daily, 9:00 a.m.-9:00 p.m. during summer months

Old riverboat, moored in the Mississippi River. Museum on the third deck of the triple-deck sternwheeler, Rhododendron. Items pertaining to the history of Clinton and Indian lore are housed in glass display cases, maintained by Clinton County Historical Society. The 193-foot showboat was acquired in 1966 from the State of West Virginia. Steam driven engines, turbines, generators, and huge paddlewheel shafts are intact. Captain's lounge furnished in Victorian style. Pilot's chair, controls; meeting room for 80 persons. Magnificent 275-seat theatre in authentic decor, used by community playhouse groups in the area.

A Riverboat Days celebration is held annually.

● **Walnut Grove Park**
½ mile north of Toronto, Iowa

Clinton County Conservation Board
Ben Martinsen, Secretary-Treasurer
758 South Bluff Boulevard
Clinton, Iowa 52732

A wooded area of 17 acres on the north bank of the Wapsipinicon River. There is an abundance of walnut, maple, cottonwood, and hackberry trees. The park provides access for canoe and float trips on the river, and there are facilities for fishing, picnicking, and camping.

Toronto is one of the county's scenic Wapsi River towns. The first settler was George Thorne of Toronto, Canada, who started a sawmill here in 1844, a gristmill in 1846, and a store in 1850. The mills became famous over eastern Iowa.

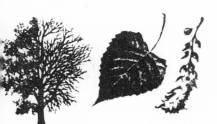

24 - CRAWFORD

Denison
E-2

● **Crawford County Historical Society**
Denison, Iowa

Howard McMinimie, President
R.R. 1
Denison, Iowa 51442
or
Harry W. Maxwell
1425 Broadway
Denison, Iowa 51442

Organized: 1966
Meetings: Second Thursday of month, or as announced
Number of Members: 312
Dues: $5.00 annual
Museum Open: Sunday and Thursday, 1:00-4:30 p.m.; groups by appointment
Admission: Free

Maintains a museum in the old McHenry House, 1428 First Avenue N, Denison, Iowa. The home was built in 1885 by William A. McHenry at a cost of $24,000. The spacious house included a ballroom, and had 6 fireplaces. The downstairs woodwork was hand-rubbed and oiled. A carriage house occupied the back lot.

● **Dow House Historical Area**
Southwest edge of Dow City, Iowa
on Prince Street

Crawford County Conservation Board
Neal Moeller, President
214 South 10th Street
Denison, Iowa 51442

A 4-acre site which includes one of western Iowa's historic landmarks, Dow House. Built in 1872-1874, the 2-story, 20-room brick and masonry home is situated on a grassy knoll overlooking Dow City and the Boyer River Valley. The soft, deep red bricks used in construction of the house were manufactured at a brickyard located near the back of the house. All partitions are made of the same bricks, and run from the basement to the top of the house. The house cost $11,000 to build and was owned by the Dow family until 1902. Through the ensuing years, it had many owners who altered and remodelled the original structure.

Simeon E. Dow arrived in the area in 1855 and began taking up land with soldiers' warrants purchased in the East. Dow continued in land trading the rest of his life, and in the 1870's and 1880's, the Dows were clearly the leading family of the community which bears their name. This region was originally covered with tall grass and well adapted to stock raising. Mr. Dow brought cattle with him when he came to the area, and is reported to have had the first purebred shorthorn cattle by 1856. He collaborated in the building of the first schoolhouse in the area in 1858 and donated a tract of land for the cemetery. He was active in various businesses (grain elevator, cheese factory, mill, hardware store, and farm implements) and served as postmaster, probate judge, and county treasurer. In the 1890s, Dow was beset by severe financial reverses from which he never recovered.

Dow House is being restored as an example of a 19th Century family home ——during Iowa's formative years —— with period furnishings, interpretive exhibits, and historical

4 - CRAWFORD
(continued)

Dow House Historical Area
(continued)

artifacts. The grounds will be landscaped to resemble a yard as it would have appeared in the 1870's. Picnic sites have been laid out within the area. The property is owned by the Crawford County Conservation Board, and is managed under a cooperative agreement with the Town Council of Dow City and Crawford County Historical Society (see above).

● **Lincoln Farm Marker**
7 miles north of Denison and
1 mile east of Schleswig, Iowa

A marker erected in 1923 by Denison Chapter of The D.A.R. identifies a land grant to Abraham Lincoln.

This is one of two parcels of land in Iowa owned by Lincoln. (Lincoln also owned 40 acres of land in Howard Township in Tama County, 4 miles north and 2 miles west of Toledo.) He never personally visited either tract. The land grants were given to Lincoln for his service as a captain in the Black Hawk War of 1832. This grant of 120 acres is in Goodrich Township in Crawford County. Warrant 68645 was issued on April 22, 1856 and the land was located by Lincoln himself, at Springfield, Illinois, on December 27, 1859. Patents of the tracts were issued to Lincoln on September 10, 1860, in the midst of his campaign for the U.S. Presidency, and sent to the Registrar of the Land Office at Springfield on October 30, one week before the election. This land was owned by Lincoln when he was assassinated, and was sold by his son, Robert Todd Lincoln, on March 22, 1892, as a part of the Lincoln estate, to Henry Edwards for $13,000.

● **Nelson Park**
5 miles northwest of
Dow City, Iowa

Crawford County Conservation
Board
Neal Moeller, President
214 South 10th Street
Denison, Iowa 51442

A 165-acre outdoor recreational area. There are ridges along both sides of an interesting valley through which a spring-fed stream flows continuously, year round. The timber area contains oak, hickory, basswood, cottonwood, and elm. The park has been developed for picnicking, hiking, fishing, boating, swimming, camping, and nature study. Birds, deer, and small game abound in the area, which includes a small lake.

● **Site of Fort Purdy**
Broadway Street, near
Courthouse Square,
Denison, Iowa

A granite block commemorates the site of Fort Purdy, built on land owned by John Purdy. The early settlers gathered there for protection against Indian attacks at the time of the Indian scare in May 1856. The original site is 2 miles northeast of Denison, on Ridge Road.

5 - DALLAS

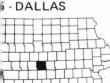

del
-5

● **Dallas Center Museum**
12th and Linden
Dallas Center, Iowa

Dawson G. Black, Secretary
303 13th Street
Dallas Center, Iowa 50063

Incorporated: January 7, 1972
Open: June through September, 1:00 p.m.-5:00 p.m. Saturday and Sunday; other times by appointment
Admission: $1.00; school children $0.50 (good for current year)

Over 5,000 antiques and items of historic interest housed in a large barn previously used by Brenton Farms. Six completely furnished rooms include a living room, dining room, kitchen, bedroom, washroom, and meat processing

25 - DALLAS
(continued)

Dallas Center Museum
(continued)

room. There is a blacksmith shop, carpenter shop, general store, doctor's office, printing shop, cobbler's shop, and millinery shop. Also on display are gasoline engines dating back to 1891, horse-drawn farm implements, and hand tools.

Dallas Center was settled in 1869 and so named because of its location near the center of Dallas County. The County, established January 13, 1846, was named for George Mifflin Dallas (1792-1864), who was Vice President of the United States in 1846 when the county was opened to white settlement.

● **Dallas County Historical Society**
Adel, Iowa

Mrs. Clair A. (Helen) Folk, President
1605 Main
Adel, Iowa 50003
        or
Mrs. Clarence (Mabel) Hill
Vice President
Minburn, Iowa 50167

Organized: October 26, 1958
Incorporated: July 27, 1966
Meetings: Last Sunday of each month
Number of Members: 150
Dues: $1.00 annual; $2.00 family; $25.00 life

Annual Harvest Home Festival Dinner held in November and tours are sponsored. A newsletter is distributed to members.

● **Forest Park and Museum**
One mile south of 16th and Willis
Perry, Iowa

Dallas County Conservation Board
Adel, Iowa 50003
        or
Mr. and Mrs. Ted Streed, Supervisors
R.R. 2
Perry, Iowa 50220

Established: August 30, 1953; purchased by Dallas County in 1967 from original owner, Eugene N. Hastie
Park Open: 9:00 a.m. until dark
Museum Open: Tuesday through Sunday, 1:00-5:00 p.m. May 1-November 1; closed Monday
Admission: Donations accepted

Several museum buildings situated in a 5-acre arboretum with over 400 trees and shrubs of 160 varieties, tagged with names. The park and museum originated through the efforts of Eugene Hastie, who sold it to Dallas County Conservation Board in 1966. An old 1-room country schoolhouse, built in 1867, is fully equipped with desks, period textbooks, and blackboards. Exhibits include an old wooden Huber threshing machine and other farm machinery, buggies, sleds, sleighs, harness rigs, 1916 Des Moines trolley car, Model T Ford, blacksmith shop, old general store, a kitchen of the 1880's, lanterns, rocks, arrowheads, fossils, and other relics. A log cabin, built in 1873, has been restored and furnished. An Exhibition Building and Visitor Center opened in 1971. A garden includes crops unusual for Iowa, such as cotton, peanuts, tobacco, and herbs.

5 - DALLAS
(continued)

● **Granger Homestead Project**
Just west of
Granger, Iowa

One of the first public housing projects in the United States, funded in 1933. It was made possible by the National Industrial Recovery Act, which included the Subsistence Homesteads Act, and the efforts of Father L. G. Ligutti, then a priest at Granger, who was concerned about housing for the poor--particularly the Italian coal miners. The plots were 3 to 5 acres in size, enough for a family to have a garden during the summer when there was no work in the mines. Fifty houses were completed by 1935. These were arranged around circles, so the lots were mostly pie-shaped. The homes included from 4 to 6 rooms; all were modern.

By 1942, the federal government withdrew from the project and it then became essentially a cooperative. The 50 houses still stand, but many have been changed considerably. A number of families living in the homes today were among the original occupants.

During the Great Depression, corn sold for 8 cents a bushel and hogs were marketed for 1½ cents a pound. Father Ligutti reasoned that needy families could help themselves by "having one foot on a little piece of land and the other foot in industry . . . Help a man get land and he becomes a capitalist. Give him a cow and he doesn't become a Communist."

Father Ligutti, who was born in Italy (1895) and came to the United States as a boy, gained fame as a result of this project. After living and working in Iowa some 50 years, he eventually became the permanent observer for the Pope, with his office in the Vatican, to help people throughout the world, and was assigned to the Food and Agriculture Organization of the United Nations.

● **Old Order River Brethren Settlement**
Near Dallas Center, Iowa

A settlement composed of members of the most conservative wing of the Brethren Church. Their religious beliefs and manners of dress are similar to the Amish, although they do drive automobiles and use electricity and telephones. This settlement dates back to the 1870's. Other members of this highly distinctive religious minority live in Ohio and Pennsylvania.

6 - DAVIS

loomfield
I-9

● **Davis County Genealogical Society**
Bloomfield, Iowa

Lowell N. Francis, Secretary-Treasurer
503 N.W. Street
Bloomfield, Iowa 52537

Organized: February 21, 1974
Meetings: Third Thursday of month, in Davis County Courthouse Lounge
Number of Members: 28

A local chapter of the Iowa Genealogical Society (see Polk County). Members have canvassed cemeteries in Davis County, and copied death and marriage records.

26 - DAVIS
(continued)

● **Davis County Historical Society**
Bloomfield, Iowa

Quentin E. Johnson, President
601 North Washington
Bloomfield, Iowa 52537

Organized: March 16, 1961
Incorporated: February 13, 1962
Meetings: Second Tuesday of each month, except August
and December
Number of Members: 100
Dues: $1.00 annual

One of the original brick homes in Bloomfield, owned by
the pioneer Dr. William Findley family, is being restored to
the mid-1800 period. The 2-story brick house is located at
302 East Franklin. A log cabin is to be moved to the site by
the Bloomfield Jaycees.

The territory now comprising Davis County was referred to
as the "Hairy Nation" by early travelers. The descriptive
term referred to the rough, hairy, unkempt appearance and
rude manners of the residents of the area.

● **Iowaville**

Near the junction of Davis,
Jefferson, Van Buren, and
Wapello Counties

Site of an Ioway Indian Village dating back to the early
1800's. (See Van Buren County also.)

Around 1823, the Ioway Indians allegedly suffered heavy
casualties at the hands of the Sac and Fox Tribes of Illinois
in the so-called Iowaville Massacre. A second-hand account
of the conflict given by the trader James H. (Jim) Jordan
has been questioned by historians.

Late in 1970, archeologists located the village and collected
an assortment of artifacts, including arrowheads, musket
balls, gunflints, bits of clay pipes, human skull fragments,
glass beads, and pieces of glass bottles (whiskey and patent
medicines). These surface finds may be classified into three
separate categories: those made by the Indians from their
own raw materials, those made in Europe for the Indian
trade, and those European-made goods left by the white
man.

It could be argued that Davis County should have been
named Black Hawk County. It was here along the Des
Moines River that the Indian Chief Black Hawk selected a
place to live and the spot where he was later buried, in
October 1838. The Indian village, called Iowaville, was in
section one in the northeast corner of present-day Davis
County. In the Black Hawk War of 1832, Chief Keokuk
favored peace and Chief Black Hawk favored war.

The Indians held as sacred the spot where Black Hawk was
buried. The grave was marked by a heap of stones,
carelessly piled. In 1839, vandals robbed the grave and
removed the body. The event was reported to General
Street, the Indian Agent at Agency, about 10 miles away. A
detail was sent from the company of Dragoons commanded
by Captain Allen at the Indian Agency. Tracks of a carriage
were discovered leading from the grave, but pursuit was
considered useless. Black Hawk's skull was later recovered,
but was destroyed by fire when the building in which it was
stored in Burlington was burned.

5 - DAVIS
(continued)

● **Lock Tenders House**

On farm on north side of crushed rock road along the Des Moines River, midway between Eldon and Selma, Iowa. The river road may also be reached by turning south off Iowa 16 at Iowaville Cemetery.

A stone house, built between 1846 and 1848, in the extreme northeast corner of Davis County at the halfway mark between Selma and Eldon. Flat limestone, taken from the Des Moines River nearby, was used to construct the building which was to be used by the Dam and Lock Tender of the Litchfield Company. Through a system of dams and locks the river was to have been made navigable for steamboats.

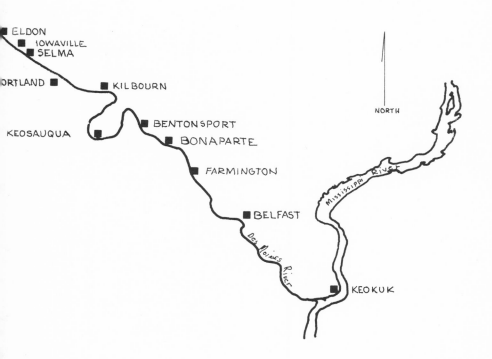

On August 8, 1846, Congress adopted a bill providing that alternate sections of public land, 5 miles wide, on each side of the Des Moines River, be set aside to aid Iowa in improving the navigation of the stream "from its mouth to the Raccoon Fork." The plat of survey filed with the Board of Public Works called for 28 dams, together with locks and canals. The first of the dams was to be at St. Francisville, Clark County, Missouri. Proceeding on upstream, dam number 2 was to be located at Belfast, Iowa, dam number 3 at Creston, number 4 near Farmington, number 5 at Bonaparte, number 6 at Bentonsport, number 7 at Keosauqua, number 8 near Kilbourn, number 9 at Portland, and number 10 one mile above Iowaville, between Selma and Eldon. Only the first 7 of these dams were completed and put into operation. Dams number 8, 9, and 10 were partially completed, while little or no work was done on the other 18.

Although dam number 10 was not completely built, the locks at this point were practically completed. The Des Moines River navigation project was the most ambitious of any attempted on Iowa's inland waters, and several hundred thousand dollars were spent on it. Because of a flood in 1851, followed by the coming of the railroads soon after, the need for river steamers on the Des Moines ended, and the venture was abandoned.

At various times in more recent years--in 1911, in the 1930's, and as late as 1974--studies by the U.S. Army Engineers and others have been made to determine the feasibility of making Des Moines a "seaport." These plans to develop the Des Moines River have included hydroelectric power, flood control, lake stabilization, and recreation, along with the navigable channel. The cost of such a project is the main obstacle.

27 - DECATUR

Leon
I-6

● **Decatur County Historical Society**
115 North Main Street
Leon, Iowa 50144

Harry Graves, President
Davis City, Iowa 50065

Orange Dorsey, Curator
Leon, Iowa 50144
or
Dr. C.D. Scott
107 West 12th
Leon, Iowa 50144
or
Miss Himena V. Hoffman
Leon, Iowa 50144

Organized: 1901
Incorporated: April 21, 1967
Meetings: Second Thursday of month
Number of Members: 171
Dues: $2.00 annual
Museum Open: 1:00-5:00 p.m., June to September
Admission: $0.50, Children $0.25

Sponsors fund raising events, such as old-time threshing festivals, variety shows, and the publication of a history of Decatur County. The Society was originally organized in 1901, but became inactive and its early records were lost or destroyed by fire. The Society became active again in 1961, but did not incorporate until 6 years later.

Museum contains furniture and dishes used by pioneers, tools, farm implements, guns, paintings, newspapers, dolls, and other mementoes related to Decatur County. Exhibits include school, church, and fireplace settings. A collection of horse drawn equipment is shown at the Decatur County 4H Fair.

● **Slip Bluff Park**
2 miles northwest of
Davis City, Iowa

Decatur County Conservation Board
H. L. Graves, Executive Officer
R. R. 1
Davis City, Iowa 50065

A 188-acre tract along the main branch of Grand River. Archeological, historical, botanical, biological, and ecological interpretive opportunities make this an interesting area for hikers, naturalists, and students. The natural character of the prairie woodland, river valley bottom, steep slopes, and bluff land is being preserved. The area is used as an outdoor classroom and will be developed for use of picnickers, fishermen, hikers, and campers. Plans include wildlife areas, bridle paths, and scenic overlooks.

● **Trailside Historical Park**
½ mile west of Garden Grove, Iowa

Decatur County Conservation Board
H. L. Graves, Executive Officer
R. R. 1
Davis City, Iowa 50065

A 3-acre park on a west-facing slope of the bluffs adjacent to Weldon River. Various scattered hardwood trees and shrubs cover the historic site. Garden Grove was a Mormon settlement, with around 200 Saints living here by the close of 1846. The park site is where the cemetery of these early Mormons was located. According to early accounts the Mormon cemetery contained 6 graves, and a 16-foot-square area was surrounded by a picket fence until about 1910. After that, the cemetery was neglected and the grave markers disappeared.

28 - DELAWARE

Manchester
C-11

● **Backbone State Park**
5 miles south of Strawberry Point, on Iowa 410

State Conservation Commission
State Office Building
300 Fourth Street
Des Moines, Iowa 50319

Established: October 1, 1919

Iowa's first state park includes 1,780 of the most scenic acres in the Middle West. Rock ledges, caves, boulders, and rock formations rise 90 to 140 feet above the curves of the Maquoketa River. A high limestone ridge, "The Devil's Backbone," extends for ¼ mile. Windblown pines jut over limestone cliffs. Trails, scenic drives, and trout streams are featured, and there are facilities for swimming, picnicking, and camping. Richmond Springs, one of the largest in Iowa, feeds a large trout and bass hatchery in the park.

- DELAWARE
(continued)

● **Bailey's Ford Access**
4 miles southeast of
Manchester, Iowa

A 23-acre area along the Maquoketa River, at the upstream limits of Lake Delhi, used for fishing, picnicking, and camping.

Delaware County Conservation Board
John Klaus, Executive Officer
469 South Tama Street
Manchester, Iowa 52057

Joel Bailey, the first surveyor in Delaware County, homesteaded 40 acres here around 1837. He built a cabin near the ford that bears his name, and provided accommodations for travelers on the stage road between Dubuque and Waterloo.

● **Baker's Stagecoach Inn**
Coffins Grove, northeast
of Manchester, Iowa

A stagecoach inn built in 1855, privately restored.

● **Bay Church and Cemetery**
Southeast of Manchester,
Iowa

The first Free Baptist Church in Iowa, erected in 1846 and rebuilt in 1873. In the cemetery, on a grassy knoll a short distance to the rear of the church, is the first Civil War Monument erected in Iowa--August 1865. This is also said to be the site of the first Memorial Day observance in the North.

Local citizens of Milo Township organized a special day of observance May 30, 1866 to honor those young men from the area who had lost their lives in the Civil War. This was 2 years prior to the time when the General Order was issued in 1868 by General John A. Logan, Commander-in-Chief of the Grand Army of the Republic, declaring May 30 as a special day for decorating the graves of war veterans and listening to patriotic speeches.

The marble monument, erected in the center of the east end of Bay Cemetery, is inscribed with the names of the fallen heroes, their ages, and the regiments in which they served. For many years, large crowds gathered here for Memorial Day services.

● **Coffin's Grove Park**
3 miles east of
Manchester, Iowa

A 22-acre tract used for picnicking and camping. Coffin's Creek, a clear-water stream with several riffles, flows through the area and provides fishing. Sand and gravel bars located on the creek are of interest to rock hounds. Trees to be seen in the park include burr oak, black ash, hickory, hackberry, mulberry, walnut, willow, and elm.

Delaware County Conservation Board
John Klaus, Executive Officer
469 South Tama Street
Manchester, Iowa 52057

A stagecoach road once crossed this land, and the tracks are still visible. A brick house or tavern built along the creek provided meals and an overnight stopping place for travelers. A large Dutch oven in the house was used to cook prairie chickens and other game shot by hunters on the prairies to the north and west.

● **Delaware County Historical Museum**
Hopkinton, Iowa

Established: 1967
Admission: Donations accepted
Open: Sunday, 2:00-5:00 p.m., June-October; other times by appointment

Mrs. Herbert (Barbara) Gearhart
Hopkinton, Iowa 52237

28 - DELAWARE
(continued)

Delaware County Historical Museum
(continued)

Five separate buildings make up the museum complex and serve as depositories for historic items. One museum is in Clarke Hall, which was formerly a women's dormitory on the campus of historic Lenox College, founded in 1859 (as Bowen Collegiate Institute) and closed in 1944, during World War II. On display are Lenox College materials, a recreated girls' dormitory room of the 1890 s, high fashions, an early kitchen, a child's room of the 1890 s old instruments and equipment from doctors' offices, early Americana, and the War Room, including Civil War items. During the Civil War, most male students at Lenox College went into military service. A soldiers monument, dating back to November 17, 1865, on the old campus along Iowa 38, is believed to be the first to be erected by private subscription in memory of Civil War veterans. There are 44 names inscribed on the 20-foot marble shaft, a reminder that by 1864, only one man over 20 remained in the town of Hopkinton; all others were engaged in war. Death claimed one-fourth of the known students of Lenox College who volunteered their services to the North. Also killed was Rev. James V. McKean, (April 30, 1833 - July 9, 1864), President of Lenox College and Captain of Company C, 45th Regiment, Iowa Volunteers.

The Reformed Presbyterian Church (1901), acquired by the Society in 1969, contains antique musical instruments, a rock collection, a natural science exhibit (birds and animals), and Indian artifacts.

The old Hopkinton Milwaukee Railroad Depot houses the primitive collection--articles depicting pioneer life in Delaware County. Farm tools and machinery of over 100 years ago, old fire engines, a general store display, a stationmaster's room, and displays on early railroading are featured. A section of track from Western Dubuque Railroad, built in the late 1850's, has been placed in front of the depot.

An old one-room, rural schoolhouse (c. 1880) has been moved to the area and restored as part of the museum complex.

In 1973, a new Agriculture Display Building was created to display early day farm machinery.

Also in Hopkinton is the Livingstone Home (private), built in 1896-97, and acquired in 1901 by an early physician, Dr. Hugh Livingstone. In Livingstone Cemetery, south of Hopkinton, many of the early Scottish settlers are buried.

● **Delaware County Historical Society**
Manchester, Iowa

Mrs. Herbert (Barbara) Gearhart,
President
Hopkinton, Iowa 52237

Incorporated: May 28, 1959
Meetings: Annually, second Tuesday in April, or when calle directors meet last Monday of each month
Number of Members: 600
Dues: $1.00 annual; $5.00 sustaining

- DELAWARE
(continued)

Delaware County Historical Society
(continued)

or

Don Appleby
Manchester, Iowa 52057

Owns and operates Delaware County Historical Museum (see above) in Hopkinton, Iowa. A Delaware County history and brochures on historic landmarks have been published, slide programs are available, and recordings are being made on local history. The Love Log Cabin, first house in Manchester (1850's) was moved to Denton Park in 1964 and restored.

A Civil War Days celebration was initiated in 1972, and is held annually during the first weekend in June. A 16-mile Monument Trail has also been established by the Society. The trail passes by 3 Civil War monuments and other historic sites between Delhi and Hopkinton.

- **Dunlap Park**
West edge of Hopkinton, Iowa

Delaware County Conservation Board
John Klaus, Executive Officer
469 South Tama Street
Manchester, Iowa 52057

A 1-acre plot of ground including an old mill dam on the Maquoketa River. This is a popular spot for fishermen and picnickers and is of historic interest. The land was first bought from the U. S. Government in 1838. A log dam was erected about 1844 at approximately the site of the present dam to provide water power for a sawmill. Later, a flour and feed mill was started and operated until 1892, when it was converted to a generating plant for electricity by a Mr. Milroy. He sold the plant to Hopkinton Electric Power Corporation in 1920. In 1924, the property was acquired by Iowa Electric Company. After this company quit generating electricity here, the old mill site and dam were sold to Herman J. Dunlap, in 1953. Mr. Dunlap donated the property to Delaware County Conservation Board on December 30, 1961. The dam and foundations of the power plant, and a well that served the old mill are still here.

- **Fountain Spring Creek Park**
3 miles northeast of Greeley, Iowa

Delaware County Conservation Board
John Klaus, Executive Officer
469 South Tama Street
Manchester, Iowa 52057

A scenic area of 176 acres containing native wildlife, trees, shrubs, and wild flowers--a paradise for the nature lover. Fountain Spring Creek, fed by Bone Hollow Branch and several large springs, runs through the entire area. Bright green watercress grows in profusion. The water temperature is low enough to support trout, and the stream is stocked periodically. The creek and road follow through a rock gorge, heavily covered with hardwood timber. Conifer trees have been planted on the higher areas, above the limestone bluffs.

The first family settled near Fountain Spring in 1834. Some years later, a mill was built nearby to grind the wheat of the early settlers. The mill was in operation until the 1920's, by which time it was used to grind feed. All that remains of the mill is a pile of rocks, traces of the millrace, and one of the millstones brought here from France.

The area has been used for hunting, fishing, picnicking, and camping for over a century.

28 - DELAWARE
(continued)

● **Hard Scrabble Park**
1 mile south of Hopkinton, Iowa

Delaware County Conservation Board
John Klaus, Executive Officer
469 South Tama Street
Manchester, Iowa 52057

A 42½-acre tract containing high limestone bluffs, hardwood timber, and Indian graves along the Maquoketa River. A nature trail has wild flowers identified, and a trail along the bluffs to Wildcat Rock rises 90 feet above the road. The park has been developed as a multiple-use outdoor recreational area with picnicking and camping facilities, and scenic overlooks of the Maquoketa River Valley.

● **Hobbs Chimney**
Southwest corner
of Delhi, Iowa

A lone chimney, all that remains of Delhi's first home, built in 1848. The limestone fireplace and chimney was built by Isaac Hamblin and his sons, the only stonemasons in Delhi for many years. The chimney is a good example of the craftsmanship of that period. The log cabin was the home of Charles W. Hobbs, first Clerk and Recorder for Delaware County, and his wife Mary, first postmistress of Delhi. Their cabin served as the postoffice. The chimney is situated on about an acre of land, owned by the Town of Delhi, with a spring and watercress bed.

● **Hook Wildlife Area**
4 miles northeast of Greeley, Iowa

Delaware County Conservation Board
John Klaus, Executive Officer
469 South Tama Street
Manchester, Iowa 52057

Natural area of 10 acres, including a large canyon, spring, variety of trees, and wild flowers including 3 varieties of wild orchids.

● **McCreery Memorial**
West of Delhi, Iowa

The site of the house where J. L. McCreery lived in 1862 when he wrote the poem "There Is No Death". He was Delaware County Superintendent of Schools, editor of the Delaware County Journal, and a poet.

● **Milo Township Forest Area**
2 miles southeast of Manchester, Iowa

Delaware County Conservation Board
John Klaus, Executive Officer
469 South Tama Street
Manchester, Iowa 52057

A 100-acre timber preserve, game area, county-school forest, limited picnic area, and access to the Maquoketa River.

● **Oneida Town Park**
3 miles south of Greeley, Iowa
on Iowa 38

Delaware County Conservation Board
John Klaus, Executive Officer
469 South Tama Street
Manchester, Iowa 52057

A 2-acre plot of historical significance. This was the site of Hickory Grove School, closed about 1905, and of a pioneer cemetery. The graves and markers have almost disappeared, but a grove of lilacs marks the cemetery.

● **Pin Oak Park**
2 miles southeast of Manchester, Iowa

Delaware County Conservation Board
John Klaus, Executive Officer
469 South Tama Street
Manchester, Iowa 52057

A 100-acre tract of land, covered with hardwood timber, adjacent to the Maquoketa River. A pioneer stage and wagon ford, with a rock bottom, was used in the late 1800's to cross the river. The old trail is still visible. The park includes hiking trails, and provides facilities for fishing, picnicking, and camping.

8 - DELAWARE
(continued)

● **Plum Creek Park**
Southeast edge of Earlville, Iowa

Delaware County Conservation Board
John Klaus, Executive Officer
469 South Tama Street
Manchester, Iowa 52057

A 29-acre tract of land that straddles Plum Creek, a tributary of the Maquoketa River. A steep rocky bluff, rising 75 feet above the creek, is covered with early spring wild flowers, and a great variety of trees grows here.

In the last decade of the 19th Century, a dam was built at this site, and a water-powered mill ground grain and feed. The park is used for picnicking, hiking, camping, nature study, and winter sports.

● **Red Schoolhouse**
4 miles northeast of Manchester, Iowa on county road D13

Delaware County Conservation Board
John Klaus, Executive Officer
469 South Tama Street
Manchester, Iowa 52057

One-room rural school and playground located on a 1-acre site near Honey Creek. The first Township School Board in Delaware County was organized in 1857, and the first Red Schoolhouse (Sub-district No. 6) was built about 80 rods north of the present location. It was used until 1871, and a new school was built the following year, at a cost of $350. This school burned in November 1904 and a woodshed served as a school until another could be built in 1905. The cost was $750, plus about $150 for furnishings. The District of Delaware Township was discontinued July 1, 1959, when West Delaware County Community School District was organized. The schoolhouse and contents, including the records and minutes of the old school board from 1857 to 1959, are being preserved as a historic landmark. An old well and shade trees are used by picnickers.

● **Silver Lake Park**
Southeast edge of Delhi, Iowa

A 13-acre park containing a marker at the site of Delaware County's first courthouse, located along a 45-acre natural lake. This hickory log building was not erected at Delhi until 1842--nearly 4 years after the county was established. Labor and other materials were contributed by the early settlers. The 18' x 24' building overlooked Silver Lake. This spot was selected for the county seat in a rather unusual manner. The men responsible for finding a suitable location saw a deer come out of a thicket and shot it. At the point where the deer fell, a stake was placed for the courthouse site. During the following winter, logs were dragged across Silver Lake on the ice and a 2-story building was erected. The roof was not added until later, due to a lack of funds. The building was also used as a school, church, meeting place, and temporary home for immigrants until they could build their cabins. In the 1850's, this first courthouse was replaced by a frame building located further west,

28 - DELAWARE
(continued)

Silver Lake Park
(continued)

where stores and houses were being built. The log courthouse was torn down in 1858. Only the marker remains where it stood. The 1853 courthouse (Memorial Hall) still stands in the city park and is used by the American Legion. The old 2-story brick county offices building was built in Delhi in 1857 adjacent to the old courthouse. The third courthouse built at Delhi was a brick structure costing $5,000. Due to changing conditions and shifts in population, the county seat was finally moved to Manchester in 1880.

● **Site of First Delaware County Courthouse**
Delhi, Iowa

A marker at the site of Delaware County's first courthouse. (See Silver Lake Park above.)

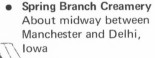

● **Spring Branch Creamery**
About midway between Manchester and Delhi, Iowa

The site of Iowa's first butter factory, built in 1872 at Spring Branch by John Stewart, a native of Ohio and a Civil War veteran. The butter won first place and a gold medal in worldwide competition in 1876 at the Centennial Exposition in Philadelphia. As a result, Eastern prejudice against Iowa butter was replaced by demand for the product, often at premium prices. At this time the best grade of butter sold for 10 cents to 15 cents per pound. Only the foundation of the creamery now remains.

● **Trout Haven**
Hopkinton, Iowa

Admission: Charge for fishing
Open: Year round

Ever-flowing spring of clear, cool (40-50 degree) water used 130 years ago by settlers. Flow averages 750,000 gallons daily. Developed privately as a pond for trout fishing.

● **Turtle Creek Recreation Area**
4 miles southwest of Delhi, Iowa

Delaware County Conservation Board
John Klaus, Executive Officer
469 South Tama Street
Manchester, Iowa 52057

A tract of 149 acres along Lake O'Delhi, an impoundment on the Maquoketa River. Most of the area is a wilderness and wildlife preserve. There are provisions for picnicking, camping, and fishing, as well as nature and bridle trails. Small boats may be launched from Turtle Creek Bay on the lake. The terrain is very rugged, with many rock outcroppings along various gullies. Hardwood timber includes oak, maple, butternut, walnut, and ironwood. A variety of shrubs and many native wild flowers may be seen. A limestone quarry along the west bank of Turtle Creek was a source of building stone in early days.

The land provided fuel and lumber for the early settlers. According to local legend, one pioneer family named Tuttle squatted on 40 acres near a spring, where they built a log cabin. This family gave the place its original name, but through the years the name changed from Tuttle Creek to Turtle Creek.

- DELAWARE
(continued)

● **Twin Bridges Park**
4 miles southwest of
Colesburg, Iowa
along Iowa 3

Delaware County Conservation Board
John Klaus, Executive Officer
469 South Tama Street
Manchester, Iowa 52057

A 20-acre area adjacent to Elk Creek, a spring-fed, stocked trout stream. A high bluff is covered with hardwood timber, shrubs, ferns, and wild flowers. This section is used for hiking and as an outdoor classroom. There are also provisions for picnicking and camping, and a playground.

- DES MOINES

rlington
H-12

● **Chautauqua Park**
1½ miles east of
Mediapolis, Iowa

Des Moines County Conservation Board
James A. Settles, Executive Officer
601½ "Corner" Main and Court Streets
Burlington, Iowa 52601

A 10-acre area where the last Chautauqua in Iowa was held. (See Montgomery County, also.) An Independent Chautauqua was established at Mediapolis in 1904 and continued for 40 years.

Jefferson Academy was founded on this site by an Act of the Territorial Legislature of Iowa in 1844. The school was reorganized as the Yellow Spring Collegiate Institute in 1852, and as Yellow Spring College in 1855. During the Civil War, most of the young men attending the school enlisted for service, walking to Burlington to volunteer, and the college closed in 1869. In 1873, the school was reopened as Kossuth Academy, but it closed before the end of the century. The last 4-year class to graduate--4 boys and 4 girls--was in 1897. The grounds and school building were next acquired by the Mediapolis Chautauqua Association. Beginning in 1904 and continuing until 1944, up to 5,000 people per day gathered here annually to enjoy musical talent and outstanding speakers, such as William Jennings Bryan, Senator Robert LaFollette of Wisconsin, and Billy Sunday. As many as 200 tents were pitched on the grounds at one time by people who came from surrounding towns and farms to attend the program which usually lasted for 10 days.

Bordering the park is the unincorporated community of Kossuth. The town was founded in 1839 and was known as Round Prairie Community until a post office was established in 1850 under the name Kossuth. About 1½ miles north is Round Prairie Cemetery, containing the graves of two Revolutionary War soldiers, William Blair and Frederick Ware. The latter served as an artificer in York County Militia of Pennsylvania, and is said to have shod a horse for General George Washington during the early part of the American Revolution. About ¼ mile northwest is one of Iowa's earliest historical monuments, erected in memory of veterans from Yellow Springs Township who died in the Civil War. Funds to erect the monument were provided by the Southern Iowa Fair, held in 1864.

Located on a high hill covered with large native trees and shrubs, which have been labelled for nature study, the area is also used for picnics, group and individual or family camping, and as a rest area.

29 - DES MOINES
(continued)

● **Crapo Park**
Burlington, Iowa

Opened: 1895

Crapo (pronounced Cray-po) Park and adjoining Dankwardt Park include about 100 acres of natural stone bluffs, deep ravines, and majestic panoramas of the Mississippi River and the hills of Illinois in the distance.

The first American flag to fly in what is now Iowa was raised by 26-year-old explorer Zebulon Pike on August 23, 1805 on the west bank of the Mississippi River in present-day Crapo Park. This historic event is commemorated by a marker placed at the site in 1905.

When Lieutenant Zebulon Pike visited the area in 1805, he described it in these words: "We landed on a flint hill on the west side of the river about 4 miles south of the Henderson at a bend in the river. The view from this hill across the river is very beautiful, showing broad prairies as far as the eye can reach, occasionally interrupted by groups of trees. We remained here for 9 hours and saw traces of Indians." Pike (for whom Pikes Peak in Iowa and in Colorado were named) was on a government mission to explore the Mississippi River Valley and select locations for military posts.

This area was neutral ground for the Indians who obtained flint for their implements from Flint Hills (Sho-quo-quon), which was the settlement's original name. (See Tama Beach, also.) Black Hawk and the Sac and Fox Indians roamed and hunted here. Black Hawk Spring may be reached on one of the nature trails. The spring flows from a rock cavern below the top of the bluffs and tumbles down to the Mississippi River not far away. Indians used the spring when camping in the vicinity, but the water is no longer safe for drinking.

Burlington, established in 1829, served as the capital of Wisconsin Territory in 1837, and of Iowa Territory when it was established in 1838, until the capital was moved to Iowa City in 1839.

The statue of General John Murray Corse (1835-1893), at an intersection near the west entrance to the park, is the first equestrian statue erected in Iowa (1896). The statue honors the valiant defense of Alatoona Pass, in Georgia, during the Civil War, when General Corse held out against heavy odds until General William Tecumseh Sherman could arrive with assistance.

The park arboretum includes every tree indigenous to this region. There are also formal gardens throughout the park, an illuminated fountain, recreational facilities, nature trails, and a tourist campground.

29 - DES MOINES
(continued)

● **Des Moines County**
   Genealogical Society
   Burlington, Iowa

   Mrs. Evelyn Benz,
     Corresponding Secretary
   919 North 8th Street
   Burlington, Iowa 52601

Organized: 1973
Meetings: Second Tuesday of month
Number of Members: 52

A local chapter of the Iowa Genealogical Society (see Polk County). Members copy wills, land patents, marriage records, and mortuary records. A family surname file is being maintained, and a number of cemeteries recorded.

● **Des Moines County**
   Historical Society
   1616 Dill Street in Perkins Park
   Burlington, Iowa 52601

   Mrs. John Collins, President
   1434 West Avenue
   Burlington, Iowa 52601
     or
   Mrs. William (Dolores) Kinneer, Jr.
   521 Court Street
   Burlington, Iowa 52601
     or
   Mrs. David (Helen) Parsons,
   Curator

Incorporated: 1940; reorganized February 1963 and again in 1968
Meetings: Second Tuesday, February through April and September through November
Number of Members: 500
Dues: $3.00 annual; business $15.00; student $0.50

When the original Society disbanded, collections and funds were transferred to the Burlington Public Library (open daily except Sunday, 9:00 a.m.-9:00 p.m.) for custody and display. Speakers, known as "Town Criers," are available from the reorganized Society to any group interested in stories of early Burlington. Arrangements may be made to tour privately owned historic homes. Historic tours to various parts of the United States are sponsored each year.

The Apple Trees, a living history museum and headquarters of the Society, is maintained in a wing of the old home of Charles Elliott Perkins, in Perkins Park, and includes antique furniture, silver, and household articles. The first orchard in the area was located here, which suggested the museum's name. The Hawkeye Log Cabin Museum in Crapo Park (see above) includes furnishings from the pioneer period prior to 1900. The cabin, located on the bluff along the Mississippi River and overlooking Black Hawk Spring, is open to visitors on Thursday and Sunday afternoons, from May through September. Victorian House Museum (Phelps House) which borders closely on Snake Alley (see below), was acquired by the Society from the Garrett-Phelps family heirs in 1974, and is also operated as a museum open to the public.

● **Grave of Chief Tama**
   3 miles north of Burlington, Iowa
   in Tama Township on the Great
   River Road (Iowa 99)

A marker indicates the site of the grave of Chief Tama (Tai-mah), a consistent friend of the white man. He moved his band to Tama Town Prairie from Burlington, where he had set up his Indian village (Sho-quo-quon) in 1820. A wild cherry was planted on Chief Tama's grave many years ago. (See Tama Beach, also.)

29 - DES MOINES (continued)

● **Hunt Woods**
2½ miles southwest of Burlington, Iowa

Des Moines County Conservation Board
James A. Settles, Executive Officer
601½ "Corner" Main and Court Streets
Burlington, Iowa 52601

Rolling timberland, comprising over 58 acres of some of the best remaining native hardwoods in Des Moines County--burr oak, white oak, shagbark hickory, walnut, basswood, and elm. There are nature and hiking trails, picnic and primitive camping areas, and an arboretum. The timber preserve is used as an outdoor classroom, permitting children to study nature and wildlife. A 1-acre burial ground is within the area. This land was part of the thousands of acres purchased by C. W. Hunt in the early 1800's.

● **Jimtown**
Along U.S. 34, 2 miles west of Danville, Iowa

A pioneer hamlet, named for James (Jim) Duke, who provided accommodations for stagecoach passengers. This first stagecoach hotel in Iowa, built in the 1840's, was located at Jimtown.

James Wilson Grimes (1816-1872), a Whig from Des Moines County, worked for the establishment of a plank road to Mount Pleasant before he became Governor of Iowa (1854-1858). The Iowa Legislature authorized the construction of three plank roads radiating from Burlington, in 1849. One of these was completed in 1851 as far west as Mount Pleasant. Timber was plentiful, and the new road was laid with good oak planks, 8 feet long and 3 inches thick, spiked on white oak stringers, 2 inches thick and 6 inches wide. The cost was about $2,500 per mile. The plank road was 30 feet wide, and built on a 60-foot right-of-way. Toll stations were 4 miles apart. A toll of 2 cents a mile was charged for a horse and wagon. A 4-horse vehicle paid 3 cents per mile and a horseman, 1½ cents per mile. Loose livestock driven over the toll road cost ¼ to ½ cent each. With the building of the C. B. and Q. Railroad parallel to the plank road, it was unable to survive the competition and work to extend the toll road to Ottumwa, as originally planned, was never completed.

The Jimtown hotel offered sleeping rooms and a barroom which became the local social center, providing spirits and games of chance. Unoccupied since 1957, the 10-room building deteriorated until it was beyond repair, and was finally burned in 1969. The doors of the inn were saved and given to the Midwest Old Settlers and Threshers Association of Mount Pleasant (see Henry County, below) for use in a stagecoach house replica.

The site of Jimtown is now a roadside park, where a marker has been erected by a chapter of the Daughters of the American Revolution.

● **Lower Skunk River Access**
½ mile east and 1 mile northwest of Augusta, Iowa

Des Moines County Conservation Board
James A. Settles, Executive Officer
601½ "Corner" Main and Court Streets
Burlington, Iowa 52601

A public recreation area of historic interest on the Skunk River. Parts of the 86 acres are covered with natural timber growth, including walnut, oak, hickory, ash, soft maple, willow, cottonwood, box elder, and elm, and there are plantings of jack pine and multiflora rose.

Augusta is situated in a small pocket in the hills along the river. The first white settler was John Whittaker who

- DES MOINES
(continued)

Lower Skunk River Access
(continued)

located at Flint Hills (Burlington) in 1832, but he and other settlers were driven back across the Mississippi River by Indians. With the Black Hawk Purchase, settlers could legally return to the Iowa side, and Whittaker staked a claim near the site of Augusta and built a log cabin. He later built a stone house, parts of which can still be seen. He also selected a site for a dam on the Skunk River, but sold it in 1835. Levi Moffitt then built a mill--one of the first in Iowa. Part of the rock dam for the mill can still be seen at the site when the river is low. One of the stone burrs from Moffitt Mill has been used as a base for the fountain in the Shakespeare Garden in Crapo Park (see above). At one time Augusta was expected to become an important town in southeastern Iowa. There were several stores and 3 churches in the early days. But plans for a railroad did not materialize and the town gradually declined.

The access area includes nature trails along the river, and facilities for picnicking, fishing, and camping. Other parts are maintained as a wildlife habitat.

● **Luckenbill Woods**
4 3/4 miles southeast of
Mediapolis, Iowa

Des Moines County Conservation Board
James A. Settles, Executive Officer
601½ "Corner" Main and Court Streets
Burlington, Iowa 52601

An undeveloped area of 32 acres, including a stand of hardwood timber, acquired as a gift of M. Virginia Sharar. The area is to be planted and restored to its appearance in 1853. The property will be preserved as a natural area and arboretum for use as an outdoor classroom. Nature trails are planned, and a small farm pond is to be converted to a swamp, where aquatic plants may be grown.

● **Malchow Mounds**
Along the Mississippi River,
about 9 miles north of
Burlington, Iowa, or 1 mile
north of Kingston, Iowa on
the west side of Iowa 99

Iowa State Preserves System
c/o State Conservation Commission
State Office Building
300 Fourth Street
Des Moines, Iowa 50319

One of Iowa's largest remaining groups of Indian mounds, named for the landowner at the time of the archeological survey by Ellison Orr, in 1934. The preserve of about 10 acres contains over 50 ancient mounds, built some 2,000 years ago (200 B.C.-200 A.D.) by Indians. These mounds are the only ones with a large Hopewellian Village immediately adjacent. An additional 5 mounds in a second group on another hill (the Poisel Mounds) have been dedicated to the Iowa State Preserves System without transfer of ownership to the state. The larger group of mounds was donated to the State of Iowa by Charles Poisel of Kingston, Iowa in memory of his parents, Albert J. and Viola L. Poisel, to be included in the Iowa State Preserves System.

● **Otter Island**
In Mississippi River,
north of Burlington, Iowa

Otter Island Advisory Committee
c/o Des Moines County
   Conservation Board
James A. Settles, Executive Officer
601½ "Corner" Main and
   Court Streets
Burlington, Iowa 52601

A wintering area for the American bald eagle, and a spring nesting area for herons. Eagles use the area from November to March, while the heron rookery is active from March to July. The island is visible from Tama Beach (see below) and Edgewater Beach. Otter Island, now owned by the City of Burlington, was previously owned by the State of Iowa, and is to be preserved as a wildlife refuge.

29 - DES MOINES
(continued)

● **Site of Old Zion**
West side of 3rd Street, between
Columbia and Washington Streets
Burlington, Iowa

The first Legislative Assembly of Iowa Territory met in Old Zion Methodist Church on November 12, 1838. The building erected to house the Legislative Assembly after Burlington was named the capital of Wisconsin Territory, was destroyed by fire on December 12, 1837. Arrangements were then made to rent the recently completed church for a temporary capitol. Four sessions of the Territorial Legislature were held in Old Zion.

Dr. William R. Ross built the church in 1837, at a cost of $4,500. It was originally a plain, 2-story, brick building, 40 by 60 feet in size. Basement walls were 2 feet thick. In 1850, a belfry and 1,450 pound bell were added, but it wasn't until June 1864 that the church was formally dedicated.

Old Zion also served as an assembly hall, public meeting place, and courthouse. The church was razed in 1881, and the site was then occupied by the Grand Opera House, in the days of Lillian Russell, Edwin Booth, John Drew, and the Barrymores. This building became the Rialto Theater, which was also torn down.

Now a parking lot, a marker, erected by the Stars and Stripes Chapter of the Daughters of the American Revolution, locates the site of Old Zion.

● **Snake Alley**
North Sixth Street,
between Washington and
Columbia Streets
Burlington, Iowa

Constructed: 1894

A curving, narrow street built on a limestone bluff and consisting of 5 half curves and 2 quarter curves, descending over a distance of 275 feet. It has been featured by Robert L. Ripley (1893-1949) in "Believe It or Not" as the "crookedest street in the world." The 58-foot drop from residential North Hill to the business district is so steep that the city council feared an ordinary straight road would wash out, and horses and buggies would go out of control rushing down the slope. The curves were designed to permit the horses to descend at safer speeds. The bricks were made locally and are tapered and set at a slight uphill tilt to allow better traction. The hand-chiseled stone curbs were tailored to fit the curves and changing grade, an unusual engineering feat and an example of fine craftsmanship. The 6 homes

- DES MOINES
(continued)

Snake Alley
(continued)

bordering the alley were built during the period 1845 to 1880. The Phelps House, at 521 Columbia, is a large rambling, Victorian estate built in 1851 and acquired in 1974 by Des Moines County Historical Society (see above). The home contains the original furnishings of the Garrett-Phelps family and is open to the public as the Victorian House Museum. Snake Alley was placed on the National Register of Historic Places in September 1974.

- **Solar Eclipse Marker**
South Hill Park
Corner of 7th and Elm Streets
Burlington, Iowa

A huge glacial boulder, set with a bronze tablet, marks the site of government observation of the total eclipse of the sun on August 7, 1869. It was here that the scientific instruments were set up by J. H. C. Coffin, of the United States Navy, and other distinguished scientists to study the eclipse. Their principal object was to secure photographs of the phenomenon. Conditions for observation were almost ideal in Iowa, and the first pictures of the corona ever taken in America were obtained. Other prominent astronomers established temporary observatories in different parts of the State, and some of the most important scientific work on the eclipse was accomplished in Iowa.

- **Starr's Cave Park**
¼ mile north of Burlington,
Iowa along Irish Ridge Road

Des Moines County Conservation Board
James A. Settles, Executive Officer
601½ "Corner" Main and Court Streets
Burlington, Iowa 52601

A 140-acre tract being maintained as a forest preserve. Flint Creek runs through the timber before emptying into the Mississippi River. The preserve is unique in that it includes a large cave and towering limestone bluffs. Hiking trails wind throughout the park.

- **Tama Beach**
4 3/4 miles northeast of
Burlington, Iowa

Des Moines County Conservation Board
James A. Settles, Executive Officer
601½ "Corner" Main and Court Streets
Burlington, Iowa 52601

A 2-acre tract in the flood plain adjacent to the Mississippi River, along the levee, which provides a public boat launching area, and opportunities for fishing, picnicking, and camping. The property is covered with brushwood, grass, and river bottom timber, and is adjacent to the unincorporated settlement of Tama Town or Hoochtown, as it was known in prohibition days.

The great bluffs bordering the Mississippi at Sho-quo-quon or Flint Hills were long a place of importance to the Indians because of the rich deposits of flint. This was neutral ground, where Indians from many tribes came for the raw material for their weapons and implements. (See Crapo Park, also.)

In 1808, Colonel J. W. Johnson, the factor for the United States Fur Factory at Fort Madison, established a trading post at the mouth of what is now Flint Creek, just below Tama Beach. The post was destroyed by fire in 1812. There followed a period of Indian occupation in 1820 when Chief Tama (Tai-mah) came here from Henderson Creek in Illinois. After a short time, he moved on to the prairie north of Burlington, to a place now known as Tama Town Prairie. Chief Tama, a friend of the white man, gave his name to Tama County, Tama Township, and the town of Tama. A memorial marker 3 miles north of Burlington on

29 - DES MOINES
(continued)

Tama Beach
(continued)

the Great River Road (Iowa 99) has been placed near Chief Tama's burial plot. (See Grave of Chief Tama, above.)

● **Zion School Museum**
1¼ miles south and 2½ miles west of Dodgeville, Iowa or 7½ miles southwest of Mediapolis, Iowa

Des Moines County Conservation Board
James A. Settles, Executive Officer
601½ "Corner" Main and Court Streets
Burlington, Iowa 52601

An old country schoolhouse built of native limestone from a nearby quarry. The 1-acre tract, covered with lush bluegrass and a few hickory trees, was deeded to Zion School District in 1846. The 1-room school was in use until the early 1960's. It is equipped with slate blackboards, pot-bellied stove, old desks, books, and other school furnishings typical of the 1900 period.

30 - DICKINSON

Spirit Lake
A-3

● **Cayler Prairie**
9 miles southwest of Spirit Lake, Iowa
or 4½ miles west of Iowa Lakeside Laboratory on county road

State Conservation Commission
State Office Building
300 Fourth Street
Des Moines, Iowa 50319

Acquired: 1960

120 acres of unplowed, ungrazed prairie noted for its variety of prairie flowers and grasses and used extensively as a study area by biologists. A total of 265 species in 53 plant families have been identified here. The State Preserve includes rolling upland prairie, intermediate and lowland prairie, potholes, hilly morainal areas, and moist prairie, typical of Iowa country before it was cultivated.

● **Deerland**
3 miles southwest of Spirit Lake, Iowa on U.S. 71

B.D. Blair, Owner
Lake Park, Iowa 51347

Established: 1965
Admission: $0.50; under 8, $0.35
Open: Daily during summer, 10:00 a.m.-9 p.m.

A children's zoo featuring over 30 tame deer, seals, bears, monkeys, birds, small animals native to Iowa, and domestic animals.

● **Dickinson County Historical Society**
Spirit Lake, Iowa

Byron Smith, President
R. R.
Spirit Lake, Iowa 51360

Organized: March 1961
Meetings: January, April, July, and October
Number of Members: 70
Dues: $1.00 annual

Compiles historical data, and genealogical records; preserves old pictures and articles; marks historic sites; and sponsors Old Settlers Picnic. Operates Dickinson County Museum (see below).

● **Dickinson County Museum**
1708 Keokuk Avenue
Spirit Lake, Iowa

Mrs. Dale E. (Faye) Peterson, Curator
507 - 11th Street
Milford, Iowa 51351

Dedicated: June 7, 1970
Admission: Free
Open: During summer months (June-July-August), afternoons daily except Monday, 1:00-5:00 p.m.

Operated by Dickinson County Historical Society to preserve and display items indicative of the County's heritage. Originally located in the Lakes Art Center in Okoboji, Iowa, but moved in 1973 to the former Chicago, Milwaukee and St. Paul Railroad Depot in Spirit Lake. A section of track (120 feet) has been left on the west side of the depot. A large framed map of Dickinson County shows the homesteads and names of owners in 1883, and advertisements of businesses of that time. Also on display are Civil War items, a World War I collection, a showcase of

0 - DICKINSON
(continued)

Dickinson County Museum
(continued)

early doctor's equipment and instruments, and a knitting machine brought to the lakes area in a covered wagon shortly after the Spirit Lake Massacre. The machine was owned by Reverend Samuel Pillsbury who moved here with his family in 1863 and lived in the Gardner log cabin.

● **Egralharve Mineral Spring**
West side of West Okoboji Lake, just north of Vacation Village

One of a number of springs in the Iowa Great Lakes Region. The spring elevation is about 50 feet above the level of West Okoboji Lake, and about 400 feet back from the shoreline. The water, which flows at the rate of 40,000 gallons per day, is supercharged with minerals and gave rise to a commerical venture in the earlier part of the 20th Century. The springs, privately owned, are also unusual in that they support life usually considered marine and found nowhere else except within the limits of the Arctic Circle.

● **Freda Haffner Preserve
(Arends' Kettlehole)**
4 miles northwest of Milford, Iowa, or southwest of Iowa Lakeside Laboratory. Take U.S. 71 north of Milford, Iowa 1 mile to Junction with Iowa 32 and continue west 1½ miles until the highway curves north. At this curve, turn on gravel road and go west 2¼ miles. The preserve is on the north side of this road.

Henry Arends
(Lives next to preserve area)

Iowa Chapter,
The Nature Conservancy
c/o Larry Eilers
Department of Biology
University of Northern Iowa
Cedar Falls, Iowa 50613

A 110-acre preserve on the east side of the Little Sioux River, located in the glacial terrain formed by the last glacier to enter Dickinson County —— the Cary lobe of the Wisconsin Glacier. Included in the natural area is a large glacial sink or kettlehole with steep sides and a marsh at the bottom. It is believed that the depression was formed when a huge chunk of glacial ice buried in the glacial drift melted, leaving the kettlehole filled with water. Aquatic plants now grow in the marsh.

The kettlehole is surrounded by upland sandy prairie, and is located west of West Okoboji Lake. A diversity of habitats exist--the dry, gravelly rim of the kettlehole supports short grass and plants; tall grass prairie remnants cover the upland portions of the tract; and sedges dominate the prairie sloughs in the low areas. Nearly 250 species of plants have been found, including the pasque flower, a small locoweed, and butterfly weed or orange milkweed.

The preserve, which had been grazed before it was acquired by The Nature Conservancy in 1972, is one of the few remaining prairies left in Iowa and serves as a nature study and research area for Iowa Lakeside Laboratory, students, and others.

● **Gardner Log Cabin**
Arnolds Park, Iowa
(Signs direct U.S. 71 traffic to the site)

The State Historical Society of Iowa
402 Iowa Avenue
Iowa City, Iowa 52240
or
Iowa Great Lakes Area
  Chamber of Commerce
Box A
Arnolds Park, Iowa 51331

Acquired: By State of Iowa in 1943
Admission: Free
Open: 11:00 a.m.-6:00 p.m. daily, Memorial Day through Labor Day

A log house constructed by Rowland Gardner after he arrived at West Okoboji in July 1856. Two families resided in the cabin during the following winter and, in March 1857, both families were killed by renegades from the Sioux tribe, led by Inkpaduta (Scarlet Point). Only Abigail (Abbie), the 13-year-old daughter survived. She and 3 women were taken to South Dakota as captives. Two of the women were later killed. Families in other cabins in the Iowa Great Lakes area--a total of 33 persons--were also killed in the Spirit Lake Massacre. In 1891 Mrs. Abigail Gardner Sharp returned to the area, purchased the cabin,

30 - DICKINSON
(continued)

Gardner Log Cabin
(continued)

and preserved it until her death in 1921. After the cabin passed into state ownership in 1943, efforts were made to restore and furnish it. In 1975, the cabin was restored to its 1856 appearance. A Visitor Center near the cabin contains displays and exhibits of pioneer life and housing in Iowa. A mass gravesite for some of those killed during the uprising, the Gardner family burial plot, and the Spirit Lake Massacre Monument (dedicated in 1895) are also here on Pillsbury Point.

● **Horseshoe Bend**
3½ miles southwest of
Milford, Iowa

Dickinson County Conservation Board
Robert K. Walters, Executive Officer
1013 Okoboji Avenue
Milford, Iowa 51351

A 180-acre tract along a large bend of the Little Sioux River, where it turns back north. Some of the area is covered with thick timber. There are recreational trails for hiking and horseback riding. The park is also used for fishing, picnicking, winter sports, and nature study. Songbirds, deer, and other wildlife may be seen.

● **Inkpaduta Trail**
From Peterson, Iowa to
Arnolds Park, Iowa

See Clay County for information.

● **Iowa Great Lakes**
North central Dickinson County

The Iowa Great Lakes are of glacial origin, dating back about 12,500 years. Many such lakes were formed at the edge of the glacial advance, on the very top of the Iowa Watershed Divide, between the Mississippi and Missouri Rivers. In all, Iowa has over 50 natural lakes formed by the action of glaciers.

Four of Iowa's largest natural lakes are in Dickinson County--Spirit Lake (5,684 acres), West Okoboji (3,939 acres), East Okoboji (1,875 acres), and Silver Lake (1,058 acres).

West Okoboji Lake is recognized as one of the three most beautiful blue water lakes in the world. The others are Lake Louise in Canada and Lake Geneva in Switzerland.

The *Queen*, was constructed in 1884 by the Dubuque Boat Company at a cost of about $7,500 and operated as an excursion boat on Big Spirit and West Okoboji Lakes for 89 years--"the flagship of the Iowa Great Lakes Navy." The 74-foot-long ship was the first iron hulled vessel on the Iowa Great Lakes, and its interior woodwork was done in the B.C.R.&N. car shops in Cedar Rapids. In May 1973, the 45-ton *Queen* was purchased by Adventure Lands of America, Inc., for $33,000 and moved overland by flatbed truck to a recreation complex near Altoona, Iowa.

At one time the Okoboji Steamboat Company had a line of 4 steamers, *Okoboji, Queen, Des Moines,* and *Iowa.* These passenger boats operated on East and West Okoboji Lakes and met the Milwaukee trains at Arnolds Park and the Rock Island trains at the head of West Okoboji Lake to take passengers "to all points on the lake."

) - DICKINSON
(continued)

● **Kurio Kastle**
On U.S. 71
Arnolds Park, Iowa 51331

Mrs. Wilbur Gildemeister
2403 Jackson
Spirit Lake, Iowa 51360

Established: 1932
Admission: $0.25; children, $0.10
Open: During summer, 9:00 a.m.-9:00 p.m.

Natural and wildlife exhibit, including mounted fresh and salt water fish, birds, animals, and a 1,400 pound turtle; Indian garments and artifacts; and mineral specimens.

● **Lakes Art Center**
On U.S. 71
Okoboji, Iowa

Mrs. Louise Vanderpool, President
Okoboji, Iowa 51355

Established: 1965
Meetings: 1st Monday of the month during summer
Number of Members: 250
Dues: $5.00 individual; $8.00 couple; $10.00 family
Open: Gallery, 1:00-5:00 p.m. during June, July, and August

Art exhibits, lectures, shows, musicals; instruction in various art mediums (oil, watercolor, other).

● **Marble Beach**
North of Spirit Lake, Iowa
on Iowa 276

Rodney Parsons
Spirit Lake, Iowa 51360

Established: 1967
Open: Daily during summer

Replica of William Marble Cabin at original site. Members of this family were the last victims of hostile Sioux Indians during the Spirit Lake Massacre in March 1857. There are museum displays at the site.

● **Meadow No. 7 (Viola) Rural School**
On U.S. 71, 3/4 mile south of Arnolds Park, Iowa or 2 miles north of Milford, Iowa

Established: Moved to present location April 22, 1962
Admission: Donations accepted
Open: Daily during summer; other times by request

One-room rural schoolhouse, built sometime prior to 1885 (when courthouse records start) in Meadow Township, Clay County. Preserved and furnished with desks, blackboards, books, map racks, organ, and old school records. Initials and names are carved on desks. Wooden pegs and square iron nails were used in construction.

Displays include Indian bones, arrowheads, stone hammers, lithograph stones, antique farm equipment, hair pictures, old skates, irons, and horsehide coats. An Indian burial mound is on the premises.

● **Silver Lake Fen Area**
Southwest of Lake Park, Iowa at the Southwest corner of Silver Lake, between the fish rearing pond, the lake shore, and the county road

Iowa State Preserves Advisory Board
c/o State Conservation Commission
State Office Building
300 Fourth Street
Des Moines, Iowa 50319

A rare plant preserve of 15 acres. The fen contains unusual plants that grow only in cold, hard water, and boggy areas. Marsh birds, such as the yellow-headed blackbird, are commonly seen here. Since this is a very fragile environment, viewing is limited to the edges.

30 - DICKINSON
(continued)

● **Spirit Lake State Fish Hatchery**
On isthmus between East Okoboji
and Spirit Lake
Spirit Lake, Iowa 51360

State Conservation Commission
State Office Building
300 Fourth Street
Des Moines, Iowa 50319

Fish factory or hatchery in operation over 60 years. Brood fish (walleye and northern pike) are brought here for stripping and may be seen in holding pens. The entire process of fertilization and the hatching of the "fry" are explained to visitors. A slide show on spawning techniques may be seen. Live Iowa game fish are on display in the hatchery aquaria.

In the Biology Building, scientific studies and investigations are constantly under way to improve fish management techniques and angling success. A biologist is on hand to explain the operation to groups.

31 - DUBUQUE

Dubuque
C-12

● **Bankston Park**
6 miles southeast of
Holy Cross, Iowa

Dubuque County Conservation Board
Ray C. Briggs, Executive Officer
1990 Bennett Street
Dubuque, Iowa 52001

A 120-acre park including heavy, hilly woodland along the middle fork of Little Maquoketa River. Natural rock outcroppings appear along the slopes, and there are natural springs in the bottomland. An old family burial plot is located in the area. Parts of an old dike remain from English Mills, a grinding mill that has gone out of existence. The park is used by hikers, picnickers, and campers.

● **Basilica of St. Francis Xavier**
Dyersville, Iowa

Dedicated: 1889

A twin-towered church given the rank of Minor Basilica in November 1956--one of only 18 in the United States. The term "Basilica" is applied by the Pope to churches of unusual architectural design, native nobility, and antiquity. As a Minor Basilica, the church has its own heraldic shield and takes precedence over other churches with the exception of cathedrals. The imposing twin spires are 200 feet high.

● **Crystal Lake Cave**
5 miles south of Dubuque, Iowa,
off U.S. 52

Opened to Public: 1932
Admission: $1.50; children 6-12 years, $0.75
Open: May 1 to November 1; hours during May and from
Labor Day to November 1, 9:00 a.m.-5:00 p.m.;
hours from June through Labor Day, 8:00 a.m.-
6:00 p.m.

A 3,000-foot-long tunnel passing through a cavern, winding back to a small underground lake of crystal clear water. Stalagmites and stalactites, and rock formations resembling animal and human figures, line the cave. Temperatures of 48 to 50 degrees prevail throughout the year. The cave was discovered in 1880 when miners were looking for lead ore.

● **Dubuque City Hall**
Dubuque, Iowa

Built: 1857

Originally a combined municipal office facility and market house, a combination dating from medieval tradition. The City Hall was officially opened in January 1858. The building was designed to resemble Boston's renowned Faneuil Hall (1742), "The Cradle of Liberty." The architect was John Francis Rague. Born in Scotch Plains, New York on March 24, 1799, Rague later made his home in

- DUBUQUE
(continued)

Dubuque City Hall
(continued)

Dubuque, where he died in September 1877. The area surrounding City Hall is referred to as The Market Place. The ground floor of the building was divided into market stalls with large open windows, which permitted farmers to back their wagons up for the sale of goods during spring, summer, and fall. As the need for more office space increased, the market function of City Hall was discontinued. But farmers continued to sell produce on the large open sidewalks around the building for many years. The farmers' open air market was started up again during the summer of 1974. Space is provided on the sidewalks for carts and stalls each Saturday.

Dubuque has been under the flags of 4 countries: France (1673-1763), Spain (1763-1803), England (1780, when the land from the Turkey River to the lead mines was seized and held by the British and their red allies), and the United States (since 1803, the time of the Louisiana Purchase).

● **Dubuque County Historical Society**
2241 Lincoln Avenue
Dubuque, Iowa 52001

John A. Baule, President
P. O. Box 305
Dubuque, Iowa 52001
or
Mrs. Kenneth Mercer
P. O. Box 305
Dubuque, Iowa 52001

Organized: 1950
Meetings: Second and fourth Wednesday of month, 7:30 p.m.
Number of Members: 400
Dues: $5.00 annual; $10.00 family; $25.00 sustaining; $100.00 life.

Sponsors monthly lectures, an old-fashioned ice cream social on July 4th, and an annual Christmas party. Other activities include educational school tours on Dubuque history, marking historic sites in Dubuque County, making tape recordings, and publishing "Dubuque: Its History and Background." Owns and operates Ham House Museum (see below).

The Orpheum Theater, built in 1910 in Dubuque, was designed by the George Rapp firm, leading theater designers. The Flemish Renaissance style represents an architectural transition between the Victorian playhouse and the palatial theaters of the 1920's. The theater is on the National Register of Historic Places and is being restored to its original appearance, to be used as a civic center.

● **Dyersville Historical Society**
Dyersville, Iowa

Ray Goedken, President
622 Eighth Avenue, S.E.
Dyersville, Iowa 52040

Organized: 1960
Meetings: No regular time
Number of Members: 25
Dues: $1.00 annual

Collects small items, letters, documents, pictures, and other historical articles. Housed in Dyersville Public Library.

● **Fourth Street Elevator or Fenelon Place Inclined Railway**
West Fourth and Bluff Streets
Dubuque, Iowa

Fare: $0.10, one way

An inclined railway cable car that runs to the summit of a 300-foot bluff. Built in 1882 to relieve the horses and pedestrians from having to climb the staggering hill. From the platform at the summit is an unobstructed panoramic view of Dubuque and environs, the Mississippi River, and across into Illinois and Wisconsin.

31 - DUBUQUE
(continued)

● **Grave of Julien DuBuque**
South of Dubuque, Iowa, beyond
the end of Rowan Street

Dubuque County Conservation Board
Ray C. Briggs, Executive Officer
1990 Bennett Street
Dubuque, Iowa 52001

A circular Galena limestone tower erected in 1897 on the Mississippi River bluffs, at the mouth of Catfish Creek, contains the grave of Julien DuBuque, the founder of the City of Dubuque, and reportedly the first white man to settle permanently in what is now Iowa. The monument site is approximately 180 feet above the river. A bronze plaque inside the monument bears the following inscription:

JULIEN DUBUQUE
MINER OF MINES OF SPAIN
FOUNDER OF OUR CITY
"DIED MARCH 24, 1810"

In 1788, DuBuque, a French-Canadian, began mining lead with permission of the Indians and the Spanish authorities. The "Mines of Spain" were located in this area, at the mouth of Catfish Creek. DuBuque died in 1810 and was buried by his Indian friends on a cedar-covered bluff overlooking the Mississippi River. His remains were later unearthed and then reburied October 31, 1897.

Fox Indian Chief Peosta was a friend of Julien DuBuque, who married Petosa, daughter of the Chief. Peosta died in 1814 and was buried at his request beside DuBuque atop the high, narrow bluff that juts out towards the Mississippi River. When it was decided to erect the 28-foot-tall stone tower at the gravesite in 1897, the remains of both DuBuque and Peosta were removed and identified. The bones of DuBuque were reburied under a cement slab inside the tower, but Peosta's were not. His bones and those of Petosa, DuBuque's wife, became a part of the collection of Richard Hermann. The bones of Chief Peosta were wired together and the entire skeleton stood on a pedestal, with his name on the base. Petosa's bones were packed away in cotton. Following Hermann's death, the collection went to Dubuque County Historical Society in 1966, and the bones were displayed at Ham House Museum in a room containing Indian artifacts. As a result of complaints about the public display of Chief Peosta's skeleton, his remains and those of his daughter Petosa were reburied about 50 feet from DuBuque's grave in a simple ceremony on May 12, 1973.

The 12-acre Julien DuBuque Monument Preserve has picnicking facilities.

Some time before Julien DuBuque appeared, there was another white man, also a French-Canadian, in this area. Jean Marie Cardinal (or Cardinell), hunter, trapper, and fur trader, penetrated to the upper reaches of the Mississippi River and resided in the Prairie du Chien, Wisconsin area (1754 or earlier). He was probably at the site of Dubuque, Iowa at intervals during the latter part of the 1700's. He was also a trader of some renown in St. Louis. His wife Careche-Coranche (or Marie Anne) was a Pawnee Indian.

- DUBUQUE
(continued)

Grave of Julien DuBuque
(continued)

The 6 daughters and 2 sons were all baptized in the log church at St. Louis on May 30, 1776, at which time their parents were married. Mrs. Cardinal was baptized the following day. Their late marriage was not unusual at that time for those living in the wilderness, where ministers or priests were not to be found. It was common practice among the French living in the Indian country to take their children with them to a priest to have the children baptized and their own marriage legalized at the same time.

There are many accounts which refer to Jean Marie Cardinal and unauthenticated stories about his activities during the period of the American Revolution. It has been established, however, that during the British attack on the village of St. Louis, Cardinal was killed May 26, 1780.

Ham House Museum
2241 Lincoln Avenue
Dubuque, Iowa 52001

Open: Daily, 12:30 - 4:30 p.m., from Memorial Day to Labor Day
Admission: $1.00; children, $0.50

Ham House, a 22-room Victorian mansion was built in 1857 by miner-contractor Mathias Ham. Actually, this was built as an addition to the original farmhouse constructed of native limestone in 1839, using Illinois limestone rejected for use on the U.S. Customs House for which Ham was the contractor. (The Customs House was completed in 1866. It was later used as the Post Office, and was razed in 1933.) Located on a bluff, at the entrance to Eagle Point Park, the 4-story castle-like house has been restored and serves as a museum displaying Indian artifacts, costumes, and pioneer and industrial items. Exhibits include natural history, Indian Rooms, Clothing Rooms, River Boat Room, Yesteryear Room, World War I Room, and a John Deere Room. The watchtower provides a panoramic view of the river and surrounding area. At Christmas-time each year, an open house is held in an old-fashioned Christmas setting. Antique ornaments, cards, dolls, and toys of bygone days are on display.

The William Neuman (or Newman) 2-room log cabin, built prior to 1827, is reputedly the oldest building still standing in Iowa. It has been removed from its original site at Second and Locust Streets and restored. The cabin is said to have been built and occupied originally by French hunters and miners. It is now located on the grounds of Ham House Museum, as is an old red railroad caboose, Burlington car No. 13814. The old wooden caboose, built prior to 1910, was used for many years to transport railroad personnel from Dubuque to East Dubuque. The Humke 1-room rural schoolhouse, also on the grounds, has been restored and completely furnished.

COUNTY AND COUNTY SEAT; LOCATION ON MAP	NAME AND LOCATION	DESCRIPTION
31 - DUBUQUE (continued)	• **New Melleray Abbey** 10 miles southwest of Dubuque, Iowa on U.S. 151	*Founded:* 1849 *Open:* Visitors welcome on weekdays; tours available A Trappist monastery founded by a religious group from County Waterford, Ireland. Its appearance and atmosphere are typical of the Old World. Monks live under the same rigid rules of discipline they have followed for more than 1,300 years; their day begins at 2:15 a.m. and ends at 7:00 p.m. During their long day, the monks farm 800 acres of land, raise livestock, make candles, process honey, and bake bread for religious uses. A constant vigil is kept in the chapel. There are daily prayers and hymns. The Observance of Christmas, by the Abbot and the community of about 120 monks, is much the same as it was in monasteries of over 800 years ago. Most of the limestone buildings, of Victorian Gothic architecture, were built around 1875 by the monks, with stone cut from a nearby quarry.
	• **New Wine Park** Southwest of New Vienna, Iowa, about 1 mile off Iowa 136 Dubuque County Conservation Board Ray C. Briggs, Executive Officer 1990 Bennett Street Dubuque, Iowa 52001	A 126-acre wooded area offering nature study, hiking, picnicking, fishing, and camping. A section of an old country road has been preserved as a walking trail. A stream runs through the park. Wine is the Austrian word for Vienna.
	• **Old Shot Tower** End of Fourth Street Dubuque, Iowa	*Constructed:* 1855 An old stone and brick shot tower, constructed by George A. Rogers to make lead pellets or shot--a reminder of frontier days. The shot was formed by dropping molten lead from the top floor, through screens and into vats of water at the bottom of the tower. The tower had a capacity of 6 to 8 tons of finished shot per day. The shot was adequate for most weapons of the period, and was produced here until around 1863. The tower was later used by a lumber company as a lookout tower to sight rafts on the river. The 150-foot tower was gutted by a disastrous fire in 1911, but has been restored.

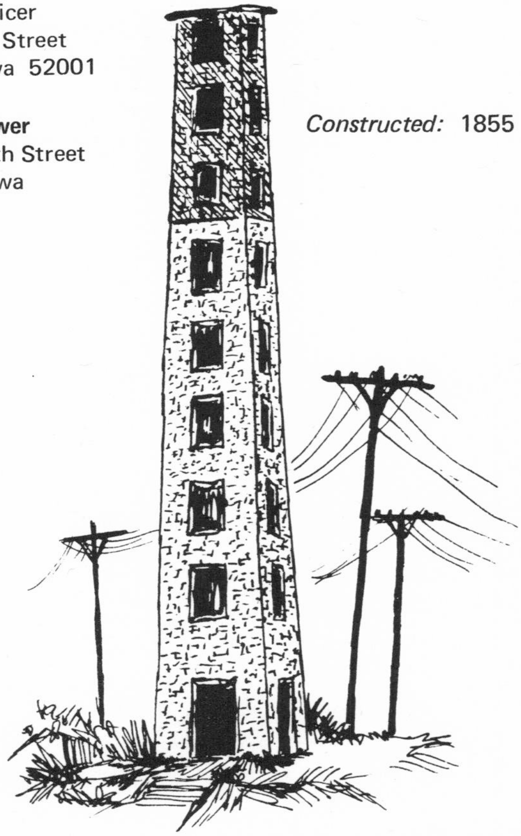

- DUBUQUE
(continued)

● **Swiss Valley Park**
4 miles southwest of
Dubuque, Iowa

Dubuque County Conservation Board
Ray C. Briggs, Executive Officer
1990 Bennett Street
Dubuque, Iowa 52001

A hidden valley with heavily wooded hillsides, named for the resemblance to alpine foothills. Catfish Creek flows through the 514-acre park. The creek, which is a certified trout stream, got its name from the great numbers of catfish that swarmed at its mouth where it joins the Mississippi River. It was here that Julien DuBuque built his cabin in 1788 when the Fox Indians gave him permission to work the lead mines. (See Grave of Julien DuBuque, above.) One of the first villages settled by white men in Iowa after the area was opened to settlement in 1833 was located here, and named Catfish. The town of Dubuque later swallowed up the little village. One of the worst flood disasters in Iowa history occurred here during a 4th of July thunderstorm in 1876 when the creek washed out the settlement of Rockdale, killing 39 persons.

Nearly every tree native to Iowa grows in the woods. Nature trails have been laid out, with small carved signs identifying and explaining the plants. An old farm has been remodelled for a nature center, complete with both outdoor and indoor lecture areas where films and slides may be shown. The valley abounds in wild flowers and birds. Prairie grasses have been planted, together with trees and shrubs to attract wildlife. The park is also used for picnicking, hiking, camping, fishing, and horseback riding.

● **White Pine Hollow State Forest**
3 miles northwest of Luxemburg, Iowa

State Conservation Commission
State Office Building
300 Fourth Street
Des Moines, Iowa 50319

About 15 percent of the original area of what is now Iowa was forest land. It has been estimated that about 40 percent of this original timber is still present. Of course, truly virgin woods, not cut over or grazed, are rare. This timber is a survival of the northern forest dating back to glacial times. It is the largest remaining stand of white pine in Iowa, with many trees over 200 years old in an undeveloped area of 712 acres. Spring-fed streams, dense forest, limestone bluffs, and hillsides covered with Canadian Yew, reminiscent of the far north country, may be seen.

- EMMET

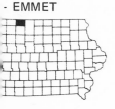

therville
A-4

● **Country Schoolhouse**
Emmet County Fair Grounds
18th Street and 3rd Avenue South
Estherville, Iowa

Dorothy Story
1314 North 13th Street
Estherville, Iowa 51334

Open: By appointment

Restored country schoolhouse, appropriately furnished.

● **Emmet County Historical Museum**
107 South 6th Street
Estherville, Iowa 51334

Admission: Free
Open: Thursday and Sunday, 2:00-5:00 p.m., from April to December; other times by appointment

An extensive collection of historical items located in a building on the ground formerly occupied by Fort Defiance.

32 - EMMETT
(continued)

● **Emmet County Historical Society**
Box 101, Estherville, Iowa 51334

Louis F. Obye, President
408 North 5th Street
Estherville, Iowa 51334
or
Miss Ivadell Ross, Treasurer
1724 North 6th Street
Estherville, Iowa 51334

Organized: June 11, 1964
Annual Meeting: September
Number of Members: 250
Dues: $3.00 annual; $30.00 life

Owns restored country schoolhouse (see above), located on Emmet County Fairgrounds, and Emmet County Historical Museum (see above), in Estherville business district.

● **Estherville Meteorite**
1½ miles north of Estherville, Iowa

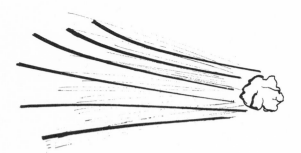

On May 10, 1879, Iowa experienced one of the largest meteorite falls on record. Others have occurred over Iowa in Iowa County and Winnebago County. The meteorite exploded and broke into 3 large pieces. The largest piece, weighing 431 pounds, fell on the Sever Lee farm. A huge hole was made where it landed and buried itself 14 feet in the ground. The rough black surface of the meteorite contains pieces of sparkling metal (iron nodules). A marker, originally located on the northeast ¼ of Section 35, Township 100 north of Range 34, Emmet County, 482 feet away from the fall, has been relocated along Iowa 4.

Other smaller portions of the huge meteorite, one weighing 151 pounds and the other 92½ pounds, were found later at other locations. Some 5,000 bits, ranging in size from a pea to lumps weighing a pound, were also picked up by persons living in the area. Large specimens of the Estnerville Meteorite are now on display in museums in widely separated cities of the world. Smaller fragments may be seen in the Estherville Public Library and the State Historical Building in Des Moines.

● **Fort Defiance State Park**
1 mile southwest of Estherville, Iowa on Iowa 245

State Conservation Commission
State Office Building
300 Fourth Street
Des Moines, Iowa 50319

Site of a military fort built in 1862-63 by Captain W. H. Ingham and Company A of the Northern Border Brigade. One of a string of fortifications built to protect settlers from marauding Sioux Indians, it was abandoned by the troops after 15 months. The 181 acres of heavily wooded hills support an abundance of wild flowers. There are nature trails and recreational facilities. In 1911, a monument was erected in Estherville City Park by the D A R to commemorate Fort Defiance.

● **Okamanpedan State Park**
3 miles northeast of Dolliver, Iowa on county road

State Conservation Commission
State Office Building
300 Fourth Street
Des Moines, Iowa 50319

A tract of 18½ acres along the shore of Tuttle Lake (formerly Okamanpadu or Okamanpedan Lake), located on the Iowa- Minnesota border. The lake is the headwaters of the East Fork of the Des Moines River.

Okamanpedan, the Sioux Indian name for the lake, meaning "nesting place of the herons," was at that time a nesting area for blue herons. The birds built their nests in the tall trees around the lake. A government surveyor, Joseph Nicolas Nicollet, visited the region in July 1838 and recorded the lake as Okamanpedan. Accompanying Nicollet as his aide was young John Charles Fremont (1813-1890) who was to gain fame as an explorer ("The Pathfinder"),

- EMMETT
(continued)

Okamanpedan State Park
(continued)

soldier, and the first Republican candidate for President of the United States (in 1856, when he lost to James Buchanan). This was also used as a campsite by Major Thomas West Sherman. In later years, the name of Okamanpedan Lake was changed to Tuttle Lake for Calvin Tuttle who settled on its shores in 1856. The park has facilities for picnicking, boating, and fishing.

● **Swan Lake (Ghost Town)**
Near Gruver, Iowa on farm owned by Robert Woods

Swan Lake, platted in the 1870's, was once the county seat, although a courthouse was never built here. The town was abandoned in 1899 when the railroad was built to the north, at the site of Gruver. Some of the buildings from the town of Swan Lake are still in use on the farm. Lumber and timbers from Fort Defiance were used in the big old barn, formerly the livery stable.

To the southeast, and visible from the site of the town of Swan Lake, is West Swan Lake, a shallow glacial lake or marsh. Geese nest here in this state-owned game management area of 1,088 acres. East Swan Lake, a drained lake bed surrounded by upland prairie, is located about 5 miles to the southeast--another public hunting area comprising 788 acres.

FAYETTE

● **Brush Creek Canyon State Park**
2 miles north of Arlington, Iowa, on Iowa 154

State Conservation Commission
State Office Building
300 Fourth Street
Des Moines, Iowa 50319

t Union
10

One of the few almost undisturbed wilderness areas remaining in Iowa--a "living museum." The 216-acre park contains deep canyons, rock chimneys, rushing brooks, moss-covered boulders, lichen, and many rare Iowa plants, such as the American yew, ground pine, paper birch, quaking aspen, big-tooth aspen, walking fern, and prairie grasses. Birds are abundant, and the clear streams are stocked with trout. The pine-scented air, the abundance of wild flowers, and the quiet one finds only in deep woods are attractions for anyone trying to escape from the signs and pressures of civilization.

The beginning of Brush Creek Canyon goes back millions of years when a sea covered the entire Midwest during the Cambrian Period (about 600 million years ago). Sediments were deposited in a thick layer on the sea bottom that stretched to the Appalachians. As the land rose in a later period of geologic time, the water retreated, leaving a deposit of limestone. The canyon cuts through the ancient limestone formation. Brush Creek empties into the Volga River. From the escarpment, huge blocks of limestone have broken away, and some have slid all the way into the river valley.

● **Buffalo Ranch Museum**
310 Lovers Lane
Off Iowa 150, at west edge of Fayette, Iowa

Admission: $1.00; students 12-18, $0.50; children 5-11, $0.40; under 5, free with parents; school children in groups, $0.25.
Open: Daily

A herd of live buffalo, in addition to an old-time general store and saloon with items dating back to pioneer days. On

33 - FAYETTE
(continued)

Buffalo Ranch Museum
(continued)

display and in playing condition are an old organ, early music boxes, early phonographs, and an Aurephone (a roller organ patented in the 1870's and manufactured in Worcester, Massachusetts). There are also juke boxes and several models of early Dictaphones in the collection.

● **Clermont Historical Society**
Clermont, Iowa

David Appelman, President
Clermont, Iowa 52135

Organized: April 20, 1967
Meetings: Quarterly
Dues: $1.00 annual

Organized to assist in plans for Larrabee Appreciation Days, July 22-23, 1967 and to gather material for a historical file. A 106-page book, *Historic Clermont*, has been published, containing pictures and information about the town of Clermont and its early residents. The Society sponsors vesper services (Union Sunday School) each year.

● **Clermont Museum**
Clay and Mill Streets
Clermont, Iowa

Historical Governor Larrabee
Home, Inc.
Henry Follett, Secretary
Clermont, Iowa 52135

Museum Founded: 1912
Bank Building Acquired: May 1, 1970
Admission: $0.50; children under 8, free
Open: Daily, 1:00-4:00 p.m.; Sundays, 1:00-5:00 p.m., May
      30 through November 1

A museum housed in the old Clermont State Bank Building located in the Clermont business district. The bank was first established by William Larrabee in 1874 in an old store, located just north of the flour mill. The bank was reorganized in 1905, and in 1909 moved to the new building. Here it remained until it was closed in 1929. The building was then used by various businesses, most recently as a grocery store and, on the second floor, a doctor's office.

Collections on display include those formerly located in the school building built by the Larrabee family at a cost of $100,000 and donated to the town of Clermont in 1904. Included are the William Larrabee, Jr. collection of shells, fossils, and sea life from the Caribbean area; the Gus Becker collection of fossils from northeast Iowa; original oil paintings; marble busts of noted statesmen; and antiques from the community (second floor).

The Larrabee family made other gifts to the town of Clermont. These include a statue of Col. David B. Henderson, which stands in front of the Episcopal Church; a statue of Abraham Lincoln (the first in Iowa), located in Lincoln Park, across from the railroad station; and a large, wind pipe organ, presented to the Union Sunday School, and housed in the old Presbyterian Church, built in 1863.

3 - FAYETTE
(continued)

● **Dutton's Cave Park**
3 miles northeast of
West Union, Iowa

Fayette County Conservation Board
David L. Smith, Executive Officer
Box 269
West Union, Iowa 52175

A 45-acre area consisting of a deep gorge cut into the limestone formation and covered with hardwood timber; Dutton's Cave; and 4 large springs, with a water temperature of 56 degrees, that flow continuously through the valley. The limestone cave extends back into the bluff for approximately a mile. The area is used for picnicking, hiking, and camping.

● **Montauk**
Clermont, Iowa

Historical Governor Larrabee
Home, Inc.
Henry Follett, Secretary
Clermont, Iowa 52135

Built: 1874
Opened to the public: Memorial Day, 1968
Admission: $1.25; children, 8-16, $0.50
Open: Daily, 10:00 a.m.-5:00 p.m., May 30 through November 1; escorted tours with guides are available

The two-story brick and native limestone home of Iowa Governor (1886-1890) William Larrabee, farmer, miller, banker, and one of Iowa's largest landowners. The name "Montauk" refers to Montauk Point, in New York State, at the eastern terminus of the Long Island Railroad. Mrs. Larrabee's father, a sea captain, swung his ship around the point as he headed for home. Larrabee was born in Ledyard, Connecticut on January 20, 1832. He was one of the early graduates of the United States

Military Academy at West Point. In 1867, he was elected State Senator and served in the legislature until 1885. His chief interests in legislation were agricultural aid, education, transportation, and prohibition. He was elected Governor in 1885, and served two terms. Larrabee was Iowa's only one-eyed Governor, having lost the sight in his right eye in a gun accident when 14 years old. Brick for the house was manufactured in Clermont. The stone foundation walls are 24 inches thick. Williams Quarry, north of town, was the source of the stone.

Original furnishings in the home were used by the Governor's last surviving child, Anna, until her death in December 1965 at the age of 97, so the interior is much as it was when Larrabee was living. Still to be seen are a handmade bed in which all seven of the Larrabee children were born, the Governor's desk and papers, chairs, tables, glass cases, paintings and statuary, table service, a cast-iron kitchen stove, and floor coverings.

The old well house, laundry, creamery and ice house, workshop, and barn have been restored and furnished. An information center is also located in the barn.

33 - FAYETTE
(continued)

Montauk
(continued)

Large statues of Civil War heroes (Grant, Sherman, Dodge, and Farragut), and thousands of trees planted by the Governor, are on the 80-acre estate, which overlooks the town of Clermont and the Turkey River Valley. Descendents of Governor Larrabee arranged for the property to be open to the public.

● **Oelwein Area Historical Society**
Oelwein, Iowa

Cliff Avery, President
621 First Avenue N.W.
Oelwein, Iowa 50662

Incorporated: December 19, 1973
Meetings: Last Tuesday of month
Number of Members: 65
Dues: $2.00 annual

The Society has sponsored the reprinting of the 1878 *History of Fayette County, Iowa*, with a newly prepared comprehensive index, the 1910 *Past and Present of Fayette County, Iowa* (2 volumes), and the 1898 picture book *Souvenir of Oelwein Record*. An annual antique show is held and a newsletter goes to members.

34 - FLOYD

Charles City
B-8

● **Ackley Creek Park**
2 miles southwest of
Marble Rock, Iowa

Floyd County Conservation Board
Lyle Boyer, Executive Officer
R.R. 4
Charles City, Iowa 50616

A scenic 40-acre tract bisected by Ackley Creek, which includes a flood plain along the spring-fed stream, steep bluffs (40 to 50 feet high) heavily wooded with hardwood trees, and typical Iowa shrubs and grasses. Most of the site has never been cultivated. The park is being preserved as a segment of our rapidly disappearing landscape, but is used for picnicking, camping, hiking, and nature study in a relatively undisturbed atmosphere.

● **Beginning of the Farm Tractor Industry**
Charles City, Iowa

Charles W. Hart and Charles H. Parr began building stationary gasoline engines in 1896 and started experimenting with machines to be used in farming. The new name "tractor" was coined (from traction motors) and the tractor industry founded in 1901 by the Hart-Parr Company. A 1913 model tractor is on display under plexiglass on the courthouse grounds. Oliver Corporation, successor to Hart-Parr, offers conducted tours of the plant every weekday at 10 a.m.

● **Flora Ellis Wildlife Sanctuary**
West edge of Charles City, Iowa

Floyd County Conservation Board
Lyle Boyer, Executive Officer
R.R. 4
Charles City, Iowa 50616

About 10 acres of hardwood timber, along the Cedar River, conveyed as a gift and preserved as a bird and wildlife sanctuary for the use and benefit of the general public. The property is used as an outdoor classroom by public and nonpublic schools for nature study, and by river fishermen.

● **Floyd County Historical Society**
107 North Main Street
Charles City, Iowa 50616

Mark Ferguson, President
400 Ferguson Street
Charles City, Iowa 50616

Organized: April 29, 1954
Meetings: Annually in fall
Number of Members: 360
Dues: $1.00 annual; $20.00 life

Operates Floyd County Historical Society Museum (see below). Sponsors booth at Floyd County Fair and conducts historic tours of county.

84 - FLOYD
(continued)

- **Floyd County Historical Society Museum**
  107 North Main Street
  Charles City, Iowa 50616

  Allen Andres
  300 Clark Street
  Charles City, Iowa 50616
  or
  Charles City Chamber of Commerce

Museum Opened: April 20, 1963 (The building escaped serious damage from the tornado that struck Charles City on Wednesday, May 15, 1968.)
Admission: $0.50; children, $0.10
Open: Thursday, Friday, Saturday, Sunday, 1:30-4:00 p.m., May 1 to October 1; other times by appointment

A museum donated by John G. Legel, Jr. to Floyd County Historical Society in 1961, in memory of his parents. The museum preserves a drug and grocery store, dating back to 1873, which was purchased by John G. Legel, Sr. in 1884. A collection of over 10,000 items includes pharmaceutical equipment of the 1890's, quaint medicines and remedies, prescription counter with rare balances and pill machines, botanical drugs, soda fountain and candy jars, tobacco counter, grocery items in old boxes and barrels, drygoods, and hardware. Period rooms show furniture, carpets, pictures, books, toys, and kitchen equipment in a "home of the past." Also to be seen are an old schoolroom, blacksmith shop and tool collection, stone implements, Indian artifacts, art objects, minerals, textiles, documents, newspapers, and clippings. A reference library contains material on Iowa and Floyd County.

- **Glacial Rock**
  3 miles west of Nashua, on Iowa 54 then 3/4 mile south on gravel road; rock is in the middle of a field, on the east side of the road.

Said to be the largest glacial rock in the Midwest. This glacial erratic was deposited by the Wisconsin Glacier, the last of the glaciers to invade Iowa, more than 50,000 years ago.

- **Girlhood Home of Carrie Lane Chapman Catt**
  Southeast of Charles City, Iowa

Two-story frame farmhouse, the girlhood home of Carrie Lane Chapman Catt (1859-1947), international leader of women's suffrage and peace movements. Although born in Ripon, Wisconsin, she came to Iowa with her parents when only 7 years of age, and lived most of her formative years here.

In 1883, when only 24, she was named superintendent of schools in Mason City. In 1890, she succeeded Susan B. Anthony as president of the National American Woman Suffrage Association. With the adoption of the 19th Amendment to the U.S. Constitution, the association was dissolved and the League of Women Voters founded in 1920.

The women's suffrage movement in the United States was a long struggle, dating back to 1848, when Lucretia Mott and Elizabeth Cady Stanton first crusaded for the right for women to vote. A constitutional amendment was first introduced in the U.S. Congress in 1875. In succeeding years the measure was discussed, tabled, or defeated until its final passage on May 21, 1919 by a vote of 304 to 90 in the House of Representatives and 66 to 30 in the Senate. Iowa was the 10th state to ratify the 19th Amendment. With the ratification by the 36th state (Tennessee), the amendment went into effect on August 16, 1920.

34 - FLOYD
(continued)

**Girlhood Home of Carrie Lane
Chapman Catt**
(continued)

Twice widowed, Carrie Lane Chapman Catt lived to be 88. A marker was placed at the homesite by the Floyd County Federation of Women's Clubs on October 20, 1938.

● **Lithograph City (Devonia)**
About 14 miles northwest of Charles City, Iowa in the northern part of Floyd County (N ¼, Section 25, Twp. 97N, Rge. 17W)

What was at one time a thriving community has once again become just a field. About 1910, Clement L. Webster, a geologist from Marble Rock, Iowa, discovered some unusual stones near the border of Floyd and Mitchell Counties. Keeping his discovery secret until he could complete his research, he found the large limestone deposit in the area contained lithograph stone of superior quality.

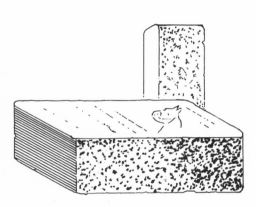

Some 114 years earlier, Alois Senefelder, a Bavarian, had discovered lithography, the simple method of producing printed impressions from stone. The process became very popular throughout Europe and spread to the United States, so lithograph stone was extremely important to the graphic arts. Until Webster's discovery, the porous limestone used in lithography came exclusively from Bavaria, and importing it to America was expensive. Webster found financial backers and proceeded to establish a settlement at the site of the limestone deposit. By 1915, Lithograph City included 15 houses, a hotel, general store, blacksmith shop, lumber yard, stone crushing and polishing plant, dance hall, and museum. The museum soon became nationally known for its displays of semiprecious gems, crystals, minerals, soil specimens, lithograph stones, and various kinds of marble. The town had just begun to prosper when it was found that zinc and copper could be used for lithography in place of stone. Since the new process was less costly, the demand for lithograph stone ended and Lithograph City declined.

After 1915, residents of the town changed its name from Lithograph City to Devonia, but the town continued to decline. After efforts to establish a post office failed, the town died completely, and by 1938 it was plowed under, the victim of progress and scientific advancement.

● **Mathers Forest**
Southeast edge of Nora Springs, Iowa

Floyd County Conservation Board
Lyle Boyer, Executive Secretary
R.R. 4
Charles City, Iowa 50616

Acquired: 1963

A 50-acre parcel of land on the Shell Rock River, acquired from Victor Mathers and maintained as a song bird sanctuary and game preserve. Virgin hardwood timber includes red and white oak, ash, hard maple, basswood, walnut, butternut, elm, and hackberry, and there are many flowering plants. A large spring flows through the center of the forest and into Shell Rock River. The area is used for boating, fishing, hiking, picnicking, camping, and as an outdoor classroom.

- FLOYD
(continued)

● **Meyer Forest**
3½ miles north and 2 miles west
of Charles City, Iowa

Floyd County Conservation Board
Lyle Boyer, Executive Officer
R. R. 4
Charles City, Iowa 50616

An undeveloped area of 102 acres, containing native timber and underbrush. It is maintained as a wildlife and forest preserve, and used as an outdoor classroom and public hunting area in season. Deer and squirrels are common.

● **Mutchlar Log Cabin**
Conservation Park
Floyd, Iowa

Floyd County Historical Society
107 North Main Street
Charles City, Iowa 50616

A historic log cabin, over 110 years old, moved to the present site and restored.

● **Nora Springs Mill Dam Park**
Northwest part of
Nora Springs, Iowa

Floyd County Conservation Board
Lyle Boyer, Executive Officer
R. R. 4
Charles City, Iowa 50616

A 27-acre tract of land along the Shell Rock River. The original old mill was located at this site, but it was damaged by a flood in 1962 and was torn down. The site was acquired from the U.S. Government in 1855, and a flour and saw mill erected. The dam was later used to generate electricity for the town. In those days, the electricity was turned off at 9:00 p.m. until 6:00 the following morning. The 8-acre millpond is used for boating and fishing, and picnic areas are provided along the river.

● **Sherman Buffalo Herd**
1 mile east of Nora Springs, Iowa

A herd of 50 buffalos (bison). Privately owned, but the animals may be seen from the road or visited with permission.

- FRANKLIN

Hampton
-7

● **Beeds Lake State Park**
3 miles northwest of Hampton, Iowa

State Conservation Commission
State Office Building
300 Fourth Street
Des Moines, Iowa 50319

Opened to the Public: 1938

The 330-acre park includes a tree-girdled 130-acre lake formed by a 170-foot-long dam located on Spring Creek. The 12 to 14 mile-long stream is fed by numerous cold water springs that flow year round. Indians used the heavily wooded area before the coming of the white man. Buffalo and elk roamed the area. Other wildlife included otter, beaver, muskrat, badger, wolves, grouse, and prairie chickens. The lake was originally formed in 1857, when T. K. Hansbury (or Hansberry) built the first dam and gristmill. William Beed, a Hampton merchant, put in the long dike and improved the property when he bought it in 1864. Beed, a native of Devonshire, England, was considered "far in advance of the times in sponsoring recreational lake and park activities . . ." Early accounts also state that Beed paid 10 cents for each muskrat trapped on the shores of the lake. This was done because Beed did not want the muskrats to weaken the dam by tunneling through the dike. The mill was enlarged until it was 4 times

35 - FRANKLIN
(continued)

Beeds Lake State Park
(continued)

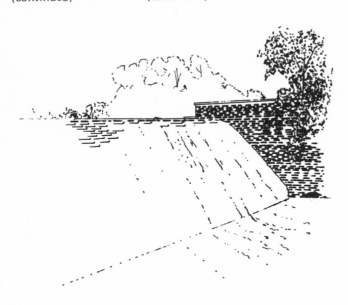

the size of the original building, and was 3 stories high. The only other mills in the area were at Iowa Falls and Ackley. The mill ceased to operate in 1904, and was demolished in 1916. Stone from the mill was sold to farmers and, by late in 1917, the 40-acre lake was drained and the land placed in cultivation or pasture. All that remained of the old mill was the basement and a few scattered rocks. There followed several efforts to establish a park or recreational area, but it was not until 1933 that the land was acquired for this purpose.

The present dam's unusual spillway was built in 1936-37 by the Civilian Conservation Corps. It is constructed of blocks of varicolored stone, sloping abruptly for 40 feet to the rock foundation. A 650-yard-long earthen dike or causeway bisects the lake toward its west end, providing additional bank fishing. This dike is where Beed originally built his dam. It was re-shaped and graded in 1967, and bridges at each end allow access to the west part of the lake. Flora native to the area provides excellent cover for birds and wildlife. A refuge at the west end of the lake attracts many species of waterfowl and shore birds. The campground extends along the lake shore.

● **Burkley Park**
1½ miles west of Geneva, Iowa along south side of Iowa 134

Franklin County Conservation Board
Dennis Carlson, Executive Officer
P.O. Box 143, Hampton, Iowa 50441

A 6½-acre tract which includes a wildlife refuge and nature study area and a stand of hardwood timber and large coniferous trees. The property was acquired as a gift of Mr. and Mrs. Arthur J. Burkley, and includes a 2-story stone house with full basement built sometime during the period 1855 to 1862--one of the first homes constructed in Franklin County.

● **Franklin County Historical Society**
Hampton, Iowa

James Fox, President
R.R. 3
Hampton, Iowa 50441

Incorporated: October 21, 1974

● **Loomis Memorial Park**
4 miles north and 2 miles east of Alexander, Iowa

Franklin County Conservation Board
Dennis Carlson, Executive Officer
P.O. Box 143, Hampton, Iowa 50441

An old rural schoolhouse located on a 1-acre tract and preserved as a historic landmark. The former Wisner Township School is complete with old double-seated desks, slate blackboards, bell, and other furnishings. The old school well is on the grounds, which may be used by picnickers. The frame building has also been used as a community meeting place and voting precinct.

● **Mallory Park**
4½ miles south and 2 miles west of Hampton, Iowa

Franklin County Conservation Board
Dennis Carlson, Executive Officer
P.O. Box 143, Hampton, Iowa 50441

A 71-acre recreational area which includes hardwood timber and pasture land along the south fork of Maynes Creek. Mr. and Mrs. Maynes made camp here in 1852. It was in this area that the first permanent white settlement was established in Franklin County. The park includes bridle trails and hiking trails, and is used as an outdoor classroom for nature study, and for picnicking, fishing, and camping.

35 - FRANKLIN
(continued)

- **Maysville School House**
South of Hampton, Iowa

Originally the first post office in Franklin County. A marker identifies the townsite.

- **Oakland Valley Game Preserve**
1½ miles southwest of
Popejoy, Iowa

Franklin County Conservation Board
Dennis Carlson , Executive Officer
P.O. Box 143, Hampton, Iowa 50441

A 2-acre game management area of historical interest. The settlement of Oakland Valley was laid out in 1855 when the B.C.R. and M.C.C. Railroad (later the Rock Island) was expected to go through here. The Public Square, included in this preserve, was donated to the town by Jess Dodd. When the railroad was located about 1½ miles to the northeast, the town of Popejoy started to build up and Oakland Valley declined until it was eventually turned back to farm land. The site is now a recreational and picnic area and is used as an outdoor classroom.

- **Popejoy Park**
½ mile southwest of
Popejoy, Iowa

Franklin County Conservation Board
Dennis Carlson , Executive Officer
P.O. Box 143, Hampton, Iowa 50441

A 67-acre tract along the Iowa River developed for boating, fishing, picnicking, camping, hiking, and winter coasting. One section is maintained as a wildlife habitat and is used for nature study. Timber covers about 35 acres of the park. Native trees include oak, hickory, basswood, red elm and white elm, and additional varieties, such as walnut and white ash, have been planted.

- **Robinson Park**
2 miles north and 1 mile east of
Hampton, Iowa

Franklin County Conservation Board
Dennis Carlson , Executive Officer
P.O. Box 143, Hampton, Iowa 50441

A 30-acre tract covered with hardwood timber, set aside for a recreational area, wildlife refuge, and outdoor classroom for the study of natural sciences. Otter Creek flows through part of the area. There are bridle and hiking trails, and facilities for picnicking, fishing, and camping.

- **Site of First Motor Vehicle Fatality in Iowa**
2 miles south of Hampton, Iowa, along U.S. 65

A sign marks the site of the first motor vehicle fatality in Iowa. On September 29, 1905, F. A. Harriman, a 32-year-old attorney from Hampton was killed when his car struck a bridge timber on the old Maysville Road and overturned. Mr. Harriman and four business companions were returning from a bank meeting in Geneva about 10 o'clock at night. Recent rains had left the approach to the bridge badly rutted, according to a contemporary account. The car hit the bridge at "a high rate of speed"--about 30 miles per hour--throwing all five men from the car. Since this first fatality, there have been over 30,000 persons killed in Iowa as a result of automobile accidents.

- **W K W Park**
(Mott Township Forest Area)
1 mile north and 1 mile east of
Hampton, Iowa

Franklin County Conservation Board
Dennis Carlson , Executive Officer
P.O. Box 143, Hampton, Iowa 50441

A 54-acre forest set aside as a wildlife preserve and outdoor classroom, also used for picnicking and camping. About ¾ of the area is covered with hardwood timber, including many species of native trees and shrubs. In addition, many varieties of native wild flowers grow in the timber and open areas. Otter Creek winds its way through the tract.

The name of the park was formed from the first letter of the last name of the 3 persons who previously owned this land. They are Wulbrandt, Klousia, and Wolf.

36 - FREMONT

Sidney
I-2

● **Forney's Lake**
2½ miles northwest of Thurman, Iowa

State Conservation Commission
State Office Building
300 Fourth Street
Des Moines, Iowa 50319

A shallow marsh where huge concentrations of wild geese--snow, blue, Canada, and white-fronted--and ducks may be seen during the spring and fall migrations when they stop to feed and rest. As many as 100,000 to 300,000 waterfowl funnel through the area on their way to and from their nesting grounds on Baffin Island in the Arctic Circle. The peaks of the flights vary according to the weather and water levels, but usually occur from March 15-27 and around November 1 of each year. Concentrations in the fall are smaller-- usually not in excess of 50,000 birds. The area is also frequented by pelicans, gulls, and fur-bearing animals.

● **Fremont County Historical Society**
Sidney, Iowa

Gilbert Benson, President
Sidney, Iowa 51652
or
Ralph H. Greenwood
P.O. Box 218, Tabor, Iowa 51653

Organized: 1963
Meetings: As called
Number of Members: 102
Dues: $1.00 annual; $10.00 life

Identifies and restores historic spots, old trails, and Indian camps. A building has been acquired in Sidney for a museum, opened in 1971.

● **Manti Memorial Park**
3½ miles southwest of
Shenandoah, Iowa

Fremont County Conservation Board
Jack Gibson, Executive Officer
P. O. Box 232
Sidney, Iowa 51652
or
Manti Memorial Association
P. O. Box 54
Shenandoah, Iowa 51601

A 12-acre memorial park, where about 40 Mormon families settled in 1849-52. Alpheus Cutler (1784-1864) was leader of the Cutlerites, a faction of the Latter Day Saints Church, which became dissatisfied with polygamy and other doctrines of Brigham Young. After their settlement in Kansas failed, the Cutlerites moved to Manti. Fisher Creek, which runs through the park toward the East Nishnabotna River, was named for the Edmund Fisher family, first to arrive. A log schoolhouse was erected in 1850, and the first and only church was built the following year. The last buffalo known to exist in southwest Iowa was killed in 1858 near Fisher's Grove, part of the Manti settlement. After 1860, most of the Cutlerites joined the Reorganized Church of Latter Day Saints, which had taken a firm stand against polygamy.

The town of Manti (a name from the Book of Mormon) had a chair and furniture factory, clock and watch factory, shoe factory, wagon works, an iron worker, blacksmith, harness maker, and many stores and shops. The town's future looked bright until the railroad came to Shenandoah in 1870. Many residents moved away and Manti became a ghost town, then farm land. A house, formerly the stagecoach stop, and a big barn still stand on a farm near the park. Other houses built by the Mormons are in the immediate neighborhood. The frame schoolhouse is one which replaced the original log building about 1868, and has been used as a community building. The 26-acre Shenandoah city park, which includes a grove of hickory trees, is adjacent to the memorial. The original Manti Cemetery and a small man-made lake, 30 feet deep, are other attractions. Fishing, boating, picnicking, and camping are popular activities.

- FREMONT
(continued)

● **Pinky's Glen**
2 miles west of Tabor, Iowa

Fremont County Conservation Board
Jack Gibson, Executive Officer
P. O. Box 232
Sidney, Iowa 51652

Acquired: 1960

A 48-acre recreational park and school forest area, formerly known as the Weatherhead Tract, acquired as a gift from Glen ("Pinky") Weatherhead of Tabor, Iowa. The natural timber, together with hardwood trees native to Iowa which have been planted in an 18-acre section, provides an outdoor classroom used by schools and nature study groups. Native trees include red cedar, oak, honey locust, and box elder. Underbrush includes gooseberry and buckbrush. Song birds, small animals, and wild flowers are abundant. The area includes steep slopes and a meandering stream. Picnicking, hiking, fishing, and camping are permitted.

● **Tabor Historical Society**
Tabor, Iowa

Mrs. Jack (Wanda) Ewalt, President
Tabor, Iowa 51653

Organized: June 1965
Meetings: Fourth Tuesday of month, 8:00 p.m.
Number of Members: 180
Dues: $2.00 annual; $20.00 life

The Society has acquired and preserved the Todd House (see below). Publications include reprinting the "Reminiscences" of John Todd, a prime source history of settlement of the area, border troubles over slavery, runaway slaves and encounters with slave owners, and the adventures of John Brown and James Lane.

● **Todd House**
Tabor, Iowa

Admission: $0.25
Open: Sunday afternoons during summer; other times by appointment

The historic Reverend John Todd House (original building built in 1853) has been restored and furnished. This frame house, built of native lumber, was a "station" on the Iowa Underground Railroad and headquarters for the Free Kansas Fighters and John Brown during his stays in Tabor. Sharps rifles were concealed in the cellar before being shipped to Harpers Ferry, Virginia. Original flooring and woodwork, hand-hewn beams and lath, adobe and (later) limestone foundations may be seen; also Pre-Civil War letters, diaries, papers, and home furnishings of the period.

Across the street from the Todd House is Tabor City Park. When John Brown and his men camped and drilled here in 1857, it was an open, treeless square. A bronze marker indicates the campground.

Several buildings remain of Tabor College, incorporated in 1866 and operated by the Congregational Church until 1926. It was reopened in 1936 as a private enterprise but later closed. Still to be seen are Woods Hall (1869), dormitory, library, museum, and World War II barracks for POW camp guards; Adams Hall (1898), conservatory, housing for POW's in World War II, and, for a time, an elementary school (K-3) in Fremont-Mills Community School District; and the Congregational Church (1875),

36 - FREMONT
(continued)

Todd House
(continued)

designed by J. K. Nutting who also designed the Little Brown Church at Nashua (see Chickasaw County). The old Tabor College Music Hall (1875) has been moved to Orange Street, between Center and Main Streets, and is now the Tabor Town Hall and Library. On display are the bell from the locomotive of the Tabor and Northern Railroad, which made its last run in 1929; an 1854 plat of Tabor; and paintings by local artists.

● **Waubonsie State Park**
7 miles southwest of Sidney, Iowa on Iowa 239

State Conservation Commission
State Office Building
300 Fourth Street
Des Moines, Iowa 50319

Established: 1926

Named for Chief Waubonsie, of the Pottawattamie Indians, who lived in the area for many years prior to 1846. The 1,208 acres of natural scenic beauty contain grass-covered loess hills, densely wooded ravines, high bluffs affording views of 4 states (Iowa, Nebraska, Missouri, and Kansas) and the Missouri River bottomlands, and evidence of ancient Indian villages. The park is a botanical preserve of native trees and wild flowers, some of which (paw paw and desert yucca) are peculiar to this area. Seven miles of foot trails and 8 miles of bridle paths wind along the wind-swept ridges and down into the steep, narrow gorges and valleys. There are pleasant areas for picnickers and modern facilities for campers. Sunrise services are held here annually on Easter Sunday.

37 - GREENE

Jefferson
E-4

● **Greene County Historical Society**
Jefferson, Iowa

Harold Radebough, President
Rippey, Iowa 50235

Organized: April 1966
Meetings: First Friday of the month
Number of Members: 200
Dues: $2.00 annual

Sponsors tours to places of interest in the county, and maintains old cemeteries. A country schoolhouse has been moved to Greene County Fairgrounds and restored. The schoolhouse is open during the Greene County Fair, or by appointment. The Society also owns and operates Greene County Historical Society Museum (see below).

● **Greene County Historical Society Museum**
North side of square,
Jefferson, Iowa

Dr. H. B. Donovan, Curator
304 North Wilson
Jefferson, Iowa 50129

Established: 1970
Admission: Donations accepted
Open: Monday, 7:00-9:00 p.m.; Wednesday, Friday, and Sunday, 2:00-4:00 p.m.

A 2-story building with historical displays, including the first dental chair in Greene County, brought in by covered wagon in 1867. In the basement of the museum building are a typical pioneer kitchen, living room and bedroom, and a grocery store.

● **Henderson Park**
1 mile south of Jefferson, Iowa on Iowa 4

Greene County Conservation Board
Byron Hobart, Executive Officer
613 South Chestnut
Jefferson, Iowa 50129

A 39-acre tract along the Raccoon River preserved as a wildlife habitat and for nature study. Recreational uses include boating, hiking, fishing, picnicking, and camping.

- GREENE
(continued)

● **Hyde Park**
5 miles west and 2½ miles south
of Churdan, Iowa

Greene County Conservation Board
Byron Hobart, Executive Officer
613 South Chestnut
Jefferson, Iowa 50129

A tract of land along the Raccoon River, consisting of 57 acres of timber and high bluffs overlooking the river. As a recreational area, the park offers boating, fishing, picnicking, and camping.

● **Log Cabin Replica**
Southeast of Jefferson, Iowa

Constructed: 1937

A miniature replica of the home of the first county judge in Greene County, William Phillips, erected on the original site. The Phillips log cabin was also used as a courthouse.

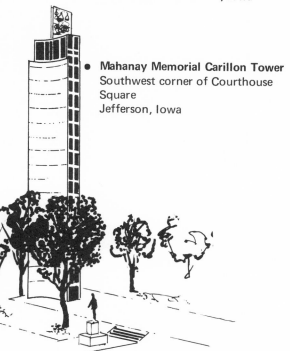

● **Mahanay Memorial Carillon Tower**
Southwest corner of Courthouse Square
Jefferson, Iowa

Established: October 1966

A 165-foot tower, built at a cost of about $350,000 with funds provided by William Floyd Mahanay, a native of Jefferson, who died in 1947. Carillon music is played periodically during the day and bells chime each quarter hour. The Deagan New World Carillon includes 32 bells, and the 14 bells at the top of the tower were cast in Holland. From the enclosed observation platform, reached by elevators, visitors have a panoramic view of the city and surrounding countryside. The tower is lighted at night.

The courthouse, dedicated in 1917, is constructed of Bedford stone and contains murals denoting historical stages of development of Greene County. A tile mosaic of the Greene County seal forms the center of the rotunda floor. The Horn of Plenty is a reproduction of the San Francisco Exposition cornucopia showing world championship Greene County corn. On the courthouse grounds is a bronze statue of Abraham Lincoln by the English sculptor Hastings.

● **Seven Hills Forest**
(Allen Forest)
2 miles southwest of Jefferson, Iowa

Greene County Conservation Board
Byron Hobart, Executive Officer
613 South Chestnut
Jefferson, Iowa 50129

An area of 80 acres of rolling hills and native hardwood timber, offering scenic views of the Raccoon River and the town of Jefferson. Intended uses include picnicking, horseback riding, hiking, nature study, and camping. Winter sports include sledding, tobogganing, and snowmobiling.

● **Squirrel Hollow Park**
5 miles northwest of
Rippey, Iowa

Greene County Conservation Board
Byron Hobart, Executive Officer
613 South Chestnut
Jefferson, Iowa 50129

A 56-acre park in southeastern Greene County, located on a high bluff overlooking the Raccoon River. Much of the area is covered with hardwood timber. Many of the improvements--a stone shelterhouse, fireplaces, foot bridges, trails, and roads--were completed by the Civilian Conservation Corps in the 1930's. It is a desirable area for fishing, picnicking, hiking, nature study, and camping, and is maintained to preserve the natural beauty of the site.

37 - GREENE
(continued)

● **Stagecoach Trail**
4 miles east of Jefferson, Iowa

A marker identifies the old Des Moines-Sioux City stagecoach trail (1850-1866) where it passed through this area, near Pleasant Hill Church in Grant Township.

● **Telephone Museum**
Jefferson Telephone Company
Jefferson, Iowa 50129

Admission: Free
Open: Monday through Friday, 8:00 a.m.-5:00 p.m.

A unique collection of historic telephonic equipment and other articles.

● **Totem Acres Zoo**
Southeast edge of Jefferson, Iowa
Jefferson Telephone Company
Jefferson, Iowa 50129

Admission: Free

An interesting collection of animals including deer, llamas, buffalo, and mountain goats; also exotic birds.

38 - GRUNDY

Grundy Center
D-8

● **Beaman Arboretum**
East edge of Beaman, Iowa, adjacent to Beaman-Conrad school grounds

Grundy County Conservation Board
Samuel K. Gooden, Executive Officer
P. O. Box 56
Grundy Center, Iowa 50638

A 5-acre tract, planted in 1934 by nurseryman and former Grundy County Representative Ellis Leppley, with a wide variety of native trees and shrubs, labelled for identification. Used primarily as a wildlife preserve and outdoor classroom for nature study, there are hiking trails and limited picnic facilities.

● **Beaver Arboretum**
8 miles north of Grundy Center, Iowa, at junction of highways Iowa 14 and 57

Grundy County Conservation Board
Samuel K. Gooden, Executive Officer
P. O. Box 56
Grundy Center, Iowa 50638

A small (1 acre), triangular tract of ground established as a forestry or arboretum, containing types of trees and shrubs native to Iowa. It is used as an outdoor classroom and for picnicking, and serves as a shelter for wildlife.

● **Grundy County Historical Society**
Mrs. Roger J. (Nancy) Hook, President
R.R. 1
Grundy Center, Iowa 50638

Organized: 1974
Meetings: Second Wednesday of month
Number of Members: 50
Dues: $5.00 annual; $8.00 couple; $10.00 family; $1.00 student

Society members are indexing cemeteries in Grundy County and engaged in other activities to preserve local history.

● **Herbert Quick School House**
In Orian Park on G Avenue
Grundy Center, Iowa

City Clerk
Grundy Center, Iowa 50638

A typical early Iowa rural schoolhouse. In this building, the noted Iowa author, Herbert Quick (1861-1925), received all of his formal education. He became a teacher in Grundy Center schools at the age of 17, and continued his teaching career for 20 years. He read law, became a lawyer in Sioux City, and then went into newspaper and magazine work. His career as an author began in 1902. His best known books are *Vandemarks Folly, The Hawkeye, The Invisible Woman,* and *One Man's Life* (his auto-biography). The school building was originally located in Colfax Township and was moved to its present location in 1933 as a tribute to one of Iowa's great writers. The old wooden blackboards, double seats, schoolmaster's desk (used by Quick), stove, lamps, tin dinner buckets, water bucket and dipper, old maps, and textbooks are preserved.

- GRUNDY
(continued)

● **Miller Memorial Park**
8½ miles west of Grundy Center, Iowa, along Iowa 175

Grundy County Conservation Board
Samuel K. Gooden, Executive Officer
P. O. Box 56
Grundy Center, Iowa 50638

A 3-acre roadside park or rest area, which includes the site of the birthplace of Ida M. Miller, the first white child born in Melrose Township. A boulder marker with bronze plaque identifies the site. A small stream borders the north side of the area. Picnic tables are available.

● **Roadman Park**
Along Iowa 57, about 1 mile west of Dike, Iowa

Grundy County Conservation Board
Samuel K. Gooden,
Executive Officer
P. O. Box 56
Grundy Center, Iowa 50638

A 10-acre area including some timber, fishing ponds, and an early log cabin, restored after being moved from another location. Activities include picnicking, hiking, and camping. The park is named for Dr. C. J. Roadman, who previously owned the land.

- GUTHRIE

thrie Center
F-4

● **Guthrie County Historical Society**
Guthrie Center, Iowa

Mrs. Frances Passmore, President
Panora, Iowa 50216

Organized: 1941
Meetings: Second Sunday of month, alternating between Guthrie Center and Panora
Number of Members: 40
Dues: $1.00 annual

Activities include the marking of historic sites of local interest, compiling lists of all veterans buried in Guthrie County, and issuing a supplement to the original Guthrie County Centennial History published in 1951. A county historical museum is maintained (see Turn of the Century Museum, below). A rural schoolhouse has been preserved and furnished, and may be visited during the Guthrie County Fair.

● **Guthrie County School**
Panora, Iowa

Organized in 1876, this is the only example of a county high school to be established in Iowa under an 1870 law. County high schools were first authorized on March 12, 1858, but none were fully organized in Iowa under this law. Local feeling that existed to the detriment of the county high school after it was established became less intense with the passage of time. In 10 years, attendance had increased from less than 50 pupils to around 200 by 1886, and the influence of the county high school upon the teachers became "more apparent each term," according to a report from the Guthrie County Superintendent of Schools.

The Guthrie County School was in existence until 1930. In all, there have been 3 buildings on this site. A 2-story wooden frame building originally served as the courthouse when Panora was the county seat. After Guthrie Center emerged as the winner in the county seat "war," the building became a school. This was soon outgrown and was replaced by a brick building designed by early Iowa architect William Foster. The cornerstone of the third and present building was laid in 1898. After the Guthrie County School was discontinued in 1930, this last building was used by the Panora-Linden Community School District

39 - GUTHRIE
(continued)

Guthrie County School
(continued)

until 1974. At that time, a new junior-senior high school was opened at the west edge of town and the old building was sold to the town. It was then leased to Guthrie County Conservation Board early in 1975 to be preserved as a memorial and museum. Alumni of the school have located pictures and other articles for display. The gymnasium, which had been added to the old Guthrie County School building, has been dedicated as a Veterans Memorial Auditorium.

Panora is a contraction of panorama, the word used by the pioneers to describe the view from the site selected for the town.

● **Iowa Watershed Divide Marker**
West of Guthrie Center, Iowa

A sign marking the Missouri and Mississippi Rivers Watershed Divide. The highest point in southern Iowa (1,415 feet above sea level) is in the town of Adair, located near the Adair-Guthrie County border (see Adair County). From there, water flows east into Middle River and on into the Mississippi River, and west into Turkey and Nodaway Creeks and on into the Missouri River.

● **Lenon Mills**
South edge of Panora, Iowa

Guthrie County Conservation Board
Samuel E. Robinson, Chairman
703 North 2nd Street
Guthrie Center, Iowa 50115

One of several early mill sites in the county. The Panora Woolen Mill was built in 1861-62 by James and John Cline, when Panora was the county seat. In 1877, the mill was converted to a water-powered flour mill which operated until 1940. This was a frame building, since torn down (1959). The dam is the only one remaining on the Middle Raccoon River. A historical marker, made from one of the old millstones, is at the site. Bluffs line the west bank of the river. Native trees include ash, elm, cottonwood, locust, and oak. Fishing, picnicking, and camping are permitted.

● **Nation's Bridge Park**
4½ miles north of Stuart, Iowa

Guthrie County Conservation Board
Samuel E. Robinson, Chairman
703 North 2nd Street
Guthrie Center, Iowa 50115

A 38-acre site bounded on one side by the South Raccoon River. The area includes mature timber, heavy underbrush, bottomland, bottomland marsh, and uplands. Most of the area is in its natural, undisturbed state. Fishing, picnicking, camping, and nature trails are featured.

● **Sheeder Prairie**
6 miles west of Guthrie Center, Iowa on Iowa 44, then 1 mile north and ½ mile east

State Conservation Commission
State Office Building
300 Fourth Street
Des Moines, Iowa 50319

Acquired: 1961

A 25-acre native prairie, set aside as a natural monument to preserve the original flora. This is the most recently acquired of the 4 areas of virgin prairie now owned by the State of Iowa. Sheeder Prairie offers an outstanding display of prairie wild flowers through the seasons. More than 180 species have been identified, including pasque flower, butterfly weed, wood lily, phlox, rattlesnake master, gentian, blazingstar, and various sunflowers. The prairie is used by students attending the annual Teachers Conservation Camp at Springbrook State Park during the summer months.

- GUTHRIE
(continued)

● **Springbrook State Park**
7 miles north of Guthrie Center, Iowa
and 1 mile east on Iowa 384

Park Officer
P. O. Box 142, R. R. 1
Guthrie Center, Iowa 50115
or
State Conservation Commission
State Office Building
300 Fourth Street
Des Moines, Iowa 50319

Acquired: 1926

A 680-acre beauty spot, heavily wooded, and containing a great variety of flora. Once called King Park, it was renamed for a small spring-fed stream, which was dammed to create a 27-acre lake of clear, blue water. The road used by pioneers of the mid-1800's runs through the park. Miles of nature trails wind through the hills and valleys and around the lake. Every kind of bird native to Iowa may be seen in the sanctuary, as well as deer, squirrels, rabbits, and other wildlife. Because of the abundance of plants and animals and the central location of the Park, the Iowa Teachers Conservation Camp is held here at the Conservation Education Center each year from June until August (2 sessions of 3 weeks each), sponsored by the State Conservation Commission, the State Department of Public Instruction, and the University of Northern Iowa. The Center was designated a National Environmental Education Landmark in 1973 by the National Park Service.

● **Turn of the Century Museum**
Panora, Iowa

Guthrie County Conservation Board
Samuel E. Robinson, Chairman
703 North 2nd Street
Guthrie Center, Iowa 50115

The former Chicago, Milwaukee, St. Paul, and Pacific Railroad depot has been repaired and repainted and converted to a museum. The railroad maintained a depot in Panora for 89 years. The second depot, built sometime before 1902 and later enlarged, was abandoned in 1968 after which it was moved to the present site.

The 2.3-acre site also includes a machinery building, with open court, where antique farm equipment and vehicles are on display, and a museum building with exhibits of hand tools, household equipment, personal effects, an old printing press, lathe, dental chair, old telephone equipment, and other items of historic interest. A blacksmith shop, log cabin, and other additions are in future development plans.

- HAMILTON

bster City
D-6

● **Bell's Mill Park**
5 miles northeast of
Stratford, Iowa

Hamilton County Conservation
Board
Brian Holt, Executive Officer
R. R. 1
Webster City, Iowa 50595

Established: 1924

All that remains of a once bustling and prosperous gristmill on the Boone River is an old iron mill wheel, identified by a memorial plaque. The first mill was built near here in 1853, and was rebuilt in 1867. About 1870 the mill was sold to members of the Bell family, who kept the mill wheel busy day and night.

The mill was the scene of a tragedy in 1883 when Van Perry, son of the miller, fell into the millrace and was

40 - HAMILTON
(continued)

Bell's Mill Park
(continued)

pulled under the mill wheel. When the father investigated to see what had stopped the wheel, he found his son's body. The gristmill was closed on March 2, 1888 when the owner, Benjamin Bell, died (see Vegors Cemetery, Webster County) and a flood washed out the dam. The mill building remained until 1903 when it was torn down; the lumber was used to build a barn near Stratford. At low water, some of the foundation timbers may still be seen at the dam site.

The 8-acre park includes the old Charles Smith log cabin, the Marion Center School (moved from its original location about 7 miles away), and a shelter house. Facilities are provided for picnicking, camping, and fishing.

A sorghum mill, located uphill from the river, has been in operation for over 30 years. A 25-ton steam-powered mill and boiler were obtained in 1970 from a mill on the Turkey River at Clermont and installed in a metal shed which also houses a collection of odds and ends. Sorghum stalks are cut into 4-inch lengths and fed into a huge press. The juice runs into a trough which feeds into a storage tank before being poured into the steam pans. From 10 to 14 gallons of juice are required to make a gallon of syrup, which takes 3 to 4 hours of cooking. The juice must be skimmed periodically to remove the green plant chlorophyll as it floats to the top. If this is not done, the syrup has a bitter taste. The finished sorghum is poured into cooling pans and then into jars, ready for sale. The sorghum mill is open daily except Sunday, in season.

In back of the sorghum mill is the Iowa Mystery House, where water appears to run uphill, a plumb bob hanging from the ceiling seems to point to the horizon instead of down, and a broom stands by itself.

● **Bonebright Museum**
Wilson Brewer Memorial Park
Webster City, Iowa

Admission: Free

Two adjoining log cabins housing relics of early Iowa. The cabins, built in 1850 and 1856, were moved to the old Wilson Brewer place. On display are tools, field implements, home furnishings, cooking utensils, and other articles that belonged to Hamilton County pioneers. It was the expressed wish of Frank Bonebright (1868-1934) to "enlighten the future generations and thereby inspire them with keen appreciation of the indomitable courage and persistent accomplishments of the pioneer progenitors."

● **Briggs Woods**
2 miles south of Webster City,
along Iowa 17

Hamilton County Conservation Board
Brian Holt, Executive Officer
R. R. 1
Webster City, Iowa 50595

Established: April 17, 1919

A park of 497 acres, adjacent to the Boone River, which has been a popular recreational area for many years. The original 60-acre tract was given to Hamilton County by Mrs. Thirza Briggs Aldrich in memory of pioneer settlers Ulis and Ellen Briggs. Old-growth hardwood trees cover most of the area. Edible mushrooms are to be found in the cool, moist humus of north-facing slopes. The public is permitted

HAMILTON
(continued)

Briggs Woods
(continued)

to gather mushrooms, nuts, wild berries, and fruits, but wild flowers and other plants may not be disturbed. Visitors may engage in picnicking, camping, fishing, boating, swimming, hiking, and nature study. A wild flower trail has been laid out by the Town and Country Garden Club, and Boy Scouts have made signs identifying the trees and plants. There is an 80-acre artificial lake and a 9-hole golf course in the park, and during the winter months, there are opportunities for skiing, coasting, and ice skating. Facilities are available for handicapped persons.

● **Hamilton County Historical Society**
Webster City, Iowa

George V. Goeldner, President
745 Walnut Street
Webster City, Iowa 50595

Incorporated: October 15, 1941
Dues: $3.00 annual

The Society became inactive after it was originally organized, but was reactivated in 1974. The 1912 *History of Hamilton County, Iowa* by J. W. Lee was reprinted in 1975, and an 1875 map of Hamilton County reproduced.

HANCOCK

ner
6

● **Armstrong House**
(Hancock County Memorial Museum)
Britt, Iowa

Mrs. R.O. Hochhaus, Museum Curator
625 3rd Street, S.W.
Britt, Iowa 50423

Constructed: 1896
Admission: $0.50; children, $0.25
Open: 1st and 3rd Saturdays and 2nd and 4th Sundays, April to October; also on Hobo Day in August and during Christmas Fair in November; other times by appointment

A large frame house, built in 1896 for Britt banker Lewis Larson, was presented to Hancock County Historical Society July 7, 1969. In 1914, the house and bank were purchased by H. C. Armstrong from Mr. Larson. Mr. Armstrong's sons--Niel, Dean, and Gordon--donated the house to the Society, in memory of their parents. The house was opened to the public in 1970, and is maintained as the Hancock County Memorial Museum.

Woodwork in the house is yellow pine and oak. Doors are thick and heavy, and hand carvings decorate the staircase. Marble was used for a fireplace and a sink, and there are small stained-glass windows upstairs. The library includes a desk and chairs used by Governor John Hammill (1875-1936). Other furnishings and exhibits include kitchen utensils, a butter churn, soap kettle, curtain stretchers, wall telephone, an organ, period chairs, hand-crafted floor lamps, early carpenter tools, clothing, and a dentist's foot-powered drill.

● **Concord Park**
½ mile south of Garner, Iowa

Hancock County Conservation Board
Anson Avery, Chairman
Goodell, Iowa 50439

Old Concord Courthouse Square, located in a 2-acre park with camping and picnicking facilities. For nearly 3 decades, prior to 1898, Concord was the county seat of Hancock County. A 2-story brick courthouse, valued at $10,000, was first occupied in 1869. With the completion of the new courthouse in Garner, the old courthouse and grounds at Concord were sold. In 1906, a tabernacle was erected on the grounds and used for religious meetings by the German Methodist Episcopal Church, as well as for high

41 - HANCOCK
(continued)

Concord Park
(continued)

school graduation exercises. This frame building had a seating capacity of approximately 700 people. Wooden benches were used.

● **Eagle Lake Park**
3 miles east and 1 mile north
of Britt, Iowa

Hancock County Conservation Board
Anson Avery, Chairman
Goodell, Iowa 50439

A 21-acre park, owned by the State of Iowa and operated by Hancock County under a management agreement, located on Eagle Lake, a natural lake. The park is used for picnicking and camping, and there are hiking trails. An additional 46 acres on the west shore of Eagle Lake is a forest preserve, being maintained in its natural state. The area is used as an outdoor classroom for teaching the natural sciences.

● **Eldred-Sherwood Park**
3 miles east and 1 mile north
of Goodell, Iowa

Hancock County Conservation Board
Anson Avery, Chairman
Goodell, Iowa 50439

A 100-acre recreational area and wildlife preserve, containing an artifical lake (22 acres), with facilities for picnicking, swimming, fishing, hiking, and camping. Trails have been developed for nature study, and a reforested area is utilized as an outdoor classroom. A variety of native prairie wild flowers grow here.

● **Hancock County Historical Society**
Garner, Iowa

Alfred Josten, President
1140 Maben Street
Garner, Iowa 50438

Organized: July 12, 1966
Incorporated: May 12, 1967
Annual Meeting: First Wednesday in May
Number of Members: 373
Dues: $1.00 annual; $20.00 life

Meetings feature programs on historical subjects, and are held in various towns in Hancock County. The Armstrong House (see above) was acquired in 1969 and is maintained as a memorial museum.

● **Pilot Knob State Park**
4 miles east and 1 mile south of
Forest City on Iowa 332

State Conservation Commission
State Office Building
300 Fourth Street
Des Moines, Iowa 50319

A 369-acre tract of hills and ridges, heavily wooded with native hardwoods and containing a wide variety of shrubs and flowering plants, provides an outstanding nature study area. Rare specimens found here include the sundew plant and a floating bed of sphagnum moss at spring-fed Dead Man's Lake, a variety of pond lily found nowhere else in Iowa, and a unique species of red-back mice. Pilot Knob, one of many odd-shaped glacial formations in the area, is one of the highest elevations in Iowa, rising about 300 feet above the surrounding valley. In pioneer days this morainal deposit of clay, gravel, and boulders left by the edge of the Wisconsin Glacier when it rapidly melted over 50,000 years ago, was a landmark used to guide travelers. From the 40-foot-high stone lookout tower

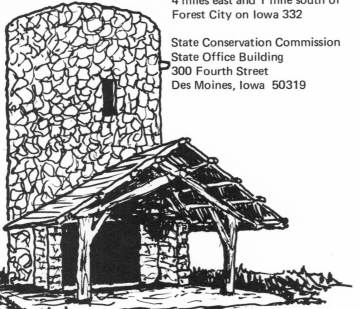

- HANCOCK
(continued)

Pilot Knob State Park
(continued)

on Pilot Knob may be seen a larger area of fertile land than from anywhere else in Iowa. The bird's eye view extends in all directions as far as 35 miles. The pattern of fields, meadows, woodlands, farms, and nearby towns varies with the seasons. Parts of the park have been set aside as a State Preserve, but picnicking and camping are permitted in designated areas.

● **Timberland Museum**
3 miles southeast of
Pilot Knob State Park

Arlo Johnson, Owner
Forest City, Iowa 50436

Established: 1940
Admission: $0.35; children under 12 free
Open: Sunday only, May 15 to November 1; other times by appointment

Contains early pioneer and Indian relics of the area.

- HARDIN

lora
-7

● **Bigelow Park**
3 miles northwest of Alden, Iowa

Hardin County Conservation Board
Irwin Burns, Executive Officer
Ackley, Iowa 50601

A 10-acre park located on the northern boundary of Hardin County along the Iowa River. Native grasses, prairie wild flowers, shrubs, and timber are preserved in their natural state, and the area is used as an outdoor classroom. Boating, fishing, and picnicking on the north side of the river are also permitted.

● **Ellsworth Museum**
First floor of Caroline Hall
Iowa Falls, Iowa

William Schmidt
Ellsworth Community College
1100 College Street
Iowa Falls, Iowa 50126

Open: During college hours, or by appointment

A valuable collection of more than 500 mounted bird and animal specimens, birds' eggs, Indian artifacts, and rock specimens. The wildlife collection was purchased in 1904 from Morton Peck, a former instructor at the college. His father, George Peck, a self-taught taxidermist, built a log cabin on the banks of the Cedar River late in the 19th Century to house the original collection. He left the area in 1908 for a "lack of open living space" and, by the 1930's, the collection had to be placed in storage due to a shortage of display space. Reconstruction of the museum was begun in 1959. Many of the species on display, such as the whooping crane, have become rare and may no longer be collected. Sketches and identification cards have been added to the displays for the benefit of visitors.

● **Flowing Well Park**
4½ miles south of Alden, Iowa
on Iowa 359

Hardin County Conservation Board
Irwin Burns, Executive Officer
Ackley, Iowa 50601

A place that has been popular with travelers for many years because of the flowing well and the sheltered beauty of the area. The old wagon road went through the park. Native trees and bushes attract song birds, and beaver are established in the area. The 6-acre park provides facilities for picnickers and fishermen. Buckeye Cemetery is adjacent to the park.

42 - HARDIN
(continued)

● **Gehrke Wildlife Area**
4 miles southeast of Buckeye, Iowa

Hardin County Conservation Board
Irwin Burns, Executive Officer
Ackley, Iowa 50601

A 6-acre area of wet marshy land fed by springs, with trees on the higher elevations. The tract offers nesting and habitat for wildlife.

● **Hardin County Historical Society**
P. O. Box 187
Eldora, Iowa 50627

Mrs. Howell (Emma) Boyd, President
1713 12th Street
Eldora, Iowa 50627

Kermith Huehn, Curator
Eldora, Iowa 50627

Incorporated: December 1970
Meetings: Second Monday of month; annual meeting in January
Number of Members: 115
Dues: $10.00 annual
Museum Open: Sundays, except during winter months, or by appointment

The Society owns and maintains a 17-room Victorian house as a county museum and historical library. One of the last remaining log cabins in Hardin County has been acquired and is being moved to Eldora for restoration. The 1883 *History of Hardin County* has been reprinted with an added name index.

● **Iowa River Green Belt**
Along the Iowa River from Iowa Falls south to Union, Iowa

Hardin County Conservation Board
Irwin Burns, Executive Officer
Ackley, Iowa 50601

More than 1,000 acres, scattered along the Iowa River with its timbered bluffs, providing an opportunity for fishing, picnicking, boating, hiking, camping, and nature study. Certain areas are set aside as wilderness preserves and wildlife habitat, and are used as outdoor classrooms. Some of the few fully timbered, wild areas left in this part of Iowa are included in the Green Belt. Iowa author Herbert Quick referred to this area as the "Iowa River Gorge."

The lush woodland is primarily oak and hickory with maples, birch, and aspen. Wild flowers found here include hepatica, spring beauty, bloodroot, Mayapple, Jack-in-the-pulpit, showy orchis, marsh marigold, wood anemone, and rue anemone. Great numbers of birds also frequent the area.

Evidence of Indian villages and campsites occurs throughout the area. Stone arrowheads, knives, hammers, and other tools have been recovered from the numerous archeological sites. The Indians found the area ideal for hunting nearly 10,000 years ago.

Following along this 30-mile stretch of the Iowa River, early settlers founded Hardin City in 1854 at a horseshoe bend in the river. The settlement grew to become one of the largest towns in central Iowa, with a post office (1855-81), numerous stores, a mill, and hotel. Eagle City was located several miles on upstream and had a post office from 1878 until 1885. Along the river upstream from Steamboat Rock (see below), placer gold was panned during a short-lived "gold rush." Extensive clay beds in the area were used to supply a pottery factory.

- HARDIN
(continued)

● **Ira Nichols Bird and Flower Preserve**
Iowa Falls, Iowa

Hardin County Conservation Board
Irwin Burns, Executive Officer
Ackley, Iowa 50601

A 16-acre natural area, maintained as a bird, wildlife, and botanical preserve. The land was purchased by Mr. Nichols in 1930 and is enclosed by a high chain link fence. The refuge is surrounded by bluffs and is crossed by Elk Run before it enters the Iowa River. A variety of birds may be seen year-round, and the preserve includes native woodland wild flowers, shrubs, and trees. Footpaths and nature trails afford access to the area, which is used as an outdoor classroom. There is a small picnic area.

● **Long Memorial Park**
1 mile east of Union, Iowa

Hardin County Conservation Board
Irwin Burns, Executive Officer
Ackley, Iowa 50601

A 6-acre park along the Iowa River, which provides an opportunity for fishing and boating. This was the site of an old mill. There are picnicking and camping facilities, while another part of the area is set aside as a wildlife refuge.

● **Pine Lake State Park**
North of Eldora on Iowa 118

State Conservation Commission
State Office Building
300 Fourth Street
Des Moines, Iowa 50319

Established: 1921

A 548-acre area with 2 connected lakes, Upper Pine Lake (101 acres) and Lower Pine Lake (65 acres), formed by impounding Pine Creek near its junction with the Iowa River. When the dam was constructed in 1922 to create Lower Pine Lake, it became Iowa's first state-owned artificial lake. The first geological survey in the territory in 1848 showed the Pine Lake area to be mostly sandstone undermined by crevices, caves, and springs. The native sandstone has been used in the construction of the lodge, cabins, and retaining walls. Hiking trails lead to native white pines over 250 years old, and a variety of other trees, wild flowers, and shrubs. Several Indian mounds are located within the park. Recreational facilities include a 9-hole golf course, campground, picnic areas, bathhouse and beach, and snowmobile trails.

● **Steamboat Rock-Tower Rock-Fallen Rock Park**
South edge of Steamboat Rock, Iowa

Hardin County Conservation Board
Irwin Burns, Executive Officer
Ackley, Iowa 50601

Within this 21-acre park, which is part of the Iowa River Green Belt (see above), are 2 unusual limestone formations-- Steamboat Rock, ranging in height from 20 to 30 feet above the Iowa River, and Tower Rock, rising from 30 to 90 feet above the water. At one time Steamboat Rock, from which the town is named, projected out into the river, and looked like a steamboat. Unfortunately, this protruding point has broken off. Tower Rock has many names and initials inscribed on it, some dating back to the early 1860's. At its base is a large clear spring. Fallen Rock shades a deep bank of boulders where a number of rare plants may be seen which usually are found only much farther north. These include paper and yellow birch, white pine, various ferns, red baneberry, mosses, and liverworts. The plants have descended from those growing here since the last glacier retreated from what is now Iowa. The cool, damp habitat has enabled these plants to resist the intrusion of prairie plants that have taken over elsewhere in this vicinity.

43 - HARRISON

Logan
F-1

● **Bertrand (Steamboat) Laboratory
and Artifact Exhibit Room**
De Soto National Wildlife Refuge,
south of Refuge Headquarters, off
U.S. 30 between Missouri Valley, Iowa
and Blair, Nebraska

Admission: Free
Open: Daily, 9:00 a.m.-5:00 p.m. Closed November 15 to
April 15

The wreck of the sternwheeler Bertrand, one of over 250
steamboats lost to the Missouri River between 1819 and
1897. The excavation site is located in the central part of
De Soto National Wildlife Refuge.

During the mid-19th Century, steamboats played a major
role in the settlement, development, and progress of our
Nation. The Missouri River was used to ship large quantities
of supplies to the military forts, fur trading posts, frontier
settlements, and mining camps of the West. The Missouri
was a hazardous river for steamboats, with its constantly
changing course, shifting sandbars, snags, and floating
debris.

The Bertrand was built at Wheeling, West Virginia in 1864
for the Montana and Idaho Lines, at a cost of about
$65,000. The steamboat measured 161 feet from bow to
stern, was 40 feet wide, and weighed 215 tons. The
sternwheeler was double- hulled and was further
strengthened by a covering of ½" iron plates around the
bow.

The Bertrand, under veteran riverman Captain James Yore,
was on her maiden voyage from St. Louis, Missouri and
headed for Fort Benton, Montana Territory when it hit a
snag or a sandbar, split amidships, and sank on April Fool's
Day, 1865 at De Soto Bend, about 4 miles downstream
from the river village of De Soto, Nebraska Territory. This
was just 13 days before President Abraham Lincoln was
assassinated. The boat sank in a matter of minutes, barely
allowing time for crew and passengers to get off, but
without loss of life. Subsequently, the Missouri River
changed channels at least 4 times, the wreck was covered
with sand and silt, records of its location lost, and the boat
was then all but forgotten. The wreckage was left a mile
away from the new main channel. Part of the
superstructure and some cargo were removed following the
sinking, but the treacherous water and the shifting
sandbars, plus the limited facilities then available, made any
major salvage attempt impossible. However, stories
persisted of gold and mercury still in the hold, and this
encouraged treasure hunters to search for the boat. The
4½-foot-deep hold of the 161-foot-long hull was crammed
with cargo when the Bertrand left St. Louis. This included
450 steel flasks of mercury, weighing 176 pounds each;
about $4,000 in gold and silver coins; possibly 5,000
gallons of whiskey; and a wide variety of consumer goods
destined for Montana merchants. The total value of the
mercury alone was said to be about $250,000 at today's
prices, making the Bertrand the most valuable of the wrecks
occurring on the Missouri River before the turn of the
century.

- HARRISON
(continued)

**Bertrand (Steamboat) Laboratory
and Artifact Exhibit Room**
(continued)

In the fall of 1967, Jesse Pursell and Sam Corbino, both of Omaha, obtained a permit from the Government to search for the Bertrand. Electronic metal-detecting equipment was used and core samples were taken to locate the boat. On February 28, 1968, test borings produced bits of lead, tin, wood, leather, tallow, glass, and firebrick. The neck of a bottle with a strong odor of whiskey was also recovered, and probes indicated the rough outline of a large boat. The site was excavated and a portion of the hull was finally exposed in October 1968. The first items of cargo removed were Dr. J. Hostetter's Celebrated Stomach Bitters, a patent medicine containing about 36 percent alcohol. On November 25, 1968, a box of Superior Palm Soap, from Goodwin Anderson and Company of St. Louis, labelled "Stores--Bertrand" was found, which served to identify the sunken steamboat, 103 years after it went down. The hull was covered with 30 feet of sand, 18 feet under the water table. Continuous pumping was necessary to keep the excavation dry while salvage operations were in progress. After removal of all cargo, the well points and pumps were pulled and the excavated hole refilled with water within 6 hours. The Bertrand was placed on the National Register of Historic Places March 24, 1969. The steamboat will remain in its watery grave until preservation and display methods are worked out. There is a historical marker at the site.

The rare find gives a perfect cross section of 19th Century frontier life. Typical items include stoneware crockery, glassware, lanterns, matches, gunpowder, Howitzer shells, picks, shovels, axes, plows, miners' hats, miners' boots, men's clothing, baby shoes, toys, canned peaches and cherries, peanuts and almonds in the shell, Drake's Plantation Bitters, and Kelly's Old Cabin Bitters. (Bitters were really booze, sold as medicine to escape paying Federal liquor taxes.)

The terms of the formal "treasure trove" contract provided that the Government would receive 40 percent of the gross value of the mercury or quicksilver, gold, and whiskey, and the treasure hunters 60 percent. Everything else became the property of the Federal Government. Only 9 of the mercury flasks were recovered, no gold was discovered, and the whiskey found was of no monetary value. However, an estimated two million separate items were removed from the cargo hold. Nearly all of this priceless cargo, which went to the Government under the salvage agreement, was in good condition, although waterlogged. On October 18, 1972, Pursell and Corbino filed a lawsuit against the U.S. government to recover the costs of their salvage operations, estimated at more than $100,000. The case is still in the courts (1975).

It took over 4 years to study, clean, and catalog the relics salvaged. More than 2 million artifacts recovered from the Bertrand remain in a controlled-environment building.

43 - HARRISON
(continued)

Bertrand (Steamboat) Laboratory and Artifact Exhibit Room
(continued)

Meanwhile, some of these items may be seen in the Bertrand Laboratory and Artifact Exhibit Room at the headquarters of De Soto National Wildlife Refuge.

Here displays tell the saga of this Missouri River steamboat. In a Country Store replica are the bottles, cans, boxes, and other containers with the original contents as found in the boat.

● **De Soto National Wildlife Refuge**
Iowa — Nebraska

U.S. Department of the Interior
Fish and Wildlife Service
Bureau of Sport Fisheries
and Wildlife

Refuge Manager
De Soto National Wildlife Refuge
Route 1-B
Missouri Valley, Iowa 51555

This public use area, part of a network of National Wildlife Refuges, is a major feeding and resting place for geese and ducks migrating along the Missouri River Valley. Up to 100,000 snow and blue geese use this migration stopover during their flights between Arctic nesting grounds and Gulf Coast wintering areas. Up to 250,000 ducks, mostly mallards, also congregate at the refuge. The peak months of waterfowl use are March and April, and October and November. About 3,700 acres of the 7,800 acres included in the refuge are planted on a share basis with neighboring farmers. The refuge's share of this food is left standing for wildlife. Nature foods supplement these crops for wildlife species. Bald eagles may also be seen perched in trees along De Soto Lake. In addition, wading and shore birds, including piping plover and least terns, nest within the refuge. Many species of songbirds may be found throughout the year. Mud banks provide burrowing sites for bank swallows. Ring-necked pheasants and quail inhabit the area. Among the mammals to be seen are white-tailed deer, raccoons, muskrat, opposum, beaver, fox, squirrel, cottontails, mink, and coyote.

There are designated areas for mushroom picking and for swimming, in season. Ice fishing is permitted in January and February. Boating and water skiing are permitted in accordance with State and Federal regulations. Picnic facilities are available at a number of locations.

The first record of white men in this section of the Missouri Valley was on August 3, 1804, when the Lewis and Clark Expedition stopped overnight at a campsite just below the old river loop known as De Soto Bend. Herds of buffalo (bison) grazed on the prairie of these rich river bottoms. Later, river boats, belching smoke as they hauled cargo and passengers on the Missouri, helped open up the West.

- HARRISON
(continued)

De Soto National Wildlife Refuge
(continued)

In 1960 construction of a new channel for the Missouri River was completed, cutting off the old river bend or oxbow and forming De Soto Lake, a 7-mile-long, 800-acre impoundment. A levee protects it from flooding. This old bend in the Missouri River, now isolated from the main river channel, provides habitat for waterfowl and fish, and is the main recreational attraction of the refuge.

● **Harrison County Historical Society**
106 East 6th Street
Logan, Iowa 51546

Mrs. W. E. Darrington,
President
Persia, Iowa 51563

Organized: 1968

Maintains and operates Harrison County Historical Village (see below). The 1891 history of the county has been reprinted.

● **Harrison County Historical Village**
(formerly **Preston Niles Pioneer Village and Museum**)
3 miles northeast of Missouri Valley, Iowa on U.S. 30

Harrison County Conservation Board
Ken Berney, Executive Officer
R. R. 2
Box 44
Woodbine, Iowa 51579

Established: 1938
Admission: $0.75; children, 6-12, $0.25
Open: Tuesday through Saturday, 10:00 a.m.-5:00 p.m.; Sunday, 1:00-6:00 p.m.; May through September. Closed Monday.

Collection of 10,000 items, contained in 9 buildings. Included are pioneer Iowa relics, early farm machinery, tools, Indian artifacts, war relics, antique toys, a peddler's wagon, and dioramas of Iowa history. The saddle and pack saddle used by General Grenville M. Dodge while he surveyed for the Union Pacific Railroad in Iowa is on display. One building is devoted to the history of corn. A pioneer log cabin (1853), old schoolhouse, chapel, and an 1856 stage depot are in the pioneer village.

● **Magnolia Memorial Log Cabin and Museum**
Magnolia, Iowa

Mrs. Frank Thomas, Caretaker
Magnolia, Iowa 51550

Constructed: 1926
Open: During summer; other times by appointment

A log cabin, closely resembling those built by the pioneers, has been built by members of families of early settlers in the area. The cabin is used as a museum and is the gathering place for the Old Settler's Reunion held in August each year in Harrison County's oldest town. Hundreds of relics are on display--many brought here by families in their covered wagons.

The Masonic Museum, in Magnolia, houses additional relics. The remains of the first courthouse in Harrison County--a brick building--is now used by the local American Legion post.

- HENRY

. Pleasant
-11

● **Benjamin Chapel**
9 miles northwest of Mount Pleasant, Iowa on the Salem-Trenton road

Guy Messer
R. R. 2
Mount Pleasant, Iowa 52641

Open: By appointment during summer months

A rural church typical of the late 1800's and early 1900's. The white frame building was constructed in 1877 as a Methodist Church in a circuit with 2 other churches nearby. Services were held here until the early 1940's, when the church was left to deteriorate. In 1974, a small group of neighbors decided to restore and preserve the church. Much of the original furniture remains in the building.

44 - HENRY
(continued)

● **Camp Harlan (Later Camp McKean)**
1½ miles west of Mt. Pleasant, Iowa

Marker Dedicated: June 8, 1930

A marker across from the Country Club has been erected at the site of a Civil War camp. The 4th Iowa Cavalry and the 25th Iowa Infantry trained here. At the old spring house may be seen initials of Civil War soldiers who carried water from here to the camp.

● **Geode State Park**
6 miles southeast of New London, Iowa or 4 miles southwest of Danville, Iowa

State Conservation Commission
State Office Building
300 Fourth Street
Des Moines, Iowa 50319

A 1,641-acre heavily wooded area with limestone bluffs, a 205-acre artificial lake, and an old stone quarry along the Skunk River which is one source of the geode, Iowa's state rock. These concretions are usually hollow and when broken open the cavities are lined with quartz crystals, calcite crystals, or other accessory minerals.

A tiny cemetery, reached by trail, contains grave markers bearing epitaphs dating back as far as 1816; the latest date is 1855. Some of the settlers buried here were born before the signing of the Declaration of Independence. Old-timers in the region say the graveyard was used by one family from around 1815 until 1860. There is evidence that several of those buried here perished in a plague that struck the family early in the last century.

In the southwest corner of the park the Skunk River flows along to the Mississippi. Certain areas are set aside as wildlife and forest preserves. Hiking, fishing, swimming, picnicking, and camping are popular activities.

● **Harlan House (Harlan Hotel)**
122 North Jefferson
Mount Pleasant, Iowa 52641

Joe McMillan, Owner

For 16 years this was the home of James A. Harlan (1820-1899). He built the house in 1857 and lived here during his entire career in the national government. It was also here that he died in 1899.

Harlan was President of Iowa Wesleyan College, the first elected State Superintendent of Public Instruction (1847), U.S. Senator from Iowa, and was appointed Secretary of the Interior by President Lincoln, who was his close personal friend. The cabinet post was held by Harlan from 1865 until 1866, when he resigned to return to the U.S. Senate. Whether Harlan was among those admitted to the dying President's room at the time of Lincoln's assassination, is a matter of dispute. However, the close friendship between Senator Harlan and President Lincoln was recognized by the Senator's associates when he was chosen as a member of the Congressional Committee to escort the body of Lincoln from Washington, D.C. to Springfield, Illinois. James Harlan is one of two Iowans to be elected to the Hall of Fame at the national capitol in Washington, D. C.

The Harlan House is now a hotel and eating place. The central section of the brick structure with mansard roof is the original house built by Harlan. The 1857 portion of the building contains many relics and documents of early Mount Pleasant and the Civil War, and Harlan memorabilia.

4 - HENRY
(continued)

- **Harlan-Lincoln Home**
  Corner of Broad and Main
  Mount Pleasant, Iowa

  Mrs. Kay Lange, Director
  Harlan-Lincoln Home
  Iowa Wesleyan College
  Public Relations Office
  Mount Pleasant, Iowa 52641

Admission: Donations accepted
Open: During Midwest Old Settlers and Threshers Reunion; other times by appointment

The former home of Senator James A. Harlan, often visited by his son-in-law Robert Todd Lincoln and family. The Harlans moved here, near the Iowa Wesleyan campus, in 1873. Abraham Lincoln's eldest son married Mary Harlan, and the couple spent their summers in this home, with their children. Built in the 1860's, the home has been restored and furnished with many original Harlan possessions and Lincoln memorabilia. The three Harlan-Lincoln grandchildren have their heights recorded on a closet door in this old home.

- **Henry County Historical Society**
  c/o Public Library
  202 North Main Street
  Mount Pleasant, Iowa 52641

  Donald E. Young, President
  305 West Green
  Mount Pleasant, Iowa 52641
  or
  Orlendes Ross
  404 West Madison Street
  Mt. Pleasant, Iowa 52641

Organized: 1956
Meetings: Sunday afternoon in January, March, May, and November
Number of Members: 80
Dues: $2.00 annual

Organized to promote interest in and preserve materials on local history. A collection of school transcripts, minutes of board meetings, pictures, church histories, and genealogies is kept at the Mount Pleasant Public Library. Programs on local history are provided for community groups, guided tours are arranged.

- **Heritage Museum**
  McMillan Park
  Mount Pleasant, Iowa

  Midwest Old Settlers
    and Threshers Association
  Mount Pleasant, Iowa 52641

Opened to Public: May 25, 1974
Admission: $1.00, or by membership in Midwest Old Settlers and Threshers Association; children under high school age free
Open: Daily, 9:00 a.m.-5:00 p.m., Memorial Day through Labor Day

Relics of the past, used by the early pioneers, and housed in a building covering 1½ acres. Early farm machinery and equipment, steam engines, gasoline engines, horse drawn vehicles (from farm buggies to elegant town carriages), and a typical country kitchen are on display. A huge Corless Engine, in operating condition, was used for 54 years at Iowa Malleable Iron Works in Fairfield, Iowa, to supply all the power for the company. The engine was manufactured at Murray Iron Works in Burlington, Iowa in 1903.

44 - HENRY
(continued)

● **Iowa Wesleyan College**
Mount Pleasant, Iowa 52641

Founded: 1842

The first college west of the Mississippi River. Sponsored by the Methodist Church, the college was first named Mount Pleasant Collegiate Institute. It was renamed Iowa Wesleyan University in 1849 and Iowa Wesleyan College in 1911.

Old Pioneer is the oldest college building in continuous use west of the Mississippi River. Construction on the building was begun in the early 1840's. It was completed in 1845, and included a residence for the president of the college. The building now houses the English Department.

Both Old Pioneer and Old Main are on the National Register of Historic Places and were completely renovated, beginning in 1973.

Plans for erection of gold-domed Old Main were begun by James Harlan when he became president of the educational institution in 1853. This building is noted as the birthplace of the P.E.O. Sisterhood, and the original chapter room is still preserved. In 1927, the P.E.O. Memorial Building was erected with funds given by the P.E.O. in honor of the 7 young women students who founded the Sisterhood on the campus in 1869.

● **Iowa Wesleyan College Museum**
Iowa Wesleyan College
Mount Pleasant, Iowa 52641

Contains exhibits on art, archeology, geology, and zoology, and a herbarium. Conducts collecting trips, and a joint insect survey program with the University of Iowa.

● **Lewelling Quaker Shrine**
South Main Street
Salem, Iowa 52649

Lewis Savage
R.R. 4
Mount Pleasant, Iowa 52641
or
Mrs. Marjorie Brown
R.R. 1
Salem, Iowa 52649

Dedicated: 1959
Admission: $0.50; children $0.25
Open: Sundays 1:00-5:00 p.m.; other times by appointment

This imposing 6-room sandstone house was built in 1840-1845 by Henderson Lewelling in Salem, the earliest Quaker settlement west of the Mississippi. It was in 1836 that the town was laid out with a grapevine for a measuring line. The homestead was another "ticket office" or refuge for slaves escaping on the "Underground Railroad to Freedom," long before the Civil War. The Quakers were firmly opposed to slavery and were active in helping runaway slaves escape. Secret places in the homes and other buildings were used to hide the slaves until they could be moved on to freedom. The house contains pioneer utensils and farm equipment dating back to 1834.

Mr. Lewelling was also a noted early horticulturist. He took the first grafted fruit trees to the Pacific Coast by wagon train in the late 1840's where he started the fruit-growing industry on the West Coast, and developed the "Bing" cherry. In 1969, sprouts taken from the Oregon trees were returned to Salem and planted during a ceremony at the Quaker Shrine.

- HENRY
(continued)

- **Lowell Mills**
Lowell, Iowa
9 miles south of
New London, Iowa

A plaque marks the site of 2 early mills, on each side of the Skunk River. The marker is located in a small park along the banks of the river and includes the buhr from the north mill. The inscription reads: "This French Buhr Mill Stone marks the site of the first flour mill 1838-1901 built in Henry County. Across the river was the first corn and saw mill (1837-1911) built and operated by Hiram C. Smith and James C. Caudill."

- **Midwest Old Settlers and Threshers Association**
McMillan Park
Mount Pleasant, Iowa

Herbert Hult, Secretary
R. R. 1
Mount Pleasant, Iowa 52641

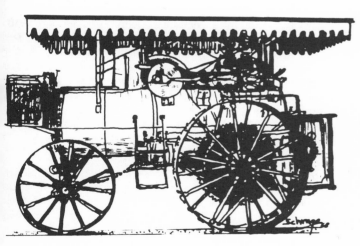

Organized: 1950
Meetings: Board meeting first Monday of each month; Annual Reunion 5 days, starting on the first Thursday before Labor Day
Number of Members: Annual Reunion attendance over 200,000
Membership: $3.00 annual; children under high school age free

During the Midwest Old Settlers and Threshers Reunion--a "steam festival"--over 100 large and small steam engines, steam locomotives, several hundred stationary engines, and more than 100 antique automobiles are in operation. On the grounds are an Old Settlers Village with log cabin, rural schoolhouse, country church, depot, general store, saloon, jail, printing shop, bank, post office, barber shop, blacksmith shop, wagon factory, shingle mill, firehouse, medicine wagon, burr mill, and bandstand. Demonstrations of threshing machine, chaff piler and baler, sorghum mill, saw mill, veneer cutter, prony brake (used to test horsepower of engines), and Baker fan powered by steam engines. Displays of old farm machinery, antiques, Indian relics, and pioneer items tell the story of our agricultural heritage. Craft demonstrations in broom making, soap making, quilting, spinning, carding, weaving, caning, glass blowing, and doll making. Narrow gauge (36-inch) steam railroad--the Midwest Central Railroad--and a vintage trolley are in operation on the grounds.

Ground-breaking ceremonies for a Repertoire Theater Complex took place on September 4, 1971. The Museum of Repertoire Americana houses a collection of theatre memorabilia--early opera house, tent, folk, and rep. Also included are artifacts of medicine shows, lyceum, and chautauqua. The museum is open by appointment, year round. An old-time tent show is performed daily during the Reunion, and there is an old fiddlers contest, checker tournament, horseshoe tournament, and a daily Giant Calvalcade of Power--"The Greatest Steam Show on Earth." The Heritage Museum (see above) is open during the summer.

Old Threshers Educational Workshops are conducted for teachers in the area. Educational tours for school children may be arranged. *Teaching Living History,* a resource guide for teachers is available upon request. *Threshers Chaff,* a quarterly newspaper containing news and information about Old Threshers activities, is published.

44 - HENRY
(continued)

● **Mud Creek Park**
6 miles south of New London, Iowa
or 2 miles northeast of Lowell, Iowa

Henry County Conservation Board
J. H. Moeller, President
Salem, Iowa 52649

A 52-acre area of scenic, botanical, geological, and archeological interest. Heavily forested bluffs extend along Mud Creek. Geodes in a variety of sizes and colors may be found here. On the ridge top are lithic remains of a prehistoric Woodland Indian encampment. Development plans call for an interpretive trail system, and facilities for picnicking, camping, and other outdoor recreation.

● **Oakland Mills State Park**
4 miles southwest of Mt. Pleasant,
on Iowa 133

State Conservation Commission
State Office Building
300 Fourth Street
Des Moines, Iowa 50319
or
Henry County Conservation Board
J. H. Moeller, President
Salem, Iowa 52649

An 85-acre wooded tract along the Skunk River, at the site of an old fishing village and mill. The dam was the first authorized on the Skunk River by the Legislature of the Territory of Iowa (January 19, 1839). The legislators, meeting at Burlington, gave this authorization based on a working model of a dam built on Hawkeye Creek by Herman Mathews, a millwright from what is now Henry County. His plan allowed for the passage of river traffic--steamboats, keelboats, and flatboats--as the proposed dam was half stone and half logs. A dam of some sort has been on the limestone ledge at the site ever since. A ferry on the Salem-Mount Pleasant road had already been established at this spot by L. B. Hughes, and a small settlement had grown up as early as 1838. Robert and James Wilson built Wilson Mill, a 4-story flouring and grist mill, and it quickly became the meeting place for the little community. While farmers waited for their grain to be processed, they discussed politics, market prices, and local happenings. The Wilsons later built a woolen mill, where a dozen people worked full time. Following the death of James Wilson, the mills changed hands and were finally purchased by Nathaniel Armstrong and Courtland Clark. Ice-harvesting became another successful enterprise at Oakland Mills.

Business at the mills eventually declined and, around 1910, the buildings were torn down and the lumber was sold. The dam was purchased by Iowa Electric Light and Power Company and, in 1911, plans were completed to build a power plant on the old mill foundations. This plant operated until 1925, when construction was started on a new dam and larger power plant, down the river and on the south bank. This hydroelectric plant was in operation until 1955, and was razed in 1965, putting an end to another era in the history of the area.

The State Park is now operated under a long-term management agreement with Henry County Conservation Board. Oakland Mills County Park includes a 10-acre tract on both sides of the Skunk River, plus the dam. These two areas provide facilities for fishing, boating, picnicking, camping, and hiking.

● **Savage Memorial Woods**
Southwest of Mt. Pleasant, Iowa

Robert W. Poulter
Iowa Chapter, The Nature Conservancy
301 South Van Buren Street
Mount Pleasant, Iowa 52641

A 12-acre tract of upland hardwood timber, overlooking Big Cedar Creek. The woods is predominantly oak on rolling hills, and has been protected from grazing for many years. It is used for nature study by colleges and schools. Acquired in 1967 by the Iowa Chapter of The Nature Conservancy as a gift of Miss Alice E. Savage, who lives in a stone house near the timber.

- HENRY
(continued)

● **Site of First Courthouse in Iowa**
Public Square
Mount Pleasant, Iowa

The site of the first courthouse in Iowa, marked by a granite boulder with bronze plaque, placed by the James Harlan Chapter of the Daughters of the American Revolution in 1929. The building, constructed in 1839, was used until 1872. A cupola for the substantial two-story brick courthouse was never built. The commissioners did not actually occupy the building until their regular meeting on April 6, 1840.

- HOWARD

esco
-9

● **Crossman Prairie**
3 miles east, 3 miles north, and 1 mile east of Riceville, Iowa

A 10-acre tract, about half of which is native lowland prairie, with the remainder old field succession. Aspen and orchids may be seen on the original prairie; golden rod and asters predominate on the area that was once cultivated. The prairie is named for Glenn Crossman.

Acquired: 1945

● **Hayden Prairie**
5 miles southwest of Lime Springs, Iowa on county road, or 4 miles west and 4½ miles north of the junction of U.S. 63 and Iowa 9, west of Cresco, Iowa

State Conservation Commission
State Office Building
300 Fourth Street
Des Moines, Iowa 50319

A remnant of true prairie in the Iowa Drift area, maintained in virgin condition by one family for 78 years before it was acquired by the State of Iowa--the first unit of the State's Botanical Monument system. The gently rolling preserve has an abundance of various prairie grasses, reaching heights of 4 to 8 feet. Altogether, 149 species of native flowers and shrubs, representing at least 36 plant families, have been identified here. These include pasque flower, prairie clover, golden Alexander, yarrow, oxeye daisy, coreopsis, lead plant, wild indigo, and various sunflowers and asters. This is a popular area for nature study, and is used by biology classes.

When the white man first arrived in Iowa, about 85 percent of its area was beautiful prairie covered with tall prairie grass and a wide variety of wild flowers. Fire and an occasional high water table kept trees from becoming established on these prairies. About 500 acres (only 0.015 percent of the original area) have been preserved in 4 state-owned natural prairies. Ada Hayden Prairie is the largest of these--240 acres. Other smaller natural prairie areas exist in state parks or have been preserved by County Conservation Boards or by private owners, or exist in rural areas along railroad rights of way, country roads, cemeteries, and on rural school grounds.

● **Howard County Historical Society**
Cresco, Iowa

Anna G. Chance, President
Cresco, Iowa 52136

Organized: 1926
Meetings: Third Saturday of month, at Cresco City Hall
Number of Members: 120
Dues: $2.00 annual

A restored historic building and an old rural schoolhouse are maintained on the Howard County Fairgrounds where antiques are displayed each year. The Society sponsors tours to places of historic interest, a spring coffee and bake sale, and a fall book sale, and has published a cookbook. An original 1853 log cabin has been relocated in Beadle Park (between South Elm and S.W. 2nd on S.E. 2nd Avenue S.W. in Cresco) and appropriately furnished. The cabin is

45 - HOWARD
(continued)

Howard County Historical Society
(continued)

● **Lidtke Park and Mill**
Old Town, 1 mile north of
Lime Springs, Iowa

Howard County Historical Society
Cresco, Iowa 52136
or
Howard County Conservation Board
Wilton Thomas, Executive Officer
R. R. 1
Lime Springs, Iowa 52155

open from 2:00-5:00 on Sunday afternoons during the summer months.

An 1870, 3-story, brick Victorian period house, with mansard roof, has been purchased by the Society and is being restored. The home will be furnished, and the addition of a carriage house is planned.

The Society also owns Lidtke Mill (see Lidtke Park and Mill, below). The old mill is being restored to operating condition.

A 10-acre memorial park featuring picnicking, boating, fishing, and camping. Across the Upper Iowa River is the historic old mill, one of the first built on this stream. It was acquired by Herman C. Lidtke in 1917 from his father-in-law, David W. Davis, who was one of several former owners.

Lime Spring (Old Town) post office was established in 1855, the second in Howard County, and the town plat was approved April 27, 1857. When the railroad was built 10 years later, the town became Lime Springs Station, which was later shortened to Lime Springs. Construction on the mill was begun in 1857, by Melvin M. Marsh, only 1 year after the Iowa-Minnesota border was surveyed just a few miles to the north. The mill was first used for sawing timber. It was later converted to the production of wheat flour, and during the 1870's, was capable of turning out 100 barrels of flour per day. Much of this was shipped to Eastern markets. During the spring of 1894, a fire destroyed all but the stone walls of the mill--a $40,000 loss. It was rebuilt with red brick and wooden frame walls the following year, and converted to grinding feed. A generator was later installed to produce electricity, and in 1916, a new dam was built.

After Mr. Lidtke became manager-operator of Old Town Mill, he made a trip by team and wagon to Colesburg, Iowa--a distance of 105 miles one way--to get the millstones from the local mill to use at Lime Springs. The trip and the loading, which was a tremendous job in itself, took a week-- from Monday until the following Sunday.

When the William Larrabee Mill was dismantled at Clermont, the old French millstones, each weighing 2,400 pounds, were obtained and hauled to Lime Springs. These millstones were used for only 1 year in the Lidtke Mill. One stone is now set in the sidewalk and the other is built into an outside wall of the Lidtke home at Lime Springs. These millstones were made from "buhr," a very hard silicate found in the Seine River Valley. The French stones were formed of wedge-shaped pieces cemented together and bound with iron hoops, while American millstones were usually made from a single piece of stone.

- HOWARD
(continued)

Lidtke Park and Mill
(continued)

In July 1919, John M. Peterson was nearly electrocuted in an accident at the mill. At the time, the towns of Lime Springs and Chester obtained electric current from the water-powered generator at the Lime Springs Milling Co. At 10:45 each evening, lights were flicked to warn local residents that they had 15 minutes to get their kerosene lamps lighted before the current went off. On Monday morning electricity was furnished for washing, and on Wednesday morning for ironing, but the rest of the time the electricity was used for grinding buckwheat. Peterson, who had been employed at the mill for only 2 or 3 weeks, accidentally came in contact with poles of an electrical switch. The terrific charge of electricity knocked Peterson to the floor and caused the flesh to come off his feet. His footprints were burned into the cement floor of the mill, and the print of veins can still be seen in the concrete. He also lost several toes, the first finger on his right hand, and 2 fingers of his left hand. He eventually recovered and returned to work at the mill for awhile, wearing wooden shoes. He lived to be nearly 99 years old, the oldest resident in Calmar at that time (January 1967).

Some years after Mr. Lidtke took over the mill, he decided that the 2 runs of stone then being used to grind feed were not sufficient. Steel burrs were installed and production was increased from 20 sacks to 60 sacks an hour. The mill ceased operating in 1963, but the machinery is intact.

The dam at the site is 150 feet long, and the fall from the top of the mill wheel, about 13 feet. The old mill and dam, and a large stone warehouse, were purchased by Howard County Historical Society (see above) and have been leased to Howard County Conservation Board. The mill, millrace, and turbines are being restored to operating condition.

● **Norman Borlaug Birthplace**
11 miles southwest of Cresco, Iowa

The 2-story, white frame farmhouse where Norman Ernest Borlaug was born on March 25, 1914. The place was the home of his paternal grandparents, Mr. and Mrs. Nels Borlaug, with whom his parents, Mr. and Mrs. Henry Borlaug, lived and farmed for many years.

The farm home where Dr. Borlaug later lived as a youth is located near Iowa Highway 139, about 14 miles southwest of Cresco. This house was painted during the summer of 1971 by 2 Iowa State University professors and students from the Botany Club, in appreciation of Dr. Borlaug's visit to the ISU campus at Ames earlier that year.

Norman Borlaug began his education at New Oregon Township Rural School No. 8. He then attended Cresco High School, where he was a 4-year vocational agriculture student, graduating in 1932. His bachelor of science, masters, and doctoral degrees were received from the University of Minnesota. He has been with the Rockefeller Foundation since 1944, living in Mexico City.

45 - HOWARD
(continued)

Norman Borlaug Birthplace
(continued)

The famous agricultural scientist, leader of the "Green Revolution," received the 1970 Nobel Peace Prize in Oslo, Norway on December 10. By developing new high-yield types of wheat and corn, he has made a major contribution in the fight against starvation and poverty in developing countries faced with growing populations. Borlaug, the 15th United States citizen to win the Nobel Peace Prize, was the first agricultural scientist to do so since it was instituted in 1901. A Borlaug Day fete was held in his honor at Cresco, Iowa on December 19, 1970. Dr. Borlaug was further honored by the 1971 Iowa State Fair, whose theme was "Discover Mexico." Friday, August 20, the opening day of the Fair, was designated Norman Borlaug Day. At this time, the Nobel Peace Prize recipient participated in various special events ending with the ceremony in his honor at the Grandstand.

46 - HUMBOLDT

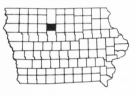

Dakota City
C-5

● **Bloody Run**
North of Humboldt, Iowa

On what is now farm land is the site of the murder of several Sioux Indians by Henry Lott in January 1854. As a squatter, Lott built the first log cabin in Humboldt County, near here, sometime around 1846. (See Lotts Creek Park, below.) He had previously been at Red Rock, in present Marion County, where he did a thriving business as an Indian trader from the spring of 1843 until he moved north in the summer of 1846. In his trading with the Indians, Lott was usually able to stay on friendly terms with them. His clearing and his cabin were a popular hangout for thirsty Indians who could come here and fill themselves with whiskey. However, on one occasion, the Indians came in force to Lott's cabin and accused him of stealing their ponies. Sidominadota (Two Fingers) and his followers became vicious, drove Lott and his family out into the snow and freezing weather, and looted and burned his log cabin.

Lott swore revenge for the death of his wife and son from exposure (see Vegors Cemetery, Webster County), but bided his time, watching and waiting until January 1854. The band of Sioux Indians under Sidominadota had broken up their camp on Bloody Run to move on to winter quarters. However, Sidominadota, craving more of Lott's whiskey, stayed behind with his squaw and children, his elderly mother, and another young squaw and her two children, in their tepees along Bloody Run. Following carefully laid plans, Lott murdered Sidominadota and most of his family, together with the other Sioux Indians. Lott tried to make it appear that hostile Indians were responsible for the massacre, but the Sioux Indians were not deceived. About 3 years later, in 1857, the Spirit Lake Massacre took place (see Dickinson County) under the leadership of Inkpaduta, another Sioux Indian. It would thus appear that the Spirit Lake Massacre and other Indian uprisings can be attributed, at least in part, to the cold-blooded murder of Sidominadota and other Sioux Indians by Henry Lott, on the banks of Bloody Run.

- HUMBOLDT
(continued)

● **Bloody Run**
(continued)

Lott, having destroyed his own cabin as part of the plot, fled southward with some furs and Sidominadota's pony. He was last seen at Saylorville, Iowa, and was finally reported killed some time later in California.

● **Frank A. Gotch State Park**
2 miles southeast of Humboldt, Iowa

State Conservation Commission
State Office Building
300 Fourth Street
Des Moines, Iowa 50319
and
Humboldt County Conservation Board
Mrs. Mary Green, Office Secretary
Courthouse
Dakota City, Iowa 50529

Established: April 1949

Frank A. Gotch (April 22, 1877-December 16, 1917), who was born near Humboldt, became world heavyweight wrestling champion April 3, 1908 at the Dexter Park Pavilion in Chicago, when he defeated George Hackenschmidt, the Russian Lion. Gotch, one of Iowa's great athletes of all time was generally acknowledged as the "fastest, strongest, most scientific heavyweight wrestler who ever appeared on any mat." He originated many of the now famous wrestling holds. In 1911, he established his training camp in Riverside Park (now Bicknell Park). Gotch was only 40 years old when he died. His mausoleum is in Union Cemetery in Humboldt.

Frank A. Gotch State Park includes 67 acres where the East Fork joins the Des Moines River. In the park is a memorial monument to Gotch, "Retired Undefeated World's Heavyweight Champion Wrestler." An annual Frank Gotch Day is observed in June.

Humboldt County Conservation Board maintains the park under a long-term management agreement with the State of Iowa. There are facilities for picnicking, camping, and fishing.

● **Humboldt County Historical Association**
Humboldt, Iowa

Mrs. Werner (Jeanette) Tigges, President
404 5th Street North
Humboldt, Iowa 50548

Organized: November 13, 1962
Meetings: First Monday of month, 8:00 p.m.
Number of Members: 287
Dues: $2.00 annual

The Association sponsors various money-making activities to provide funds for its projects, which include Old Mill Farm (see below).

● **Humboldt County Old Settler's Association**
Livermore, Iowa

Mrs. John Olson, Secretary-Treasurer
Livermore, Iowa 50558

Organized: September 25, 1885
Meetings: Annual picnic first Saturday in September
Number of Members: 70
Admission to Cabin: Donations

A log cabin was built in 1890 as a memorial to Humboldt County pioneers. Located on a half-acre of timber near Livermore, the cabin is used for a meeting place and contains ox yokes, a scythe and cradle, cider press, wood carvings, and other pioneer relics.

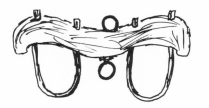

46 - HUMBOLDT
(continued)

● **Joe Sheldon Park**
1½ miles west of Humboldt, Iowa

Humboldt County Conservation Board
Mrs. Mary Green, Office Secretary
Courthouse
Dakota City, Iowa 50529

Established: February 3, 1966

An 81-acre tract acquired by J. H. (Joe) Sheldon in November 1897, and sold by his heirs to Humboldt County. The area is covered with a variety of trees--oak, hickory, walnut, elm, and willow--and overlooks the West Fork of the Des Moines River. About 2/3 of the land is utilized as a wildlife habitat and natural area for an outdoor classroom. The developed area is used for picnicking, camping, hiking, and fishing.

● **John Brown Park**
Near business district of
Humboldt, Iowa

Fountain Dedicated: September 22, 1918

One of several city parks in Humboldt, featuring a unique fountain dedicated to the memory of Fay Hessian who died from tuberculosis in 1912. The fountain was built by Reverend P. M. Dobberstein, creator of the West Bend Grotto (see Grotto of the Redemption, Palo Alto County), who died in 1954. The stone mosaic fountain is composed of some 3 million separate pieces. The stones weigh 52 tons and represent 33 states and 5 foreign countries. Semi-precious stones, ores, minerals, fossils, petrifications, corals, and shells are set in cement. A column rising from the center of the fountain is topped by a 950-pound marble statue carved in Italy. The fountain was built in sections at West Bend and transported by truck to Humboldt to be assembled at the park.

● **Lotts Creek Park**
½ mile west of Livermore, Iowa
on Iowa 222

Humboldt County Conservation Board
Courthouse
Dakota City, Iowa 50529

A 40-acre area covered with hardwood timber and bordered on the north by Lotts Creek. The stream was so named by early settlers since one of the places where Henry Lott settled was opposite the mouth of this creek. Lott, according to early accounts, was a rough, daring, wily frontiersman who traded whiskey and trinkets to the Indians for furs. (See Bloody Run, above.) Old Settler's Park is adjacent to the tract. (See Humboldt County Old Settler's Association, above.) Picnicking, fishing, and camping are permitted.

● **Old Mill Farm**
Dakota City, Iowa

Admission: $0.50; children, 8-15 years, $0.25

Old Mill Farm, located on the east side of the Des Moines River near Dakota City, was donated to the Humboldt County Historical Association in 1966 by Mr. and Mrs. Art Kunert and Mrs. Clarence Kunert for the permanent site of a museum.

The mill was destroyed by fire and the old mill dam went out later, leaving only the home. This 14-room, red brick house, which was built by Cory Brown, Sr. in 1879, has been restored. The historical museum contains mementoes of famous residents, old Humboldt College, and the old stagecoach stop and post office at Addison. Willow or Norway No. 6 School, built by Ole Biondahl in 1883, is also on the grounds and has been furnished in the 1890 period. Classes were held in the school, which was located

- HUMBOLDT
(continued)

Old Mill Farm
(continued)

southeast of Thor, until May 26, 1955. The early day schoolhouse was also used for church services and community meetings. A log cabin is being rebuilt.

- IDA

Grove
)-2

● **Battle Hill**
Near Battle Creek, Iowa

The site of an 1849 battle between Sioux Indians and a government survey party, marked by a bronze tablet cast in 1936 and dedicated in 1941. The battle gave the adjoining hill, a small stream at its foot, and the town of Battle Creek their names.

● **Ida County Historical Society**
Ida Grove, Iowa

Mrs. Jo Pullen, President
313 Main
Ida Grove, Iowa 51445

Incorporated: October 25, 1973

● **Moorehead Pioneer Park**
½ mile north of Ida Grove, Iowa

Ida County Conservation Board
Mrs. Vernette Worth,
Secretary to the Board
Ida Grove, Iowa 51445

A 260-acre tract, much of which is covered with native trees. On the site is one of the first houses built in the area-- about 1856. The original portion of the place served as a stagecoach inn. Native hardwood lumber was used in the original construction; timbers were hand hewn. The deep wheel ruts worn by the stagecoaches are still visible west of the house. The park has bridle and hiking trails, and facilities for picnicking, fishing, camping, and winter sports.

- IOWA

rengo
-9

● **Amana Colonies**
Located on and north of U.S. 6

Seven "old world" villages, the first of which, Amana, was founded in 1855 in the Iowa River Valley by the Society of True Inspirationalists under the leadership of Christian Metz (died 1867). The other 6 villages are Middle Amana, High Amana, West Amana, East Amana, South Amana, and Homestead. The towns are spaced "one hour by oxen" apart. Homes of wood, brick, or locally-quarried brown sandstone; trees; grapes; flowers; and American Lotus[1] on Amana Lake in mid- summer make the Amanas attractive. Tours may be arranged through the various factories which manufacture woolens, furniture, wines, bakery goods, and meat specialties. These industries provide the villages with the essential necessities of life. Skills have been handed down from father to son in the old world tradition. Today the new ways are blended with the old. Amana restaurants are famous for excellent meals, served family style. The annual Oktoberfest celebration honors the German heritage of the Amana Colonies.

48 - IOWA
(continued)

● **Amana Heim (Home)**
Homestead, Iowa

Open: Daily, 10:00 a.m.-4:30 p.m.; Sunday, noon-4:30 p.m.;
April 15-November 1

Built nearly 100 years ago on the south bluffs of the Iowa River in the Amana Settlement. Constructed of brick made from native clay, and timbers cut and hewed in the nearby forests, mortised and tenoned and put together without nails. Furnished with Amana-crafted walnut furniture and authentic and original pioneer items--old iron stoves, carpet looms, quilting frames, ironstone chinaware, toys, and hand implements. A hostess is available for guided tours.

● **Amana Heritage Society**
Amana, Iowa

Mrs. Alex A. Meyer, President
Middle Amana, Iowa 52307

Organized: 1968

A non-profit organization whose purpose is to preserve the history of the Amana Colonies, founded in 1855 and made up of 7 communities. The Society owns and operates the Museum of Amana History (Heritage House) (see below).

● **Indian Fish Trap**
West of bridge on
Iowa 149 south
of Amana, Iowa

Iowa State Preserves Advisory Board
c/o State Conservation Commission
State Office Building
300 Fourth Street
Des Moines, Iowa 50319

A prehistoric stone weir in the Iowa River, visible only at times of extremely low water. Fish were driven into the stone enclosure and harvested by the Indians.

● **Iowa County Historical Society**
Marengo, Iowa

Harold Moore, President
R. R. 1
Box 48
Parnell, Iowa 52325
or
Theo. C. (Ted) Ressler
Corresponding Secretary
Williamsburg, Iowa 52361

Schoolhouse Open: By appointment
Log House and Log Cabin Open: Saturday and Sunday,
1:00-5:00 p.m.; other times by appointment.

An annual picnic is held in September at Gritter School, maintained by the Society. The red brick schoolhouse was established in 1872 in English Township, 3 miles northwest of North English, in a wooded area (oak and hickory nut trees). The brick was made in a nearby brickyard. The original school, replaced by the present building, was built of logs chinked with mud or clay. Gritter School was named for the creek that flows to the north of it. As many as 60

8 - IOWA
(continued)

Iowa County Historical Society
(continued)

pupils crowded into the 1-room school some years. During the 1930's, classes usually had 30 or more pupils. The final day of school was in May 1951. The enrollment tor this term was 18--9 girls and 9 boys.

The last remaining log house and log cabin in Iowa County were moved in 1965 from Iowa Township to Marengo City Park. The original logs were cut from land owned by Henrich Meyer (1825-1907), who came from Germany to Iowa County and built a bachelor cabin in 1856. Following his marriage, the log house was built in 1861. There were 6 children who also lived here. The original stones of the foundation and basement are in the restored building. Both log buildings are furnished with heirlooms, many from Iowa County. Included are kitchen equipment, candle mold, rope bed, Boston rocker, and old cupboards.

● **Museum of Amana History (Heritage House)**
Amana, Iowa
just east of Iowa 149

Admission: $0.50; children, $0.25
Open: 10:00 a.m.-5:00 p.m., Monday through Saturday;
Noon-5:00 p.m. Sunday

A museum of Amana history, formerly the home of Dr. and Mrs. Charles F. Noe, who moved there in 1918. Mrs. Noe continued to reside in the home following her husband's death. She died in 1965. The red brick house was originally built in 1864 for Dr. Heinrich Fehr.

On display are early church records (the church was the governing body until 1932), Bibles, hymn books, articles used for communion services, handwritten testimonials (some dating back to the early 1700's when the Ebenezer Society was formed in Germany), a presiding elder's table and chair, an old church bench, old photographs, and clothing worn to church. A typical Amana living room of the 1880's includes a wood stove, wall clock, needlepoint, and handmade rugs and furniture. Upstairs in the house are displays of arts and crafts--Amana-made tinware, china, pottery, harness, shoes, soap, baskets, carpeting, mattresses stuffed with hog's hair, lithographs, and lithograph stones. In the model kinder-schule, or pre-school, toys of the early Amana days may be seen. The church room depicts an old Amana church.

48 - IOWA
(continued)

**Museum of Amana History
(Heritage House)**
(continued)

The people of western German, Swiss, and Alsatian ancestry who founded the Amana Colonies operated woolen mills, wagon shops, a furniture factory, and other industries. Skills were handed down from father to son. They lived a communal life, governed by the church elders, until 1932 when a change was made to the present capitalistic system.

49 - JACKSON

Maquoketa
D-13

● **Bellevue State Park**
South of Bellevue, Iowa
on U.S. 52

State Conservation Commission
State Office Building
300 Fourth Street
Des Moines, Iowa 50319

A beautiful 510-acre tract which includes the Dyas and Nelson Units, near the Mississippi River. From 300-foot-high bluffs is a superb view of the river, lock and dam No. 12, river barges, wooded islands, Bellevue, sand dunes, rugged woodlands, and an old mill on Mill Creek. Trails lead to unusual rock formations and conical Indian mounds associated with the Woodland Culture (1000B.C. to about 1300 A.D.). White settlers arrived in the region as early as 1833. An assortment of wild flowers grow in the park, and many ferns (including purple cliffbrake) are on the limestone ledges. Trees include tall white pines and graceful white birch. Birds common to the area are the ruby-throated hummingbird, and the rarer pileated woodpecker and the bald eagle.

● **Eden Valley Park and Refuge**
(formerly **Arnold Wulf Recreation Area**)
2 miles south of
Baldwin, Iowa

Jackson County Conservation Board
James Wendel, Executive Officer
R. R. 1
Maquoketa, Iowa 52060
        or
Clinton County Conservation Board
Ben Martinsen, Secretary-Treasurer
758 South Bluff Boulevard
Clinton, Iowa 52732

A 200-acre site noted for its natural and scenic qualities. Bear Creek runs through the valley, over half of which is made up of steep bluffs and uplands covered by dense hardwood timber and conifer plantings. A nature interpretive area includes hiking trails, and there are facilities for picnicking, fishing, and camping. This is a joint project of Jackson and Clinton Counties, although the park is located in Jackson County.

● **Home of Ansel Briggs**
Andrew, Iowa

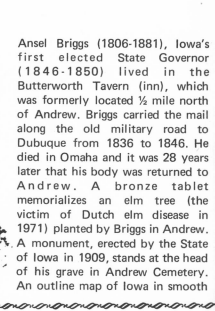

Ansel Briggs (1806-1881), Iowa's first elected State Governor (1846-1850) lived in the Butterworth Tavern (inn), which was formerly located ½ mile north of Andrew. Briggs carried the mail along the old military road to Dubuque from 1836 to 1846. He died in Omaha and it was 28 years later that his body was returned to Andrew. A bronze tablet memorializes an elm tree (the victim of Dutch elm disease in 1971) planted by Briggs in Andrew. A monument, erected by the State of Iowa in 1909, stands at the head of his grave in Andrew Cemetery. An outline map of Iowa in smooth

- JACKSON
(continued)

Home of Ansel Briggs
(continued)

polished granite is on one side of the monument, and a bronze medallion portrait of Governor Briggs is on the north side.

The stone building now occupied by the Andrew Cooperative Creamery was originally Jackson County Courthouse when the county seat was moved to Andrew in 1861 for the second time.

● **Hurstville Lime Kilns**
2 miles north of Maquoketa, Iowa, on old U.S. 61

The first of 4 lime kilns built by Alfred Hurst in 1870. The village of Hurstville had a company store; rows of identical cottages for workers lined both sides of the road. Lime from the kilns was shipped over northern Iowa, Nebraska, South Dakota, and Minnesota. Eight cords of wood per day were required to fire each kiln. The property is privately owned.

● **Jackson County Historical Society**
Box 1335, Maquoketa, Iowa 52060

J. W. Brady, President
501 South Eliza
Maquoketa, Iowa 52060
or
Mrs. Grace Holihan, Curator
R.R. 4
Maquoketa, Iowa 52060

Organized: April 25, 1903; discontinued in 1912; reorganized June 11, 1964
Meetings: Quarterly; annual meeting last Thursday evening in June; board meetings 3rd Tuesday of month
Number of Members: 280
Dues: $1.00 annual; $10.00 life

Sponsors an annual Narrative Contest among school students, and tours to historic areas in Jackson County; assists in marking and preserving historic sites; presents radio programs on station KMAQ; and issues a quarterly Newsletter. A museum is located in the Pearson Memorial Center at Jackson County Fairgrounds, and is open daily during summer months from 1:00 - 4:00 p.m.

● **Maquoketa Caves State Park**
7 miles northwest of Maquoketa, Iowa on Iowa 130

State Conservation Commission
State Office Building
300 Fourth Street
Des Moines, Iowa 50319

Established: 1921

A 152-acre wooded tract containing many geological curiosities. Trails lead through deep ravines with sheer cliffs ranging up to 75 feet in height. From the top are exciting views of the surrounding valley. Numerous caves honeycomb the limestone cliffs. Some of these bear such unusual names as Shinbone Cave, Tourist Delight Cave, Dance Hall Cave, Twin Arch Cave, Up-N-Down Cave, Match Cave, Window Cave, Dug Out Cave, and Hernando's Hideaway Cave.

Initials and dates carved in the walls of the caves date back to 1835, and Indian pottery, arrowheads, and spears found in the caverns are evidence that they were used as a dwelling place by prehistoric Indians. Later, Indians of historic times hunted and fished in the area. Under the terms of the Black Hawk Purchase of 1832, the Sac and Fox tribes were moved on west.

49 - JACKSON
(continued)

Maquoketa Caves State Park
(continued)

The first known white men to discover the great limestone caves were Joshua Bear and David Scott, two early settlers in Jackson County. This was before the Civil War, when the two men were hunting deer, following a heavy snowstorm. When first discovered, the cave ceilings were hung with milkwhite stalactites, and corresponding stalagmites rose from the floor. Unfortunately, these have been removed by souvenir hunters. The major caves are electrically lighted.

A natural bridge connects two bluffs about 50 feet above the valley floor, and a 17-ton balanced rock is perched atop a cliff, resting on a base only 1 foot in diameter. Raccoon Creek runs underneath the natural bridge and through the largest of the caves before continuing on down the ravine. The park is popular with spelunkers and practicing mountain climbers and is unexcelled in Iowa for its variety of flora and fauna. There are facilities for picnicking and camping.

● **Millrock School**
2 miles south of Baldwin, Iowa

Jackson County Conservation Board
Maquoketa, Iowa 52060

An old stone schoolhouse. Following the closing of the school, the building served as a community center.

● **Nickelodeon Museum**
Antique Room
503 West Grove Street
Maquoketa, Iowa 52060

Ronald Keller, Owner
503 West Grove Street
Maquoketa, Iowa 52060

Admission: Free
Open: 9:00 a.m.-5:00 p.m., Monday through Saturday;
9:00 a.m.-Noon, Sunday; tours by appointment
Coin operated music machines and devices, antiques, and works of art. Included in the exhibits are coin operated pianos, band organ, caliope, and music boxes; soapstone carvings; miniature sewing machines; and an old telegraph teleprinter upon which visitors can send messages to themselves. Formerly located in Decker House Inn. Decker House Inn was established by James Decker who came to Maquoketa from Watertown, New York in the 1850's. He erected a frame building in 1856, which was replaced with a more palatial, 3-story, brick hotel in 1876. A frequent visitor to the original frame Decker House and its barroom was Ulysses S. Grant. At one time, Maquoketa had 14 hotels to accommodate the fur traders, salesmen, campaigning political candidates, and occasional dignitaries. Each hotel had its own horse-drawn omnibus to meet every one of the 28 trains arriving daily. Decker House Inn was operated until recently by a fifth generation descendent of the founder. The original furniture and woodwork of the hotel were carved by local craftsmen from walnut, oak, and cherry. The broad, solid walnut staircase, shiny brass lamps, glittering chandeliers, and a rosewood piano with pearl inlays and mother of pearl keys, gave evidence of the elegance of earlier days. The piano, brought from Watertown, was said to be one of the first transported across the Mississippi River.

2 - JACKSON
(continued)

● **Paradise**
4 miles west of Bellevue, Iowa

Bevan Brothers Historical
Paradise Farm and Antique Shop
R. R. 1
Bellevue, Iowa 52031

Built: 1842
Open to visitors

Paradise Valley, edged by limestone hills, extends west from the Mississippi River at Bellevue, Iowa. Captain Elbridge Gerry Potter (1791-1875) came to Iowa in 1842 and located on the farm known as "Paradise," where he resided until his death. Potter called the place Paradise "because he went through Purgatory to find it." In the late 1830's, he had set out from St. Louis and walked to St. Paul in search of a place to build his Paradise. The area now called Iowa was first opened to permanent settlement by the Black Hawk Purchase in 1833, and Potter had come through some wild country to find a location that suited him. Potter originally bought 1,400 acres for his farm.

For the 12 years prior to 1842, he successfully operated a distilling and milling business in Lebanon, Illinois. His profits, "fully $100 per day," were wisely invested in land.

During the years he manufactured whiskey "he became fully convinced of its pernicious effects," especially after witnessing its wrecking power upon a "near and trusted relative," according to an early biographical sketch (1879). Such was his disgust with the whiskey business that "before leaving Lebanon, he deliberately removed the roof of the distillery, and reduced it to firewood. Then he took down the stone walls of the same and scattered them broadcast; then he dug up, and with his own hand, chopped in pieces the 'worm of the still'," leaving the distillery "a complete wreck and desolute ruin."

In 1843, Mr. Potter built the flouring-mills at Bellevue known as the Jasper Mills, and operated this business until 1871 when he sold out to Kilborn & Co. (see Potter Mill below). Paradise, with its rolling land watered with springs, became one of the finest stock farms in Iowa, employing 35 hired men. There were 7 hired girls to help in the kitchen, where 200 loaves of bread could be baked at one time.

Shortly after he settled at Paradise, Potter started collecting books for his library, located on the third floor of the main house. Considered Iowa's first library, it remains as it was over a century ago, with about 450 books in addition to bound copies of magazines and papers of the day. Each volume is numbered and color coded for its own place on the library shelves.

Three of the original buildings still stand at Paradise--the main house, the stone dormitory for the hired hands, and the wagon barn. Restoration of the buildings, privately occupied, is in progress.

Potter's wife, Lucretia, preceded him in death by 18 months. Both are buried, together with other members of the family, on a little hillside plot, 30 x 30 feet, which he named Infidel Cemetery.

42 - JACKSON
(continued)

- **Potter Mill (Dyas Mill)**
  South edge of Bellevue, Iowa

  Donald E. Sweitzer, Owner
  825 High Avenue East
  Oskaloosa, Iowa 52577

Admission: $0.25 donation; children free

A 6-story wooden mill with stone foundation, built in 1843 by Elbridge Gerry Potter on Mill Creek. The 100-foot-long mill has black walnut or maple floors and 20-inch square walnut beams, 48 feet long. There are 36 windows in the building, each with 20 panes. At one time the mill produced 50 barrels of flour per day, and wheat transactions ran $6,000 in a single day. The miller was paid $2.90 a day "whether the mill turns or not," but he was expected to work whenever it was necessary--day or night, Sundays included.

Potter came to Bellevue from Illinois, having previously lived in New York. He sold the mill in 1871. By the early 1900's, Iowa farmers were raising less wheat and the milling of flour was declining. After 1903, the mill was used to grind feed.

The mill ceased to operate and was sold in 1969 by the Dyas Brothers for $7,200. The property is being restored and houses examples of early Iowa relics and primitives.

- **Sagers Museum**
  6 miles northwest of Maquoketa, Iowa at entrance to Maquoketa Caves State Park

  Paul Sagers, Owner
  R. R. 2
  Maquoketa, Iowa 52060

Founded: 1950; opened 1952
Admission: $0.35; children $0.10; free to school groups with teacher upon advance appointment
Open: Daily, 10:00 a.m.-6:00 p.m. during June, July and August

A natural history museum containing specimens of wildlife, artifacts of prehistoric peoples, freaks of nature, pioneer artifacts, and displays of pioneer crafts and on the history of the area. A split rail fence is in front of the museum building.

- **Saint Donatus, Iowa**
  (Tetes des Morts)
  On U.S. 52 and 67

This picturesque French village offers "a bit of Luxemburg in America." The town was originally named Tetes des Morts (Heads of the Dead) after a nearby creek. An Indian battle took place near the stream, giving it its gruesome name. Nita Ho, the high bluff about 3 miles east of Saint Donatus is said to be the place where one band of Indians killed another, and threw the bodies from the cliff.

Niagara limestone buildings date back to the 1850's. The Parish School, formerly St. Mary's Academy, built in 1869 and destroyed 100 years later, was the first girls' boarding school in Iowa. A winding path leads past the 14 Stations of the Cross to the Chapel on the Mount, a reproduction of Chapel du Bilchen in old-world Luxemburg. On the side of a rocky hill opposite, is the twin-towered, red brick Evangelical Lutheran Church of St. John, visible for miles up and down the valley.

COUNTY AND COUNTY SEAT; LOCATION ON MAP	NAME AND LOCATION	DESCRIPTION

- JACKSON
(continued)

● **Spruce Creek Chapel**
2 miles west of U.S. 52,
between Bellevue and Saint
Donatus, Iowa

Built: 1852

A stone chapel, built by a German emigrant, Mathias Fritz. The stone was obtained locally. A crucifix and the alter inside the chapel were hand-carved by Mr. Fritz. For many years the Corpus Christi celebrations were held in the month of June at the little chapel. It may be visited at any time of the year.

● **Young Museum**
406 North Riverview
(U.S. 52, Great River Road)
Bellevue, Iowa 52031

Mrs. Harry (Helen) Nicholson
614 West Court
Bellevue, Iowa 52031

Museum Organized: June 12, 1961 (the "Joe A. Young and Grace Young Antique Institute, Historical Society and Museum"); opened to public in 1966
Admission: Free
Open: Saturday and Sunday, 2:00-5:00 p.m., June-October, and July 4th and Labor Day

A 10-room, 2-story native stone home, over 100 years old, with a river frontage, donated to the town by Joseph Albert (1871-1959) and Grace Mattes (d.-1956) Young for a museum. Displays include rare cut glass and crystal, bottles, china, miniatures, lamps, antiques, and an Early Bellevue Room containing old photographs and items of historical interest owned by Mr. and Mrs. Young. Mr. Young had a hardware, plumbing, heating, and electrical supply business in Bellevue. He invented a combination cistern strainer and cut-off, and also designed and manufactured some of the first metallic electric signs with a patented lens for added brilliance.

Bellevue is one of several colorful, historic towns along the Mississippi on the Great River Road. The oldest part of the public elementary school was originally the brick courthouse, built in 1848, when the county seat was returned to Bellevue the second time.

- JASPER

● **Ashton Wild-Wood Park**
7 miles west of Baxter, Iowa

Jasper County Conservation Board
Dennis Black, Executive Director
R. R. 2
Kellogg, Iowa 50135

A 98-acre natural area of steeply rolling terrain, high ridges, and ravines, abounding in wild flowers and native trees. The park serves as an outdoor classroom. There are bridle and hiking trails, and facilities for picnicking and camping.

wton
F-7

● **Colfax Mineral Springs**
Colfax, Iowa

At the turn of the century, the Colfax mineral springs were known worldwide. It was while drilling for coal that prospectors struck a supply of mineral water 315 feet below ground. The water was tested by experts and declared to be better than that of Carlsbad, Germany. So, Colfax became known as the "Carlsbad of Iowa." Visitors came--mainly by train-- to the spa for the medicinal water, therapeutic baths, and for rest at one of the 9 hotels. Most famous of these was the 150-room Hotel Colfax. The hotel, a Moorish type structure situated high above the Skunk River, east of Colfax on League Road, was forced to close during the Great Depression of the 1930's. Later, the building was used as a hospital for war veterans,

50 - JASPER
(continued)

Colfax Mineral Springs
(continued)

headquarters for the National Purebred Livestock Exposition and "Pig Palace," and a treatment center for alcoholics. In 1952, the old landmark was acquired by the Salvatorian Fathers, who operate the Colfax Interfaith Spiritual Center to train members for missionary work.

● **Emerson Hough Boyhood Home**
423 East 7th Street N,
opposite Emerson Hough Elementary School
Newton, Iowa

Constructed: 1855
Open: Privately owned; not open to the public

A stone, bearing a bronze plaque, marks the boyhood home of the writer of frontier life, Emerson Hough (1857-1923). Several of his stories have been made into motion pictures. The author of *The Story of the Cowboy* (1897), *The Mississippi Bubble* (1902), *The Way of the West* (1903), *The Law of the Land* (1905), *The Story of the Outlaw* (1906), *54-40 or Fight!* (1909), *The Passing of the Frontier* (1918), *The Covered Wagon* (1922), *North of 36* (1923), and *Mother of Gold* (1924) was born in 1857 in a frame house built in 1855. He attended the Newton public schools and graduated from the State University of Iowa in 1880. An advocate of conservation and preservation of wildlife, Hough was largely responsible for an act passed by Congress to save the buffalo (bison) in Yellowstone National Park. The family silverware, chinaware, and glassware and a collection of Emerson Hough (pronounced Huff) papers, including correspondence and manuscripts, are on file at the State Historical Building in Des Moines. The marker was erected in 1928 by Isham Randolph Chapter of the Daughters of the American Revolution, Newton, Iowa.

● **James Norman Hall Birthplace**
416 E. Howard
Colfax, Iowa

James E. Smith, Owner

The birthplace and boyhood home of author James Norman Hall (1887-1951), best known as the co-author of *Mutiny on the Bounty* (1932). Together with Charles Bernard Nordhoff, he wrote a number of adventure stories of the South Seas. Hall graduated from Grinnell College in 1910. After 4 years of social work in Boston and a bicycle tour of England, he joined the British army in 1914. It was following his discharge 4 years later that he and his friend Charles Nordhoff decided to go to Tahiti and "get away from it all." He continued to live there the rest of his life, but made a number of trips back to Iowa.

The 2-story house, built on Standpipe Hill, has shutters, bearing the letter "H", installed by the Hall family.

● **Jasper County Historical Society**
Newton, Iowa

Jack M. Wormley, President
403 West 10th Street South
Newton, Iowa 50208

Incorporated: October 11, 1973
Meetings: 4 times a year
Number of Members: 550
Dues: $2.00 annual; $3.50 family; $25.00 lifetime

The Society has tours to places of historic interest, records interviews with old-timers, and issues a newsletter to members.

JASPER
(continued)

● **Mariposa Park and Recreation Area**
2½ miles east and 5 miles north of
Newton, Iowa

Jasper County Conservation Board
Dennis Black, Executive Director
R. R. 2
Kellogg, Iowa 50135

A conservation-recreation area of 151 acres, which includes a 26-acre artificial lake. There are various species of pines as well as walnut and cherry, and large willow trees line the lake. The original 111 acres, including the lake, were owned and developed as an outdoor retreat by Art Holmdahl, an industrialist and conservationist from Kellogg, Iowa. The property was acquired from his estate by K.R.D. Wolfe of Marshalltown, who later sold it to Jasper County Conservation Board. Various domestic and exotic fowl, a pet crow ("Pete"), buffalo (American bison), fallow deer (white and spotted), sika (Japanese) deer, and other animals may be seen in the show area. Self-guided interpretive nature trails meander through the area, which serves as an outdoor classroom for school groups to study the sciences and conservation practices. Other popular activities include picnicking, fishing, rowing, and camping.

● **Maytag Historical Center**
The Maytag Company
Newton, Iowa 50208

Admission: Free
Open: Monday through Friday, 8:00 a.m.-5:00 p.m.

Authenic antiques, wall and floor coverings, pictures, and newspaper reproductions are used in period settings to tell the story of the washing machine industry. Beginning with the first Maytag washer--a hand-operated 1907 "Pastime" model--displays progress through the years to the latest in home laundry equipment.

● **Wagaman Mill (Lynnville Mill)**
Adjacent to the north edge of
Lynnville, Iowa

Jasper County Conservation Board
Dennis Black, Executive Officer
R. R. 2
Kellogg, Iowa 50135

An old mill (1846) on the North Skunk River, situated within a 3½-acre park and picnic area. Access to the park is across a cedar wood foot bridge over the river. The mill, a white building with red trim, has been operated by 3 generations of the Wagaman family since 1898. Originally a flour mill, livestock feed has been ground here in recent years by electricity, but the old water-powered turbines are intact. These date back to 1860 and 1917. The older model will be displayed above water, and the 1917 turbine has been restored to operating condition. Unlike the wooden mill wheels, the turbines operate horizontally in the water, about 6 inches beneath the surface, rather than vertically, and are not so common. Water turns the turbine, providing power to the burr stones. Both audio and visual interpretation of the history and working of the mill will be presented. Some of Iowa's earliest mills were built along the Skunk River as this territory was opened to white settlement.

JEFFERSON

● **Jefferson County Genealogical
Society**
Fairfield, Iowa

Mrs. Edith Reneker,
Corresponding Secretary
1104 South 2nd
Fairfield, Iowa 52556

Organized: 1973
Number of Members: 59

A local chapter of the Iowa Genealogical Society (see Polk County). Members have recorded birth and marriage records and keep scrap books of newspaper clippings of current marriages. Displays are set up at hobby shows and talks on genealogy are given at schools and to other interested groups.

field
-10

51 - JEFFERSON
(continued)

● **Jefferson County Historical Society**
Fairfield, Iowa

Ben J. Taylor, Secretary
304 South Main Street
Fairfield, Iowa 52556

Organized: March 1, 1963
Meetings: As called
Number of Members: 17
Dues: Voluntary contributions

Items of local historical interest are preserved. A Pioneer Museum is maintained in the Public Library. Exhibits also include stuffed birds and animals, Indian relics, archeological collections, and art. The Library was the first Carnegie Library built west of the Mississippi River.

The Rhodam (Rhodham, Rhodam, or Rhodeham--there are several variations in spelling) Bonnifield Log Cabin, said to be the first erected in Jefferson County, was built in 1838. The Bonnifield family arrived in what is now Jefferson County in 1837, and built their cabin in Section 4, Round Prairie Township, about 8 or 9 miles east of Fairfield. The cabin was relocated on October 25, 1907 in Water Works Park (Old Settlers Park), in Fairfield.

In the northwest part of Evergreen Cemetery is a monument to Mrs. M. E. (Auntie) Woods (1813-91), who traveled as an agent of the Ladies Aid Society among the Iowa troops with a commissary wagon under soldier escort during the Civil War. She received an honorary commission of major from Governor Samuel J. Kirkwood.

● **Site of First Iowa State Fair**
North Fourth and Grimes Streets
Fairfield, Iowa

Fairfield was the site of the first Iowa State Fair, held on October 25-27, 1854 in a 6-acre field, surrounded by a rail fence. The cost of all of the equipment at this fair was about $300. An estimated 10,000 visitors came by horseback and in wagons to see the exhibits. These included Dr. J. M. Shaffer's collection of snakes and lizards preserved in alcohol, homemade jam, and samples of Iowa corn, oats, and wheat. The featured entertainment was an exhibition of women riding horseback.

In 1925, a granite boulder with bronze tablet was placed at what was the entrance to the grounds. At the southwest corner of Central Park is a marker designating the historic 1954 Centennial Caravan from Fairfield to the Iowa State Fair in Des Moines.

52 - JOHNSON

Iowa City
F-10

● **F. W. Kent Park**
2½ miles west of Tiffin, Iowa
on U.S. 6

Johnson County Conservation Board
R. G. Dunlap, Executive Officer
R. R. 2
Oxford, Iowa 52322

A 217-acre recreational area of woodland and pasture surrounding a 30-acre artificial lake. A spring-fed stream runs through the property. The park has been developed for picnicking, fishing, water sports, horseback riding, outdoor games, and nature study.

- JOHNSON
(continued)

● **Indian Lookout**
4 miles south of
Iowa City, Iowa

A high, wooded bluff overlooking the Iowa River and its valley. The Sac and Fox Indians inhabited this region when white men first came to and settled in Johnson County. For a period of about 10 years (as late as 1838), Fox Chief Poweshiek governed over a large village located about 1¼ miles directly east of Indian Lookout on the east side of the Iowa River. The glacial ridge has become a well-known Iowa landmark, and many stories and legends are associated with the area.

● **Iowa City Genealogical Society**
P. O. Box 6112
Coralville, Iowa 52241

Miss Mary Noble,
Corresponding Secretary
620 South Johnson Street, Apt. 2
Iowa City, Iowa 52240

Organized: February 1967
Meetings: Last Tuesday of month, State Historical Society Building, 7:30 p.m.
Number of Members: 50
Dues: $3.00 annual

A local chapter of the Iowa Genealogical Society (see Polk County), organized to create and foster an interest in genealogy, preserve and disseminate genealogical and historical data, and aid members in compiling family genealogies. Occasional guest speakers are featured at meetings and workshops, and a special dinner meeting is held annually. Visitors are welcome to attend meetings.

● **Iowa State Historical Department Division of Historic Preservation**
B-13 MacLean Hall
Iowa City, Iowa 52242

Adrian D. Anderson, Director

One of the 3 Divisions of the State Historical Department created by act of the 65th Iowa General Assembly, effective July 1, 1974. The Division's purpose is to identify and help preserve historic buildings and sites in Iowa, in coordination with county and local historical societies and other groups, and nominate properties for the National Register of Historic Places. A newsletter *The Bracket* is published and distributed to those groups and individuals interested in preservation activities, methods, and techniques.

● **Iowa State Historical Department Division of State Historical Society**
Centennial Building
402 Iowa Avenue
Iowa City, Iowa 52240

Peter T. Harstad, Director

Established: 1857
Number of Members: 9,550
Dues: $5.00 annual
Centennial Building Open: Monday through Friday, 8:00 a.m. 4:30 p.m.; Saturday, 8:00 a.m.-Noon; Last Tuesday of month, 6:00-9:00 p.m.

One of 3 Divisions of the State Historical Department. The others are the Division of Historic Preservation (see above) and the Division of Historical Museum and Archives (see Polk County).

Collects, preserves, does research, and publishes material on Iowa history. The library contains 93,000 books, 30,000 pamphlets, 12,000 volumes of bound newspapers; 6,400 microfilms of Iowa newspapers and census records; manuscripts, maps, and early photographs; and Indian artifacts. Members receive the *Palimpsest, News for Members*, books, and other materials. The Society also sponsors river cruises in July, and historic tours. It is also responsible for erection of historical markers along major highways, the Gardner Cabin at Arnolds Park (see Dickinson County), and the Toolesboro Mound area (see Louisa County).

52 - JOHNSON
(continued)

Johnson County Historical Society
Coralville, Iowa

Mrs. A. B. Clemence, President
620 Ninth Avenue
Coralville, Iowa 52241

Incorporated: June 26, 1967
Meetings: As called
Number of Members: 200
Dues: $2.00

Originally organized as the Mormon Trek Memorial Foundation, Inc., the name was later changed to Heritage Museum Foundation, Inc., and finally to the present name. A brick schoolhouse, built in 1876, formerly an elementary school in the Iowa City Community School District, was acquired for a museum. A 1-room rural school has been moved on the grounds to represent schools of that era. The old Coralville City Hall is also of historic interest and has been used to display antiquities through changing exhibits.

Merrill A. Stainbrook
State Geological Preserve
4 miles northeast of North Liberty, Iowa, off County Road Y, near Mehaffey Bridge

State Conservation Commission
State Office Building
300 Fourth Street
Des Moines, Iowa 50319
        or
Johnson County Conservation Board
R. G. Dunlap, Executive Officer
R. R. 2
Oxford, Iowa 52322

An undeveloped geological area, near Coralville Reservoir, containing spectacular exposures of Devonian limestone with an abundance of fossils, together with evidence of glacial erosion. The preserve encompasses about 23 acres of hilly, partly wooded terrain. The unique geological features being preserved were brought to view during construction of a new highway. The preserve is dedicated to the memory of Professor Merrill A. Stainbrook (1897-1956), scholar, teacher, author, and researcher, who devoted much of his career to a study of fossils and rocks such as those exposed in the road cut here--the Cedar Valley limestone fossil faunas.

Around 300 million years ago, a warm, shallow, tropical sea covered the Midwest. The remains of plant and marine life were deposited on the sea floor. After a time, this sea bottom rose, exposing the Cedar Valley limestone, filled with fossils. Overlying this deposit is the State Quarry limestone. (See Old State Quarry, below.) Two million years ago, great sheets of ice covered the continent. Rock fragments and boulders, dragged along by the glaciers, cut deep parallel grooves in the bedrock, and smoothed projecting knobs of exposed rock. As the glaciers melted, the debris imprisoned in the ice was released, covering the land.

Above and to the east of the road cut, glacial striations (scratches) are visible on the surface rock. This sculpturing and grooving took place some 65,000 years ago as lobes of a continental glacier moved over the area where Solon and North Liberty are now located. These geological features were disclosed in the early 1960's during the construction of the new Mehaffey bridge and the re-routing of the county road. The work of ancient glaciers, in combination with the abundance of well-preserved fossils in the limestone, make the State Preserve a unique geological area.

2 - JOHNSON
(continued)

● **Mormon Handcart Marker**
3 miles west of Iowa City
at Coralville, Iowa on U.S. 6

A bronze tablet mounted on an 8-ton granite boulder, placed by the D A R.

In 1856, some 1,300 immigrants, converts to the Mormon faith, detrained at Iowa City, then at the end of the railroad. On the banks of Clear Creek, south of Coralville, is the site of the Mormon Handcart Brigade Camp. While encamped here, the Mormons constructed handcarts and other equipment to use on their overland journey on foot to Utah.

The handcarts were adopted by the Mormons for transporting their belongings at the suggestion of their leader, Brigham Young. Built of native oak or hickory, the carts were 6 or 7 feet long, and could carry between 400 and 500 pounds. From 1856 to 1860, a total of 10 handcart companies traveled across the plains. Each company had from 300 to 500 persons. The 277-mile journey from Iowa City to Florence, Nebraska (now on the north outskirts of Omaha) took a little less than 4 weeks. The average distance covered each day was about 15 miles.

● **Museum of Art**
North Riverside Drive and
River Street
The University of Iowa
Iowa City, Iowa 52242

Jan Muhlert, Director

Established: 1969
Dues for Friends of the Museum of Art (Organized November 1970): $10.00 annual; $15.00 family; $5.00 student; $25.00 contributing; $50.00 participating; $100 supporting; $500.00 benefactor
Open: Monday through Friday, 10:30 a.m. - 5:00 p.m.; Saturday, 10:00 a.m. - 5:00 p.m.; Sunday, 1:00 - 5:00 p.m.; closed on national holidays

A part of the Iowa Center for the Arts located on the west bank of the Iowa River. The Museum was designed by New York architects Harrison and Abramovitz, who were associated with the design of the United Nations Headquarters, Rockefeller Center, and Lincoln Center for the Performing Arts. Four floor levels provide exhibition space for widely differing groups of art objects. On exhibit are paintings, prints, antique silver, rare jade, and sculpture, including more than 100 African primitive figures and 50 Tibetan bronzes. Paintings include works by Picasso, Braque, Kandinsky, Gris, Soutine, Matisse, Gaugin, and Munch. The collection of prints offers examples of Rembrandt, Goya, and Dürer and lithographs of Honore' Daumier. The 140-seat auditorium is used for lectures, films, and other Museum events.

● **Museum of Natural History**
Macbride Hall
The University of Iowa
Iowa City, Iowa 52242

George Schrimper, Curator

Established: 1858
Admission: Free
Open: Monday through Saturday, 8:00 a.m.-4:30 p.m.; Sunday, 1:00-4:30 p.m.; closed on University and national holidays
For the first 28 years of its existence, the museum was housed in the Old Capitol (see below). Many of its collections have been obtained through expeditions financed by friends of the University and by gifts. The systematically arranged exhibits include Bird Hall (with collections of most species recorded in Iowa, including Iowa winter birds; abnormally colored and extinct or

52 - JOHNSON
(continued)

Museum of Natural History
(continued)

endangered species, and exotic birds), and a Mammal Hall. Much of the taxidermy is the work of Walter Thietje, who served for 40 years as museum curator, until his retirement in June 1971. Specimens represent nearly every mammalian order and family in the world, including extremely rare animals. One habitat group includes Atlantic Walruses collected in 1901 on the coast of Greenland by the noted explorer, Admiral Robert E. Peary.

There are other displays of geology, botany, fish, reptiles, amphibians, marine invertebrates, insects, and habitat groups. Also finely-engraved wooden Maori implements from New Zealand; Philippine exhibits; weapons, carvings, and implements from Africa, Mexico, and Java; Eskimo ivory carvings, and beadwork; arrowheads, spearheads, and axes collected along the Iowa River; and displays of museum techniques. Courses in museum methods are offered at the University.

● **Old Capitol**
Clinton Street at Iowa Avenue
Iowa City, Iowa

The seat of the first Territorial Government in Iowa was at Burlington (see Old Zion in Des Moines County), but Iowa's first permanent capitol was built at Iowa City. The cornerstone was laid July 4, 1840. Built in Greek Revival style, the building was not entirely completed until 1855, and only 2 years later the state capital was moved to Des Moines. John F. Rague, the supervising architect, also designed the Old State House at Springfield, Illinois (1839). The Old Stone Capitol housed the Territorial Legislature from 1842 until 1846, and the Iowa State Legislature from 1846 until 1857. Built at a cost of $123,000, the capitol is topped by a gold dome supported by 16 Corinthian columns.

The graceful old building housed the central administrative offices of The University of Iowa until 1971. Plans are now being carried out to restore Old Capitol as a historic landmark. The original Governor's office, Supreme Court chambers, and the House and Senate chambers on the first and second floors are being restored to their original appearance. The 200th anniversary of the birth of the United States--July 4, 1976--was set for the dedication of Iowa's restored Old Capitol.

- JOHNSON
(continued)

● **Old State Quarry**
3 miles northeast of North Liberty, Iowa on west bank of Coralville Reservoir
(Iowa River)

Johnson County Conservation Board
R. G. Dunlap, Executive Officer
R. R. 2
Oxford, Iowa 52322

Dedicated: December 24, 1969

A State Geological Preserve of about 8 acres, formerly known as Old Capitol Quarry. This quarry provided part of the limestone for the Old Stone Capitol in Iowa City as well as for the present State Capitol in Des Moines and the abutments for the old Burlington Street Bridge in Iowa City. The quarry and a lime kiln provided income to local residents during the latter half of the 19th Century. The Penn Quarry Company and D. A. Schaeffer operated the quarry from 1844 until nearly 1900. The old hand-drilled vertical holes, 1 inch in diameter and a few inches in length, may still be seen on the north wall of the quarry. Steel spikes were driven into these holes to break away huge blocks of the limestone. By 1897, the quarry was virtually abandoned.

The rock is composed largely of cemented fragments of clam-like shells of brachiopods, swept into the turbulent shallow sea of the Upper Devonian period of 300 million years ago. Lower beds of this rock, called State Quarry limestone, together with underlying beds of Cedar Valley limestone, may be seen in the road cut near the new Mehaffey Bridge, 1 mile north of this site (see Merrill A. Stainbrook State Geological Preserve, above).

● **Plum Grove**
727 Switzer Avenue
Iowa City, Iowa

State Conservation Commission
State Office Building
300 Fourth Street
Des Moines, Iowa 50319

Admission: Free
Open: Tuesday through Saturday, 1:00-5:00 p.m. April to November

The historic home of Robert Lucas, first Governor of the Territory of Iowa (1838-1841), and his wife, Friendly. This impressive red brick residence--the "Mount Vernon of Iowa"-- was built by Lucas in 1844 on 80 acres of land, and remained his home until his death on February 7, 1853. The foundation of the house was constructed of native stone quarried in the area, and the brick was manufactured in Iowa City. Each of the 7 main rooms had its own fireplace.

Although of Quaker ancestry, Lucas was a military man, rising in rank to become a major general in the Ohio militia and a colonel in the U.S. Army. He served 4 years as Governor of Ohio before his appointment as Iowa Territorial Governor by President Martin Van Buren.

Governor Lucas is buried in Oakland Cemetery in Iowa City, where Iowa's Civil War Governor (1860-1864), Samuel J. Kirkwood, is also buried. Kirkwood, a strong supporter of President Abraham Lincoln, served again as Governor of Iowa from 1876 until 1877, when he resigned to become U.S. Senator. He was also Secretary of the Interior in the cabinet of President James A. Garfield, 1881-82.

52 - JOHNSON
(continued)

Plum Grove
(continued)

Plum Grove was purchased by the State of Iowa in 1940 and restored. The home has been appropriately furnished with pieces authentic to the Lucas period by Iowa members of the National Society of Colonial Dames of America.

● **Williams Prairie**
2½ miles north - northwest of Oxford, Iowa

Iowa Chapter,
The Nature Conservancy
c/o Robert Hulbary
Department of Botany
University of Iowa
Iowa City, Iowa   52242

21 acres of unplowed, wet prairie with boggy areas. Among the plants found here are the sensitive fern, marsh fern, bunch flower, purple and yellow coneflowers, prairie fringed orchid, gayfeather, various sunflowers, and the unusual bottle gentian.

The sedge wren (short-billed marsh wren) and the bobolink may be seen here. Both of these birds are becoming rare in Iowa due to the almost complete disappearance of moist prairies.

The north side of the prairie is adjacent to a cemetery. Being only 16 miles west of Iowa City, the tract has essential usefulness for students in biology, ecology, and environmental studies.

53 - JONES

Anamosa
D-12

● **Antioch School Memorial**
Grant Wood Memorial Park
3 miles east of Anamosa, Iowa
on U.S. 64

Paint 'n' Palette Club
Mrs. Gerald F. Brown
204 N. Huber Street
Anamosa, Iowa 52205

Organized: June 1955
Meetings: Second and fourth Wednesday of each month
Number of Members: 34
Dues: $10.00 annual
Schoolhouse Open: Sunday, 1:00-5:00 p.m. during summer and fall; other times by appointment

A rural schoolhouse, built in 1872 and attended by Iowa artist Grant Wood (1892-1942) from 1897 to 1901. It contains reproductions of Wood's paintings and historical articles. Grant Wood was one of the "regional painters," together with Thomas Hart Benton and John Steuart Curry, and died just one day short of his 50th birthday. The Log Cabin Art Gallery and Studio, on the grounds, displays amateur art. An Outdoor Art Exhibit and Open House is held annually on the last Sunday in July. Grant Wood's birthplace, where he spent the first 10 years of his life, was located about 3 miles east of Anamosa. The 2-story frame farmhouse was destroyed by fire October 3, 1974. The house was about ¼ mile across a field from Antioch School. Wood moved to Cedar Rapids in 1901 with his widowed mother, 2 brothers, and a sister. His grave is in Riverside Cemetery, at the southwest edge of Anamosa.

● **Jones County Historical Society**
Monticello, Iowa

C. L. Norlin, President
323 North Chestnut Street
Monticello, Iowa 52310

or

Esther A. Sinclair
R.F.D.
Scotch Grove, Iowa 52331

Incorporated: September 7, 1973
Meetings: Every other month
Number of Members: 100
Dues: $2.00 annual

A Pioneer Complex, constructed by the Society next to a grove of oaks, near Scotch Grove in Scotch Grove Township, about ¼ mile from the Jones County Home.

In 1837, a small band of Highland Scotch families settled here in the Black Hawk Purchase. These impoverished

3 - JONES
(continued)

Jones County Historical Society
(continued)

Scottish farmers, known as the Selkirk Settlers, had been evicted from their native home in northern Scotland, and had first settled on the Red River of the North, in Canada, where Winnipeg now stands. The 1000-mile overland journey from Canada to Scotch Grove (originally called Applegate's Crossing) took 4 months. Red River or Pembina Carts, drawn by a bullock, cow, or other animal, carried their belongings. Each 2-wheeled, wooden cart was loaded with from 700 to 1,000 pounds, and was followed by the livestock. Other families came here in succeeding years, to add their log cabins to the settlement. Soon, churches and schools were also built, and later, grist mills, sawmills, and other buildings and businesses.

Near Scotch Grove, in the bluffs along the Maquoketa River, is Silurian Coral (Goniophyllum), or Pyramid Coral, found in very few other locations. A specimen is on display in the State Historical Museum (see Polk County).

● **Pictured Rocks**
4 miles southeast of
Monticello, Iowa

Jones County Conservation Board
Dean Frankfurt, Executive Officer
Central Park
Center Junction, Iowa 52212

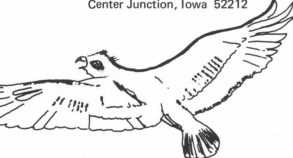

A 427-acre site stretching for 3½ miles along the Maquoketa River, preserved for its natural beauty. The terrain is rough and densely wooded. Steep natural limestone bluffs, carved by the river, tower nearly 100 feet above the water. The area abounds in animals and birds, including deer, red and gray foxes, mink, muskrat, raccoon, beaver, and turkey vultures. This stretch of the river is ideal for float trips. Other activities are fishing, picnicking, hiking, and primitive camping.

Indian Bluffs Wilderness, comprising about 3,500 acres, has also been proposed for development as a scenic wilderness region. This privately-owned land extends both north and south of Pictured Rocks, along the Maquoketa River. The area is ideal for canoeing, hiking, nature study, and scientific research, and is frequently used by college ecology classes. Scenes of rugged beauty, high bluffs, prairie, and heavy timber, with hawks soaring overhead, are outstanding feeatures.

● **Site of First Sod Turned in Madison Township**
East of Anamosa, Iowa on road to Wyoming, Iowa

A marker set up on June 4, 1913 recognizing the first prairie sod turned in Madison Township, Jones County, Iowa, on June 4, 1852. The plow was pulled by oxen driven by John Bender.

● **Stone City, Iowa**
4 miles west of Anamosa, Iowa

Post Office Established: 1873

In the 1930's, artist Grant Wood established an Art Colony at Stone City. In 1929, he painted "Stone City," which drew nationwide attention. This painting is now owned by the Joslyn Art Museum, Omaha, Nebraska.

In 1850, John A. Green settled here and opened the first Stone City quarry. The town was a flourishing community in the 1880's, situated in the sheltered valley of the Wapsipinicon River. The bluffs above the river provided a fine grade of limestone and from the quarries came the

53 - JONES
(continued)

Stone City, Iowa
(continued)

stone for many of the homes, places of business, the church, and school in Stone City. A large hotel and an opera house (where such famous performers as Jenny Lind and Tom Thumb appeared) were also built. The structure (Columbia Hotel and Opera House) was later torn down and used for building stone in Cedar Rapids. During the period of railroad growth in America, stone from these quarries was used to build many of the early railroad bridges. More recently, this stone was used in the construction of the men's reformatory at Anamosa, the Herbert Hoover Library at West Branch, and for the fireplace chimney of the first log cabin erected at the Des Moines Birthplace memorial.

The wider use of cement and other materials for building purposes after 1900 caused a decrease in the demand for limestone and Stone City was all but deserted. In December 1970, the landmark Stone City bridge, erected across the Wapsipinicon in 1882, was demolished and replaced in 1971. The old iron bridge was a favorite subject of photographers and artists.

The ruins of the Green mansion may be seen on a hill west of Stone City, overlooking the town. The massive 3-story structure was built in 1883 and had several marble fireplaces. Other stone buildings on the extensive grounds include a turret-like water tower, ice house, and barns. After Green suffered reverses and went out of business, the property was acquired by the Nissen family of Cedar Rapids for a summer residence. In 1932, the family allowed Grant Wood to use the house for a summer art school until 1934. The mansion's interior was converted to dormitories, studios, and dining and recreation rooms. The water tower became an apartment and the ice house a sort of rathskeller. Old ice wagons were used for additional dormitory space. In November 1963, a fire reduced the Green mansion to ruins.

The community room in the former schoolhouse is used for potlucks and barbecues. Tours to the stone quarries, reopened in the 1950's, and other local points of interest are conducted for visitors during the summer.

● **Wapsipinicon State Park**
South edge of Anamosa,
Iowa on U.S. 151

State Conservation Commission
State Office Building
300 Fourth Street
Des Moines, Iowa 50319

The 248-acre tract along the west bank of the Wapsipinicon River includes high rocky sandstone and limestone cliffs, open meadows and timbered hills, several caves, and an abundance of wildlife and plants of high botanical value, and Indian burials. Hiking trails lead to bowl-shaped Horse Thief Cave, said to have been used as a hideout by early-day bandits and horse thieves, and Ice Cave, which maintains a steady temperature year-round. Indian relics, flintchips, shells, skeletons, and animal bones have been found below the surface, inside Horse Thief Cave. Wapsipinicon State Park was used on June 6, 1924 to hold a national meeting of the Ku Klux Klan. The meeting lasted well into the night and next morning, after the crowd had left, a man was

- JONES
(continued)

Wapsipinicon State Park
(continued)

found hanging from a tree. Dutch Creek meanders through the park and empties into Wapsipinicon River. The oldest planting of white pine in Iowa creates an atmosphere of being "way out West" or in the Far North. There are facilities in the park for picnicking, camping, fishing, hiking, nature study, and golf.

- KEOKUK

gourney
G-9

- **Belva-Deer Park**
  5 miles northeast of
  Sigourney, Iowa

  Keokuk County Conservation Board
  Jimmy Seevers, Executive Officer
  R. R. 1, Ollie, Iowa 52576

A 360-acre tract of open and wooded land being developed as an educational facility and for outdoor recreation. A nature center and outdoor classroom, properly labeled nature trails, wayside teaching stations and educational displays, and demonstration areas are planned. Over 6,000 trees have been set out on the hills, and grain is planted for wildlife. There are several small lakes, and large areas have been set aside for picnicking and camping.

- **Bond Hill Park**
  4 miles north of
  Richland, Iowa
  on Iowa 77

A tract of 8 acres containing many of the native trees of Iowa--white oak, black oak, swamp oak, maple, hickory, walnut, buckeye, linden, hackberry, ash, and elm--preserved in its natural state for wildlife cover and nature study. The gently rolling land also supports a variety of native shrubs, and in the spring there is a profusion of woodland wild flowers carpeting the ground. A small picnic area is maintained; camping is permitted.

- **Delta Covered Bridge**
  2½ miles southeast of Delta, Iowa

  Keokuk County Conservation Board
  Jimmy Seevers, Executive Officer
  R. R. 1, Ollie, Iowa 52576

The last remaining covered bridge in Keokuk County, and one of the few left in Iowa. The bridge, open to foot traffic only, spans the North Skunk River and was built at a cost of $1,620. The contract to build the bridge was awarded to local contractors Joseph Merryfield and James Harlan. Supporting timbers were cut in 1867 and put in place over the river during the winter, using the ice for support. The bridge was built on the banks and moved into place piece by piece. Most of the wood was notched and locked together with wood bars. The distinctive arch truss or Pennsylvania type of construction is unusual. By 1973, flood waters washed out the south approach to the bridge and a new channel was cut so the river would bypass the bridge and repairs could be made.

The winding, scenic road leading from the area is known as Old Mill Road. The road passes through dense timberland, along the bluffs overlooking the river, and is bordered by wild flowers and sumac. On one of the bluffs along this early trail and near the river, a gristmill was built in 1844 by Jacob Kensler, and operated by John B. Lough. The old mill was torn down in the early 1900's.

Just west of the covered bridge area is a historic cemetery, known as the Kensler Cemetery, where many pioneer graves are marked by handmade headstones.

A shady, 1-acre roadside park and picnic area is maintained at the south end of the bridge on a wooded, sloping hillside.

54 - KEOKUK
(continued)

● **Griffin Park**
(formerly Highland Park)
½ mile east of the south edge of
What Cheer, Iowa

Keokuk County Conservation Board
Jimmy Seevers, Executive Officer
R. R. 1, Ollie, Iowa 52576

A 40-mile tract including an abandoned clay pit, surrounded by trees and undergrowth, received as a gift from Griffin Clay Pipe Company, which operated from 1962 until 1964. Coal Creek and an abandoned railroad right-of-way run along one side of the park. Small ponds, fed by springs from 2 old mine shafts, provide fishing, and the area is also open to picnicking and camping. Hiking trails have been established to provide access to the wildlife area for nature study.

What Cheer dates back to around 1865 and was later known as "The Coal City of Iowa." Before the turn of the Century, however, most of the larger coal veins were worked out and the mines closed. Then superior deposits of clay were discovered and the manufacture of various products of clay was begun. These included table and kitchen ware, flower pots, vases, and clay pipe or tile. At this period in its history, What Cheer was referred to as "The Clay City."

● **Keokuk County Historical Society**
Sigourney, Iowa

Ralph Goeldner, President
302 West Elm
Sigourney, Iowa 52591

Organized: January 21, 1963
Meetings: When called
Number of members: 60
Dues: $1.00 annual

A marker has been erected in South English, Iowa in memory of the Tally War or Skunk River War, a Civil War incident in which Cyphert Tally, a young Baptist preacher, was killed. His grave is in the cemetery at Rock Creek Church (see below).

● **Manhattan Bridge Park**
3 miles north of
Ollie, Iowa

Keokuk County Conservation Board
Jimmy Seevers, Executive Officer
R. R. 1, Ollie, Iowa 52576

A 1-acre wooded tract adjacent to Manhattan Bridge on the South Skunk River, where an old water-powered mill once operated. The mill has been torn down, but when the river is low, the remains of the old millrace may be seen. The area is now used for boating, fishing, picnicking, and camping, and as an outdoor classroom.

● **Rock Creek Church**
4 miles southwest of Ollie
and ½ mile north of Iowa 78

Founded: 1844
Open: Church always open; special services as announced

A deeply religious group, the Pioneer Separate Baptists, established a church here in January 1844. They were among Iowa's earliest settlers. The double doors of the small white church, built 2 years before Iowa became a state, are never locked. The church has been restored and contains the old narrow, straight pews, and other furnishings. Church records state that one early settler was excluded from membership because he engaged in horse trading on Sunday. A woman was excluded for dancing. The original constitution and organization of "Rock Creek Church of Separate Baptists" is kept at Iowa City in the vaults of the State Historical Society of Iowa.

- KEOKUK
(continued)

● **What Cheer Opera House, Inc.**
What Cheer, Iowa

Tommy Burriss, President
What Cheer, Iowa 50268
or
Mrs. Larry (Phyllis) Nicholson,
Treasurer
What Cheer, Iowa 50268

● **Yen-Ruo-Gis Park**
2 miles north of
Sigourney, Iowa

Keokuk County Conservation Board
Jimmy Seevers, Executive Officer
R. R. 1, Ollie, Iowa 52576

- KOSSUTH

ona
-5

● **Ambrose A. Call State Park**
1½ miles southwest of Algona, Iowa
on Iowa 274

State Conservation Commission
State Office Building
300 Fourth Street
Des Moines, Iowa 50319

● **Kossuth County Historical Society**
Nebraska and Dodge Streets
Algona, Iowa 50511

William Dau, Sr., President
Algona, Iowa 50511
or
Chester R. Schoby
R. R. 1, Algona, Iowa 50511

● **Kossuth County Historical
Society Museum**

Nebraska and Dodge Streets
Algona, Iowa 50511

Mrs. Wayne Keith, Museum Director
Algona, Iowa 50511

Organized: August 30, 1965

The 1893 brick Opera House has been restored and is used to present concerts by "big name" bands and variety programs. The 800-seat theatre has featured nationally known artists, and companies often came to the What Cheer Opera House within a few weeks of their appearance on Broadway. The attractively designed interior, with its horseshoe balcony, marvelous acoustics, and such memorabilia as old posters and the reserved seat ticket board, are preserved.

An old brick schoolhouse has been preserved. One of the 4 rooms is furnished as an old school. There is also a pioneer room, while other rooms are used to display artifacts and items of local historical significance, such as mining equipment and clay products. A log cabin, dating back to 1840, has also been moved to the site and furnished in that era.

A 76-acre area consisting of an abandoned rock quarry (Kaser Quarry), 8-acre lake, open pasture, and timber, used for recreation--fishing, boating, swimming, scuba diving, picnicking, and primitive camping--and as an outdoor classroom for nature study. The park's name is Sigourney, spelled backwards.

A wooded area of 130 acres with exceptionally large black walnut trees and oaks, overlooking the East Fork of the Des Moines River. Formerly farm land belonging to the Call family, the park includes the site of the first log cabin in Kossuth County, built in July 1854 by Ambrose A. Call. According to some historians, Inkpaduta and his band of outlaw Sioux Indians camped here before perpetrating the Spirit Lake Massacre of 1857.

Organized: 1959
Meetings: Second Tuesday in January
Number of Members: 450
Dues: $2.00 annual; $25.00 life

Activities include an annual bean supper held on George Washington's birthday, and a historical display at the Kossuth County Fair. The Society also operates Kossuth County Historical Society Museum (see below).

Dedicated: September 17, 1967
Admission: Free
Open: Friday, 2:00-4:00 p.m.; other times by appointment

A 2-story, 30-x 50-foot building, built in 1867 and formerly the public schoolhouse, G.A.R. Hall, library, and American Legion Hall, acquired by the Kossuth County Historical Society (see above) in June 1967 for a museum. Exhibits include a grandmother's kitchen, a period living

55 - KOSSUTH
(continued)

Kossuth County Historical Society Museum
(continued)

room, wearing apparel, pictures of early days, war memorials, pioneer items, and art. A record and research department contains books, histories of the county, and a file of newspapers of the Upper Des Moines region dating back to 1870.

● **Lone Rock**
City Park, southwest corner of Lone Rock, Iowa

Erich Seegebarth, Mayor
Lone Rock, Iowa 50559

A large granite glacial boulder, originally located in a field a short distance from a pioneer settlement which came to be called Lone Rock. The rock was a pioneer landmark on the trail from Fort Dodge through Algona, to Armstrong, Estherville, and Spirit Lake. At the time of the Spirit Lake Massacre, this was the turning point for the rescue party to head west.

In 1899, the Chicago and North Western Railroad built a branch line from Burt to Fox Lake which ran about 2 miles south of the town and the boulder called Lone Rock. So the town moved its creamery (started in 1895), general store, and post office to the present location, to be on the railroad.

Prior to the town's Diamond Jubilee (75th anniversary), in 1974, the 175-ton boulder was blasted from its original location and moved to the new town site, so that it would be more accessible, and to bring the town and the rock together again. With a population of less than 200, some of the residents of Lone Rock thought it might have been easier to move the town back to the rock--and if this had happened, history would have repeated itself. Main Street in the present town is on the dividing section line for Burt and Fenton Townships.

● **Pioneer Drug Store Museum**
Highway 18 West, near Algona, Iowa. Located in home office building.

Druggists Mutual Insurance Co.
P. O. 370
Algona, Iowa 50511

Established: 1971
Admission: Free
Open: Monday through Friday, 8:30 a.m.-4:00 p.m.

Recreation of a drug store, typical of the early 1900's, with a soda fountain, wire chairs and table, prescription department, display cases filled with old bottles, eye glasses, false teeth, and other items. Tours for small groups may be arranged.

● **Stinson Prairie**
4 miles west and 1 mile south of Algona, Iowa

Kossuth County Conservation Board
Mrs. Delores Lemkee, Secretary
606 East Call Street
Algona, Iowa 50511

About 32 acres of gently rolling natural prairie land, never touched with a plow, preserved as a botanical study area. Many native flowering plants grow here in this nesting area for upland game birds and song birds. The tract is included in the State Preserves System.

KOSSUTH
(continued)

● **Union Slough National Wildlife Refuge**
5½ miles east of Bancroft, Iowa; 5 different county roads pass through the refuge a few miles east of U.S. 169

Jack Womble, Refuge Manager
U.S. Fish and Wildlife Service
Box AF
Titonka, Iowa 50480

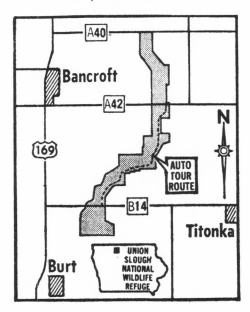

Established: 1938

A long, narrow tract of 2,155 acres of original wildland, set aside as part of a vital link in the chain of refuges making up the Mississippi Flyway, extending from the Canadian border to the Gulf of Mexico. The slough, which is actually the remains of a pre-glacial river bed, is used as a stopover for migrating waterfowl and as an animal refuge. The outlying areas of the marshland have been drained by tiling, to adapt the land to farming, and some crops are left in nearby fields to attract the wildlife. A variety of geese, ducks, herons, and pelicans may be seen, as well as deer and other mammals. In the south part of the refuge is a 50-acre stand of ash, cottonwood, elm, and wild plum. Buffalo Creek runs through this forest, the home of a large beaver colony. A variety of fungi and wild flowers may also be seen.

The refuge is open at announced times for tours, and neighboring schools and Scout groups use the refuge as an outdoor laboratory. Parking lots, self-guiding nature trails, and a blind for observers and photographers are provided.

LEE

Fort Madison
and
Keokuk
I-11

● **Bluff Park**
Park Street
Keokuk, Iowa

Affords a view of many of Keokuk's industrial plants. From this point 3 states may be seen--Illinois, Iowa, and Missouri. In addition to Keokuk, the towns of Warsaw, Illinois and Alexandria, Missouri are visible. The names of each of these 3 communities begin and end with the same letters of the alphabet--a geographical oddity once noted in Ripley's "Believe It Or Not." During the winter many American bald eagles soar over the river in this area.

● **Coleman Memorial Park**
3½ miles south of Hillsboro, Iowa along Iowa 16

Lee County Conservation Board
Carmi Lowenburg, Executive Officer
Box 245
Donnellson, Iowa 52625

A 3-acre tract on which is located the old Bailes Schoolhouse in a stand of hickory trees. The schoolhouse, built before the turn of the Century, is being restored as a monument to early-day education in Iowa. A number of former pupils of Bailes School now lie buried in the little cemetery adjacent to the grounds.

The park is named for Alex Coleman who, about 1930, constructed and paid for 13 miles of paved highway, now Iowa 16, at a cost of over $250,000.

56 - LEE
(continued)

● **Croton Civil War Memorial Park**
Croton, Iowa

Lee County Conservation Board
Carmi Lowenburg, Executive Officer
Box 245
Donnellson, Iowa 52625

Iowa's only Civil War battle scars are at Croton. The cannonballs that fell here afford the only instance in which hostile cannonfire has landed on Iowa soil. The Des Moines River formed the boundary between North and South in a battle or skirmish that was fought at Athens, Missouri, across the river from Croton, on August 5, 1861. A monument has been erected at this historic site to honor the casualties. Sprouse House, located in an 8-acre park, was used as a field hospital during the struggle. One of the casualties was William Sprouse, who later died of his wounds in his own home. The old brick house deteriorated in more recent years to the point where restoration was not feasible.

● **First Orchard in Iowa**
Montrose, Iowa

A marker placed on the grounds of Montrose Elementary School in 1930 commemorates Iowa's first orchard.

Louis Honore' Tesson, a French-Canadian fur trader, obtained a land grant from Spain in 1799 and established a trading post at present-day Montrose, making this one of the first permanent settlements established by white men in what is now Iowa. Tesson obtained about 100 apple trees in St. Charles, Missouri and brought them back on mules to his home. The grove of trees he planted was the first orchard in Iowa, thriving under the flags of Spain, France, and the United States. The orchard was submerged by the waters of Lake Keokuk when the nearby mile-long dam was built across the Mississippi in 1910-13 at Keokuk.

● **Fort Des Moines No. 1**
Montrose, Iowa

The first of three military establishments named Fort Des Moines was built in 1834 by Lt. Col. Stephen Watts Kearny and his Dragoons along the Mississippi River, at the present site of Montrose, Iowa.

Nathaniel (Nathan) Boone, a son of Daniel Boone, was captain of one of the three companies of Dragoons sent from Fort Gibson, Arkansas to Fort Des Moines No. 1. It was from here that Lt. Col. Kearny, accompanied by about 150 men, including Captain Boone and Lieutenant Albert M. Lea, left on an exploring expedition into the wilderness of the Des Moines River Valley.

56 - LEE
(continued)

Fort Des Moines No. 1
(continued)

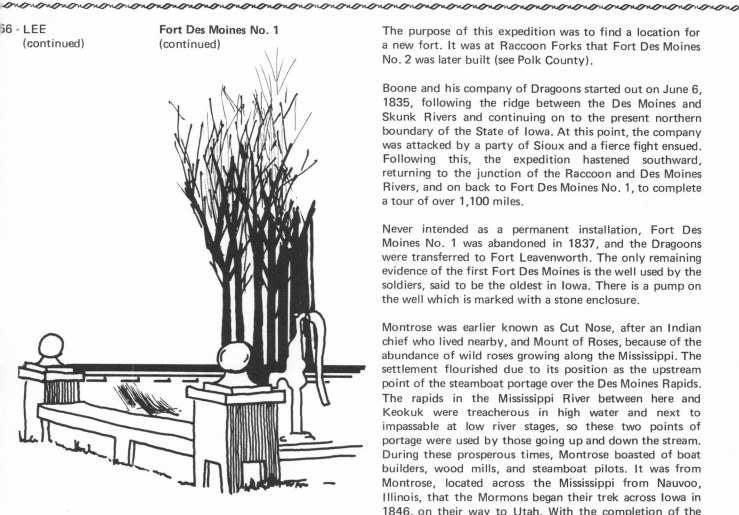

The purpose of this expedition was to find a location for a new fort. It was at Raccoon Forks that Fort Des Moines No. 2 was later built (see Polk County).

Boone and his company of Dragoons started out on June 6, 1835, following the ridge between the Des Moines and Skunk Rivers and continuing on to the present northern boundary of the State of Iowa. At this point, the company was attacked by a party of Sioux and a fierce fight ensued. Following this, the expedition hastened southward, returning to the junction of the Raccoon and Des Moines Rivers, and on back to Fort Des Moines No. 1, to complete a tour of over 1,100 miles.

Never intended as a permanent installation, Fort Des Moines No. 1 was abandoned in 1837, and the Dragoons were transferred to Fort Leavenworth. The only remaining evidence of the first Fort Des Moines is the well used by the soldiers, said to be the oldest in Iowa. There is a pump on the well which is marked with a stone enclosure.

Montrose was earlier known as Cut Nose, after an Indian chief who lived nearby, and Mount of Roses, because of the abundance of wild roses growing along the Mississippi. The settlement flourished due to its position as the upstream point of the steamboat portage over the Des Moines Rapids. The rapids in the Mississippi River between here and Keokuk were treacherous in high water and next to impassable at low river stages, so these two points of portage were used by those going up and down the stream. During these prosperous times, Montrose boasted of boat builders, wood mills, and steamboat pilots. It was from Montrose, located across the Mississippi from Nauvoo, Illinois, that the Mormons began their trek across Iowa in 1846, on their way to Utah. With the completion of the Keokuk Dam in 1913, the water level of the Mississippi was raised, submerging the formerly hazardous rapids. The special portaging, piloting, and boat repairing centered at Montrose came to a standstill, and the population of the town declined.

● **Galland School**
3 miles south of Montrose, Iowa

State Conservation Commission
State Office Building
300 Fourth Street
Des Moines, Iowa 50319

Replica of the first schoolhouse in Iowa, erected in 1830 by Dr. Isaac Galland in a clearing on the bank of the Mississippi River at a place called Ahwipetuck, which means "head of the rapids."

Dr. Galland was a botanical doctor and writer of ability and brought his family across the Mississippi River in 1829 to settle in this new and promising land, within the "Half Breed Tract." Twenty-three-year-old Berryman Jennings, a native of Kentucky, was employed by Dr. Galland as the first teacher. The schoolhouse was only 8 by 10 feet in dimension, and was constructed of unhewn logs, notched close together and mudded. The floor was made of split logs. Window panes were greased paper. Seats and benches were made by splitting a tree 8 or 10 inches in diameter in

56 - LEE
(continued)

Galland School
(continued)

halves, while crude desks were fastened to the walls beneath the windows. Pupils were required to stand unless they could furnish their own high stools. The school itself existed for only 3 years, as immigrants pushed on westward following the signing of the Treaty of 1837 which opened up additional lands of the Sac and Fox to white settlement. Abandoned as a school, the log building was used as a family kitchen for a time, then as a shelter for livestock, and finally the logs were burned for firewood. The original site was submerged in 1913 when the Keokuk Dam was built, raising the level of the Mississippi River and forming Lake Keokuk. The reproduction of the log schoolhouse, erected by the Lee County Schoolmaster's Club, is situated near the original location along the Mississippi River. Built in 1940, the monument is maintained by the State Conservation Commission.

● **Keokuk Dam**
Mississippi River
Keokuk, Iowa

Keokuk Dam and Power House was the largest lowhead hydroelectric power station in the world when completed in 1913. The 7/8-mile-long dam has 119 spillways. The locks (U. S. Lock No. 19) are the largest on the Mississippi River. The dam, power plant, and navigational locks span the Mississippi River at the foot of the rocky rapids that were long a hazard to river traffic. These rapids were first by-passed by portaging passengers and freight from Keokuk to Montrose (see Fort Des Moines No. 1, above). In 1877, a 9-mile canal was completed near the Iowa shore, allowing big Mississippi River packets to steam on past this hazard. One of the brown sandstone walls that formed the entrance to the old canal can still be seen by the present 1,200-foot locks. The locks and powerhouse are open to visitors during the summer months, free of charge.

● **Keokuk River Museum**
Victory Park at foot of Johnson Street
Keokuk, Iowa

William L. Talbot
226 High Street
Keokuk, Iowa 52632

Established: 1962
Meetings: Keokuk Museum Commission meets at 4:00 p.m. on the second Thursday of each month
Number of Members: 8
Admission: $0.75, children $0.40; tour groups of 12 or more $0.60 for adults, $0.30 for children
Open: Monday through Saturday, 9:00 a.m.-5 p.m.; Sunday and holidays, 10:00 a.m.-6:00 p.m.; mid-April to November 1

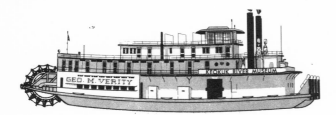

An old helical paddlewheel towboat, the George M. Verity, berthed on the riverfront, serves as a museum of upper Mississippi River history. This steamboat, built in 1927, pushed barges for 33 years on the Ohio and Mississippi Rivers, and inaugurated modern barge service between St. Louis, Missouri and St. Paul, Minnesota. She was one of the last sternwheelers to operate on the Mississippi. The boat was presented to the City of Keokuk by Armco Steel Company on December 10, 1960. Visitors have access to the machinery and interior of the steamboat. Pictures and river artifacts are displayed. The museum is sponsored and operated by the Keokuk Museum Commission.

- LEE
(continued)

● **Lee County Courthouse**
Keokuk, Iowa

One of the 2 courthouses in Lee County (the other is located at Fort Madison), originally built for a medical school in 1857. The school was later closed for lack of funds and the building was sold to the county for use as a courthouse. Originally, a third story and a cupola adorned the structure, but a windstorm blew most of this part away before the turn of the Century, and it was removed. The building is typical "river architecture."

● **Lee County Genealogical Society**
P. O. Box 303
Keokuk, Iowa 52632

Mrs. Lloyd Kelly, Corresponding
Secretary
R. R. 2
Keokuk, Iowa 52632

Organized: 1964
Meetings: Second Thursday of month
Dues: $3.00 family

Active in compiling early marriage records of Lee County, making scrapbooks of obituaries clipped from Lee County newspapers, and recording burials in Oakland City Cemetery, Keokuk, and other cemeteries in Lee County and Hancock County in Illinois. Publications include *Happy Hunting Grounds*, on early marriages of Lee County. The Society became a chapter of the Iowa Genealogical Society (see Polk County) in 1975.

● **Lee County Iowa Historical Society**
318 North Fifth Street
Keokuk, Iowa 52632

Mrs. Robert (Jane) Kerr, President
1209 Blondeau Street
Keokuk, Iowa 52632
         or
William L. Talbot
226 High Street
Keokuk, Iowa 52632

Organized: 1956
Meetings: As called
Number of Members: 250
Dues: $2.00 annual
Miller Home and Museum Open: During summer or by appointment

Projects include tours of historic sites and publications on local history.

A museum is maintained in the pioneer home, at 318 North Fifth Street, of Samuel Freeman Miller, appointed to the U.S. Supreme Court by President Abraham Lincoln in 1862. Miller, a prominent Keokuk attorney, served as Supreme Court Justice--the first to be appointed from west of the Mississippi--until his death in 1890. The home was built in 1857 for $13,000. After Miller and his family moved to Washington, D. C. in the late 1860's, the house was occupied by Captain Benjamin P. Taber, a prominent steamboat operator and pilot. He later engaged in the lumber business in Keokuk. Now on display in the restored house are Chief Keokuk's rifle, Mark Twain furniture, antiques, paintings, and early Keokuk memorabilia. The old home was acquired by Lee County Historical Society in July 1965 from the widow of Dr. Frank Brown, who owned the house following Captain Taber. The house was placed on the National Register of Historic Places in 1972. It serves as the Society's meeting place.

Other homes of historic interest, located in Keokuk, include the boyhood home of novelist and playwright Rupert Hughes (across the alley from the Miller home); the modest dwelling in which the mother of Samuel Clemens (Mark Twain) once lived; the birthplace of internationally

56 - LEE
(continued)

**Lee County Iowa
Historical Society**
(continued)

famous party-giver Elsa Maxwell (1881-1963), at 318 North Fourth Street; the General Curtis Home (see Victory Park, below); and the home of General William Worth Belknap, who served in the Civil War and was Secretary of War (1869-1876) in the Cabinet of President U. S. Grant.

The monument and grave of Chief Keokuk, of the Sac and Fox Indians, is located in Rand Park (see below), high above the Mississippi. Many old documents bearing the name of Chief Keokuk and his "X" may be seen at Lee County Courthouse (see above).

● **Mark Twain Center**
Keokuk Public Library
5th and Concert Streets
Keokuk, Iowa 52632

Donald Tillet, Librarian

Open: During Library hours
Admission: Free

A collection of many possessions of American author and humorist Mark Twain, pen name of Samuel Langhorne Clemens (1835- 1910), together with an impressive collection of his works. (See also Lee County Iowa Historical Society, above.)

● **Muir Log Cabin Site**
In front of Keokuk Municipal
Water Works pumping station,
north of Victory Park,
Keokuk, Iowa

The site of the first building in Keokuk. In 1820, Dr. Samuel C. Muir (d. 1832) built a low, double log cabin here, where it stood for nearly 20 years. Dr. Muir was the first American-born citizen to settle in what is now Iowa and was the first physician to practice in the State.

One block north of this site, under the present highway bridge, a group of 5 connected log cabins, known as Rat Row, were built in 1829 by Russel Farnham, an agent for John Jacob Astor's American Fur Company. Old Rat Row was a fur trading post until Farnham's death during the cholera epidemic of 1832.

● **National Cemetery**
West end of Cedar Street
Keokuk, Iowa

One of 85 national cemeteries in the United States and the only one in Iowa. Established in 1861, over 750 soldiers were buried here before the end of the Civil War, including at least 5 Confederate prisoners. The College of Physicians and Surgeons (which later became the University of Iowa Medical School) was located here in 1850 and, during the Civil War, Keokuk was designated a General Hospital Center. Five hospitals were established here to care for sick and wounded soldiers from southern battlefields. The cemetery is still used as a burial place for the honored dead of our wars. The 2,000 veterans buried here represent every war in which our country has been involved, except the American Revolution.

● **North Lee County Historical Society**
P. O. Box 385
Fort Madison, Iowa 52627

Mrs. John A. (Marian H.) Keenan,
President
High Point
Fort Madison, Iowa 52627

Organized: May 1962
Meetings: Fourth Wednesday of each month
Number of Members: 277
Dues: $5.00 supporting; $10.00 patron; $100.00 life
Brush College Open: As announced; groups by appointment
Historic Center Open: During summer; other times by
     appointment

6 - LEE
(continued)

North Lee County
Historical Society
(continued)

or

Mrs. James Worden
3029 Avenue H
Fort Madison, Iowa 52627

or

Mrs. Leo Winke,
Curator, Brush College
R. R. 1
Fort Madison, Iowa 52627

or

Bernard B. Hesse, IV
Director, Historic Center
601 Avenue F
Fort Madison, Iowa 52627

● **Old Fort Madison**
Fort Madison, Iowa

A red brick rural school, Brush College, over 100 years old, has been restored (in 1966) and fully equipped with the period 1885-90 in mind. This building replaced the original log schoolhouse that stood on approximately the same site, about 4 miles north of Fort Madison. Furnishings for the restoration were obtained from various old schools —— the bell from Jaybird School, the teacher's desk from a school on Chalk Ridge, wooden benches from St. Paul School, and the organ from the Old Baptist Church. The old school was also the social and cultural center of the community, the scene of amateur theatricals, spelling bees, pie socials, voter registration, and polling. An open house is held at Brush College each fall, and in May pupils from public and private schools come for classes on early Iowa History.

The old Santa Fe Railroad depot was acquired for the Lee County Historic Center. A Flea Market is held in September and "Old Times" is published quarterly.

Organized: 1965
Meetings: When called
Number of Members: 20
Dues: $5.00 annual

An organization was formed in 1965 to excavate the site of Old Fort Madison, the first fortification built in Iowa to guard the frontier and quiet the Indians on the upper Mississippi. Old Fort Madison (1808-13), named for President James Madison, proved difficult to defend. After repeated attacks by the Indians during the War of 1812, the troops were forced to abandon the fort, burning it in 1813 and escaping down the river by boats to St. Louis. The blackened lone chimney remained standing and became a landmark and monument to the high tide of Indian power. In 1908, a replica of this chimney was erected on the site of Blockhouse No. 1. The exact location of the old fort was determined by archeologists in 1965. Excavations made under a factory parking lot disclosed stone foundations and cobbled walks, and many artifacts (crockery, china, glass, silverware, musket balls, and iron hardware) were obtained. The remains of the old fort were then covered over with plastic and the excavation was filled, and plans to rebuild the 1808 fort were considered. The artifacts and excavation data were taken to The University of Iowa Archaeological Laboratory. A replica of one of the old blockhouses and stockade may be seen at the Iowa State Fairgrounds (see Polk County).

● **Rand Park and**
Chief Keokuk Monument
Off Grand Avenue
Keokuk, Iowa

In Rand Park, overlooking the Mississippi River, is a 10½-foot bronze statue of the famous Sac Chief, Keokuk (1788-1848). The statue, which rests on a 20-foot pedestal, was designed by Nellie Verne Walker, an Iowan, who was a pupil of Lorado Taft. She also executed the bronze statue of James Harlan placed in the Hall of Fame in the U.S. Capitol during February 1910. Keokuk died and was buried in Franklin County, Kansas. His remains were later returned

56 - LEE
(continued)

Rand Park and Chief Keokuk Monument
(continued)

to Iowa, in 1883, and are now beneath the statue, in his namesake city and favorite hunting grounds. Tablets on the monument, erected in 1913, tell of Keokuk's rise among the braves of his nation.

One of the finest formal gardens in the Midwest may also be seen near the Grand Avenue entrance to Rand Park.

● **Riverview Park**
North edge of Montrose, Iowa
on U.S. 61

Lee County Conservation Board
Carmi Lowenburg, Executive Officer
Box 245
Donnellson, Iowa 52625

Acquired: 1959

The Montrose Boat Harbor area (2 acres) is historically significant, as this is the location of Fort Des Moines No. 1 (see above) and is where the Mormon Trail began, across the river from Nauvoo, Illinois. There are facilities for boating, fishing, and picnicking.

● **St. Barnabas Church**
Montrose, Iowa

One of Iowa's oldest existing churches. Built as Grace Episcopal Church in 1869 on some of the first titled land in Iowa, the stone church overlooks the site of the first of three Iowa forts to be named Fort Des Moines (see above). The church was built on donated land and with much donated labor. The stone was excavated from the old Des Moines Rapids when a 9-mile navigation canal was being built. Gravestones in the adjoining cemetery date back into the 1840's. Due to a declining population for Montrose and lack of support for the church, it was closed in the late 1950's, but the old building (which houses the public library) and grounds are being preserved as a historic landmark.

● **Shimek State Forest, Donnellson Unit**
West of Donnellson, Iowa
off Iowa 2

State Conservation Commission
State Office Building
300 Fourth Street
Des Moines, Iowa 50319

Over 7,600 acres of forest are contained in the Croton Unit, Donnellson Unit, Farmington Unit, Keosauqua Unit, and Lick Creek Unit of Shimek State Forest, located in Lee and Van Buren Counties. The Donnellson Unit (860 acres) provides an opportunity for nature study, primitive camping, and picnicking. Wild turkeys and a wide variety of songbirds may be seen and heard, and there are marked nature trails.

The forest was named to honor Bohumil Shimek (1861-1937), whose parents were political refugees from Bohemia. At the time of his death, Professor Shimek was the second oldest member of The University of Iowa faculty. During his 46 years of service at the University, he served as professor of botany, head of the department of botany, director of Lakeside Laboratory (established in 1909), curator of the herbarium, and research professor. His outstanding services covered a broad range, as a pioneer, engineer, geologist, zoologist, conservationist, ecologist, educator, author, patriot, and citizen. His life was spent

- LEE
(continued)

Shimek State Forest, Donnellson Unit, (continued)

largely out-of-doors, in direct contact with the things about which he wrote. He was known for his insistence upon study in the field and the synthesis of the entire natural environment. His obituary included in the *Proceedings of the Iowa Academy of Science for 1937* describes him as "the last of the elder statesmen of natural history in the Middle West."

● **Victory Park**
Foot of Johnson Street, along the riverfront
Keokuk, Iowa

It was from here that thousands of Iowans departed to and returned from southern battlefields during the Civil War. The sick and wounded were taken to one of several general hospitals in Keokuk.

A bronze statue of Major General Samuel Ryan Curtis stands in the park. Curtis was a West Point graduate (1831) and came to Keokuk in 1847 to engineer improvements for navigation of the Des Moines River when steamboating was thriving. He built a native limestone home in Keokuk in 1849, and lived there until his death in 1866. Curtis served as a Congressman in the Iowa Legislature, and spent 3 terms in the U.S. Congress before resigning to command the 2nd Iowa Infantry Regiment. During the Civil War, Curtis was in command of the Union forces at the Battle of Pea Ridge, Arkansas, and won the first Union victory in the West. He is credited with keeping Missouri in the Union, thus preventing the Confederates from seizing territories on further west.

- LINN

● **Abbe Creek School Museum**
2 miles northwest of Mount Vernon, on Iowa 150

Linn County Conservation Board
George D. Hamilton,
Executive Officer
R. R. 1
Central City, Iowa 52214

dar Rapids
D-10

Museum Dedicated: October 25, 1964
Open: Sunday, 1:00-7:00 p.m. during June, July, and August; also limited schedule on Saturday; other times by appointment

Believed to be the oldest standing brick schoolhouse in Iowa. The 20-by 26-foot school was constructed in 1858 of soft brick, kilned locally. Initials, names, and dates (earliest is 1885) have been carved in many of the bricks on the outside of the building, which was last used as a public school in 1936. The original school on Abbe Creek was built of logs in 1844. The school was first called Sumner, or Kepler, and later came to be known as Little Brick School. In pioneer times the school was the center of community life. It served as a church on Sundays. Near the site is a marker honoring William Abbe, the first white settler in Linn County. Mrs. Abbe is buried nearby in an unmarked grave in Abbe Creek Cemetery. The original storm cave, opening into the side of the hill, and the spring which furnished the drinking water for students and teacher are on the grounds. Original primers and other books, slates, lunch buckets, desks, pot-bellied stove, pump organ, and other furnishings of mid-19th Century country schools may be seen.

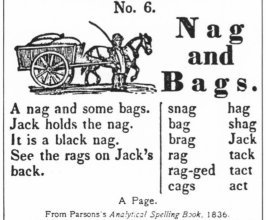

No. 6.

Nag and Bags.

A nag and some bags.
Jack holds the nag.
It is a black nag.
See the rags on Jack's back.

snag	hag
bag	shag
brag	Jack
rag	tack
rag-ged	tact
cags	act

A Page.
From Parsons's *Analytical Spelling Book*, 1836.

The schoolhouse is located along the old Lincoln Highway, America's first transcontinental highway and Iowa's first paved road across the state.

COUNTY AND COUNTY SEAT; LOCATION ON MAP	NAME AND LOCATION	DESCRIPTION

57 - LINN
(continued)

● **Bever Park Zoo**
2700 Bever Avenue SE
Cedar Rapids, Iowa

Cedar Rapids Parks Department
City Hall
Cedar Rapids, Iowa 52401

Located in 80-acre Bever Park, named for George Bever from whom part of the land was purchased in 1893. The zoo includes bears, lions, coyotes, dingos, cougars, monkeys, and birds. Nearby is Old McDonald Barnyard Zoo, where baby lambs, goats, donkeys, calves, pigs, rabbits, kinkajous, chickens, and ducks may be seen. Bever Park also offers flower displays and recreational facilities.

● **Cedar Rapids Art Center**
324 Third Street S.E.
Cedar Rapids, Iowa 52403

Stanley H. Wiederspan, Director

Admission: Free
Open: Tuesday, Wednesday, Friday, and Saturday, 10:00 a.m.-5:00 p.m.; Thursday 10:00 a.m.-8:30 p.m.; Sunday, 2:00-5:00 p.m.

Exhibits of paintings and art objects. The Grant Wood Gallery provides permanent housing for an extensive collection of Grant Wood art, including work donated by Mr. and Mrs. John B. Turner II. Grant Wood had his studio at No. 5 Turner Alley in Cedar Rapids.

In 1974, the Cherry-Burrell Corporation of Cedar Rapids (manufacturers of processing and packaging equipment for the dairy industry) donated 8 paintings believed to be the only industrial scenes done by Wood. The 1925 paintings depict workers on the assembly lines and in the manufacturing plant (then the J.G. Cherry Co.).

The "Mourner's Bench," designed by Grant Wood when he was an art teacher at McKinley Junior High School in 1923, may be seen. It was used in the principal's office by pupils awaiting disciplinary action, and bears the carved message "The Way of the Transgressor Is Hard." The bench is owned by the Cedar Rapids Community School District.

Paintings on display include John B. Turner, Pioneer (1928-30), "Woman With Plants" (1929), "Trees and Hills" (1933), and "Young Corn."

There are rotating exhibits and an Art Center School for all ages, preschool through adult.

● **Council Rock**
Just west of Waubeek, Iowa

According to legend, it was here that the Wapsipinicon River got its name. Pinicon, an Indian brave, and Wapsie, a princess from an enemy tribe formed a lover's pact and escaped together one night down the river in a canoe. A scouting party spotted them and shot Pinicon. Wapsie, in coming to his aid, upset the canoe and both were drowned. From their combined names comes Wapsipinicon.

● **Hanging Bog**
Northwest of Cedar Rapids, Iowa on county road, off Iowa 94

The Nature Conservancy
Paul A. Christiansen
103 - 10th Avenue South
Mt. Vernon, Iowa 52314

A 16-acre tract acquired by the Iowa Chapter of The Nature Conservancy in 1967. Dominated by red oak and basswood, the area contains cold springs with water seeping in many places. Terraces formed on a north-facing slope are waterlogged throughout the year, forming a bog environment. Some of the less common Iowa wild flowers, including skunk cabbage and marsh marigold, grow here. Jewel weed may be seen later in the year, and after frost has killed most other plant life, mosses and liverworts cover much of the ground.

- LINN
(continued)

● **Indian Creek Nature Center**
6665 Otis Road, SE
R.R. 3
Cedar Rapids, Iowa 52401

Curtis D. Abdouch, Director

Incorporated: January 18, 1973
Memberships: $5.00 student; $10.00 adult; $15.00 family; $50.00 supporting; $100.00 or more sustaining

A renovated red tile dairy barn, located on 6 acres of land near the Sac and Fox Trail (see below), used as a base for nature study and field trips by adults and school children. Guided nature tours may be arranged, or visitors may use self-guiding interpretive trails. The year-round facility features exhibits and botanical and wildlife displays. Classrooms are available for the educational program on nature, wildlife, ecology, and conservation. The *Nature Center News* goes to members quarterly.

● **Iowa Heritage Trail**
Begins at Mount Vernon, Iowa

Opened: 1971

A scenic drive in east-central Iowa, calling attention to some of the State's cultural, historical, educational, industrial, and religious heritage. Points of interest include the Cornell College campus, the Old Military Road (now part of Iowa 1), Wapsipinicon State Park, Grant Wood Memorial Park, Men's Reformatory at Anamosa, Stone City, Mount Hope Park, Matsell Bridge, Waubeek, Council Rock, Whittier, Springville, Abbe Creek School, Palisades-Kepler State Park, Palisades-Dows Preserve, J. Harold Ennis Preserve, Amana Colonies, Lake McBride State Park, and Herbert Hoover Presidential Library.

● **Iowa Masonic Library and Museum**
813 First Avenue SE
Cedar Rapids, Iowa

Charles Jackson, Jr.,
Grand Secretary of Grand Lodge
of Iowa
P. O. Box 279
Cedar Rapids, Iowa 52406

Established: 1844
Open: Week days, 8:00 a.m.-noon and 1:00-5:00 p.m.; other times by appointment

One of the oldest and largest Masonic libraries in the United States, established by Theodore S. Parvin who came to Iowa in 1838 as Secretary to Robert Lucas, first Territorial Governor of Iowa (1838-1841). The 65,000-volume library includes works on secret societies of the Middle Ages. The museum contains collections of Masonic interest, firearms, Indian weapons and tools, personal items owned by Parvin, Japanese armor, and the first telephone made in Iowa. The marble building was completed in 1955.

● **J. Harold Ennis Preserve**
Southeast of Palisades-Kepler
State Park

Linn County Conservation Board
George D. Hamilton, Executive Officer
R. R. 1
Central City, Iowa 52214

A 36-acre botanical preserve along the Cedar River, kept inviolate for nature study and hiking.

● **Lewis Wildlife and Timber Preserve**
4 miles south of Center Point, Iowa

Linn County Conservation Board
George D. Hamilton, Executive Officer
R. R. 1
Central City, Iowa 52214

Acquired: 1964

A 435-acre tract, donated by Ira Lewis, set aside to preserve the native Iowa landscape. There is no road access to the area. Major activities include hiking and nature study. Walnut trees are to be planted in one part of the area.

57 - LINN
(continued)

● **Linn County Heritage Society**
Box 175
Cedar Rapids, Iowa 52406

Mrs. Margaret Wagner, President
2820 12th Avenue, SW
Cedar Rapids, Iowa 52406
or
Mrs. Herman (Phyllis) Wennermark,
 Historian
746 Old Marion Road NE
Cedar Rapids, Iowa 52402

Organized: February 22, 1965
Meetings: Fourth Thursday of month, 9:30 a.m.
Number of Members: 60
Dues: $2.00 annual

Locates and secures information about old cemeteries in Linn County, and has programs on local history. An exact reproduction of the 2 volume Brewer & Wick *History of Linn County*, originally printed in 1911, was published by the Society in 1973. An every name index has been compiled, and a library is maintained in the Heritage Room of the Cedar Rapids Public Library. The Society became a chapter of the Iowa Genealogical Society (see Polk County) in March 1970.

● **Linn County Historical Museum Association**
P. O. Box 823
Cedar Rapids, Iowa 52406

Mrs. Mary Heabel, President
P. O. Box 823
Cedar Rapids, Iowa 52401
or
Roger K. Donnelly
238 Brentwood Drive, NE
Cedar Rapids, Iowa 52402

Incorporated: June 25, 1970
Meetings: Third Thursday of each month
Number of Members: 275
Dues: $5.00 annual; $8.00 couple; $10.00 family; $25.00
      contributing; $50.00 supporting; $100 life

Linn County Historical Society merged with Linn County Historical Museum Association for the purpose of preserving and displaying the heritage of Linn County and establishing a county museum.

The Association plans to assemble buildings of historical significance or construct replicas to maintain for display of materials related to the history of Linn County. The first building acquired was the original Bertram Post Office.

● **Marion Historical Museum, Inc.**
970 Tenth Street
Marion, Iowa

Dale T. Miner, President
Marion, Iowa 52302

Incorporated: September 18, 1973

The old Granger house has been renovated and restored to its appearance in the 1880's. The property was purchased in September 1973 for use as a museum.

● **Matsell Bridge Area**
2½ miles north of Viola, Iowa

Linn County Conservation Board
George D. Hamilton, Executive Officer
R. R. 1, Central City, Iowa 52214

A 1,108-acre area stretching along 4½ miles of the Wapsipinicon River. Schoonover's Mill was formerly located at Matsell Ford, but all traces of it have disappeared. This area was once the home of George W. Matsell, who was New York police chief and founder of *The Police Gazette*. The house built in the 1850's by Matsell was in the tradition of George Washington's Mount Vernon on the Potomac, and is said to have contained many hidden rooms and lookout stations. The public use area offers boating, fishing, hiking, picnicking, camping, and an opportunity for nature study and wildlife photography.

● **Morgan Creek Park**
South of Covington, Iowa or 2½ miles west of Cedar Rapids

Linn County Conservation Board
George D. Hamilton,
Executive Officer
R. R. 1, Central City, Iowa 52214

A 104-acre park with facilities for picnicking, camping, and hiking, and an arboretum.

- LINN
(continued)

● **Mount Hope Park**
2 miles northeast of Viola, Iowa

Linn County Conservation Board
George D. Hamilton,
Executive Officer
R. R. 1, Central City, Iowa 52214

A 15-acre area, including an old rock quarry, near the Wapsipinicon River, set aside for nature study, hiking, fishing, picnicking, and camping.

● **Noelridge Greenhouses and Horticultural Gardens**
Intersection of Collins Road
and Council Street NE
Cedar Rapids, Iowa

Cedar Rapids Parks Department
City Hall
Cedar Rapids, Iowa 52401

Located in Noelridge Park. The 5 greenhouses encompass 30,000 square feet and display several hundred varieties of plants. Flower shows are held in the spring, mid-summer, and fall, and tours are available. Three conservatories are planned to be associated with the greenhouses. Annual, perennial, and rose gardens cover 10 acres.

● **Palisades-Dows Preserve**
5 miles east of Ely, Iowa

Linn County Conservation Board
George D. Hamilton,
Executive Officer
R. R. 1, Central City, Iowa 52214

A 162-acre botanical and wildlife preserve along the Cedar River, used for organized nature study. Natural plant communities are permitted to develop with a minimum of influence by man.

● **Palisades-Kepler State Park**
4 miles west of Mount Vernon, Iowa
off U.S. 30

State Conservation Commission
State Office Building
300 Fourth Street
Des Moines, Iowa 50319

A 688-acre area of natural scenic beauty containing huge limestone cliffs, or palisades, from 30 to 75 feet high along the Cedar River. Numerous caves, Indian mounds, and a natural stone archway are in this historic area. A variety of Indian pottery, arrowheads, stone fishhooks, and other articles, and a molar tooth from an ancient mammoth have been found here. Deep timbered valleys provide a haven for assorted wild flowers, mosses, and ferns. Red cedar, American yew, and ground hemlock are in evidence. Points of interest include Lover's Leap, Fern Cliffs, Maple and Hemlock Junction, Indian Mounds, and Council Fire Circle. Marked nature trails wind through the park, and from Lookout Tower, atop a high cliff, is a fine view of the river and surrounding countryside. Popular activities are hiking, nature study, fishing, boating, picnicking, and camping.

● **Palo Marsh Wildlife Refuge**
½ mile north of Palo, Iowa

Linn County Conservation Board
George D. Hamilton,
Executive Officer
R. R. 1, Central City, Iowa 52214

A game management area of 144 areas on the Cedar River. The area includes hiking trails, and is used for nature study, fishing, and hunting.

57 - LINN
(continued)

● **Pinicon Ridge Park**
¼ mile northwest of
Central City, Iowa

Linn County Conservation Board
George D. Hamilton,
Executive Officer
R.R. 1,
Central City, Iowa 52214

A series of ridges built up of loess deposits in an 800-acre park along the Wapsipinicon River. An Information Center with educational displays and a wildlife exhibit (deer, geese, ducks, etc.) is located near the entrance. There are facilities for picnicking, camping, hiking, nature study, boating, fishing, and hunting.

● **Rock Island Preserve**
1 mile northwest of
Linn Junction, Iowa, or 2 miles
northwest of Cedar Rapids, Iowa

Linn County Conservation Board
George D. Hamilton,
Executive Officer
R. R. 1, Central City, Iowa 52214

A 20-acre undeveloped area preserved for scientific botanical and biological study. Prairie wild flowers and many rare specimens of plant and animal life have become established in a natural bog which makes up about half the area. The other half of the property is made up of higher ground. The area has been used by college students for many years for nature study and research.

● **Sac and Fox Trail**
Access and parking at Mount
Vernon Road SE and Bertram
Road, and off Otis Road SE

Cedar Rapids Parks Department
City Hall
Cedar Rapids, Iowa 52401

Dedicated: July 24, 1973
Open: Daily, weather permitting; closes at 10:00 p.m.

A 5-mile trail, about 10 feet wide, within a 937-acre green belt of woodland and prairie, running from East Post Road SE to the city limits near Beyerly Road SW, and along the Cedar River. The area is being kept in its natural state for hiking, bicycling, horseback riding, and nature study. No motorized vehicles of any kind are permitted on the trail. The trail was named for Indians who lived and hunted along the same pathway in the early 19th century. It is the first National Recreation Trail to be designated in Iowa. A red dairy barn adjacent to the trail houses Indian Creek Nature Center (see above).

● **Seminole Valley Farm, Inc.**
Seminole Valley Park
Along the Cedar River,
5 miles northwest of downtown
Cedar Rapids, Iowa

Mrs. James Browne, President
P. O. Box 605
Cedar Rapids, Iowa 52406
or
Cedar Rapids Parks Department
City Hall
Cedar Rapids, Iowa 52401

Dedicated: October 5, 1969
Open: Sunday, 1:00-4:00 p.m., May 1 through October 31; week days by appointment, May, September, and October only

Admission: Free; donations accepted

A non-profit corporation, organized to supervise restoration of an Iowa farm of the 1880's and open it to the public.

The faithfully restored farm includes the house, barn and farmyard, summer kitchen, smoke house, and chicken house. The farmhouse has five rooms downstairs--the formal parlor, furnished in Victorian style, with lace curtains at the 8-paned windows; the family sitting room;

COUNTY AND
COUNTY SEAT;
LOCATION ON MAP
      NAME AND LOCATION
      DESCRIPTION

- LINN
(continued)

Seminole Valley Farm, Inc.
(continued)

the kitchen, with its wood floor, braided rugs (made by artist Grant Wood's mother out of his old jeans), big iron stove, pie cupboard, and pantry filled with utensils; the master bedroom, with a rope bed; and the child's bedroom, with trundle bed, cradle, and toys. Farm machinery and tools of the last century are on display in the barn and farmyard. Members of the Cedar Rapids Garden Club have planted trees, shrubs, flowers, and vegetables typical of the early farmstead. These include fruit trees, lilacs, old-fashioned roses, hollyhocks, columbine, bluebells, iris, peonies, daisies, lilies-of-the-valley, ferns, rhubarb, and asparagus. The property is owned by the City of Cedar Rapids, which leases it to Seminole Valley Farm, Inc.

Willow Bend Village is being developed near the farm in Seminole Valley Park to represent a late 1800 Iowa village, with church, school, shops, and homes.

● **Shakespeare Garden**
Ellis Park
Cedar Rapids, Iowa

Mrs. Francis (Nancy B.) Lackner,
President
The Wednesday Shakespeare Club
11 Blake Court, SE
Cedar Rapids, Iowa 52403
or
Mrs. Nevin Nichols, Chairman
of Garden Committee
1107 27th Street, NE
Cedar Rapids, Iowa 52402

Established: 1927

A landscaped area of 1.4 acres featuring flowers and shrubs mentioned in the plays of William Shakespeare. A bust of Shakespeare (1564-1616) is a central feature of the garden. A sundial, and a wall and entrance pillars, are located along the Cedar River. A new rose or shrub is planted each year on April 23 to commemorate Shakespeare's birthdate. (Although his date of birth is indefinite, official records indicate that Shakespeare was baptized on April 26, 1564.)

● **Standing Rock**
4 miles southwest of Lisbon, Iowa

A granite glacial boulder, one of the original and possibly the only remaining landmark, used to locate the boundary of the Black Hawk Purchase following the close of the Black Hawk War of 1832. The rock may have been named by one of the original surveyors. All or parts of 22 Iowa counties were included in the Black Hawk Purchase, comprising nearly 6 million acres west of the Mississippi River.

● **Tower Grove**
1035 Second Street SE
Cedar Rapids, Iowa 52401

John A. Kuba, owner

Open: By appointment

A 9-room native red brick Victorian home, with white wood trim and cut stone foundation, built in 1879 by Frank J. Mittvalsky, who owned and operated a butcher shop and slaughter house nearby. He had been trained as a

57 - LINN
(continued)

Tower Grove
(continued)

sausage maker and butcher in what is now Czechoslovakia, and came to the United States in 1870. Mr. Mittvalsky only lived in the house for a few years before he died in 1889, leaving his wife Frances and 5 children. She later married Professor Joseph Tlapa, who taught piano, organ, and violin in the home for over 20 years. He wrote his own music and was the director of the Bohemian Singing Society and the German Singing Society. Members of the family continued to live here until 1963. The home has been restored by the present owner. Linn County Historical Museum Association (see above) has given some assistance in the restoration. The Victorian furnishings complement the maple and walnut floors, grained woodwork, and 12-foot ceilings. Tours may be arranged for groups.

● **Wakema Park**
Center Point, Iowa

Linn County Conservation Board
George D. Hamilton,
Executive Officer
R.R. 1,
Central City, Iowa 52214

A 5-acre park with playground, wading pool, lodge, and picnic area, named for an Indian brave who played a part in the early history of Center Point, one of the first settlements in Linn County. Settlers were attracted to the area as early as 1839 because of the timber and close proximity to the Cedar River.

● **Wakpicada Area**
1 mile south of Central City, Iowa

Linn County Conservation Board
George D. Hamilton,
Executive Officer
R. R. 1, Central City, Iowa 52214

A 215-acre game management area, along the Wapsipinicon River, used for hiking, nature study, horseback riding, boating, fishing, hunting, and wilderness camping.

● **Waubeek, Iowa**
About 12 miles northeast of
Cedar Rapids, Iowa

A group of New England whaling families, tired of their rugged life at sea, are said to have settled here--as far as they could get from the sea and the dangers of whaling. Waubeek is an Indian name, given to the village by Samuel T. Buckston, one of those who established the town in 1859. Prior to this, in 1855, the town of Paddington had been laid out here, and a dam and sawmill had been built. A 4-story stone flouring mill was erected in 1859, on a solid base of rock. About 1865, a woolen mill started operation, and other stone buildings were constructed at the village.

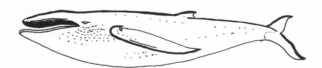

Waubeek was also where Jay G. Sigmund, "the poet of the Wapsie," lived. He was born near Cook's Ford, just up the Wapsipinicon River. His verse and stories of life along the river brought him fame from coast to coast. In 1937, a tablet was erected here in his memory. On the Wapsi, just across from Waubeek, is a 7-acre park, the Jay G. Sigmund Memorial site, where one of his poems, "The Granite Boulder," has been engraved on a marker. Picnicking and fishing are permitted.

| COUNTY AND COUNTY SEAT; LOCATION ON MAP | NAME AND LOCATION | DESCRIPTION |

- LINN
(continued)

● **Whittier, Iowa**
About 6 miles northeast of
Cedar Rapids, Iowa

A Quaker settlement dating back to 1850, named for the poet John Greenleaf Whittier. The white-painted, frame Friends (Quaker) Meeting House, which may be visited, has woven rag rugs on the aisles.

● **Wickiup Hill Area**
2 miles west of Toddville, Iowa,
or 2½ miles northeast of Palo, Iowa

An undeveloped area of 178 acres preserved for hiking, nature study, wilderness camping, fishing, and hunting.

Linn County Conservation Board
George D. Hamilton,
Executive Officer
R. R. 1, Central City, Iowa 52214

OUISA

lo

● **Joliet and Marquette Historical Marker**
Near Toolesboro, along Iowa 99

French-Canadian trapper-explorer Louis Joliet (1645-1700) and Father Jacques Marquette (1637-1675), a French missionary and explorer, were the first white men to see Iowa and set foot on its soil. They entered the Mississippi River, after coming down the Wisconsin River, and for 8 days paddled along the eastern border of Iowa. On June 25, 1673, the party landed on the west bank of the Mississippi, probably at some point near the mouth of the Iowa River. They were met by friendly Illinois Indians and remained to rest and smoke the calumet or peace pipe with them at their village.

Joliet wrote his name with 2 "l's" in the many autographs which are in existence. However, the name has been spelled more commonly, as on this historical marker, with only a single "l."

● **Louisa County Historical Society**
Wapello, Iowa

Mrs. Sylvia S. Chatterton, President
Grandview, Iowa 52752
or
Mrs. Lyle Weber
903 Main Street
Columbus Junction, Iowa 52738

Incorporated: November 30, 1964
Meetings: Quarterly, in February, May, August, and November, at various locations in Louisa County
Number of Members: 150
Dues: $3.00 annual

Early in 1968, a 5-acre tract in the Toolesboro area was purchased by Louisa County Historical Society to develop as a historic site. A museum was later built by the State Historical Society of Iowa near the Toolesboro Indian Mounds (see below), along the Great River Road, on the land donated by Louisa County Historical Society. The Society also maintains a museum on the second floor of the City Hall in Wapello.

Five miles south of Wapello, along the Iowa River, Chiefs Black Hawk, Keokuk, Poweshiek, and Wapello held war council to deliberate on an attack on Fort Armstrong (see Scott County). War parties were launched from this area during the Black Hawk War.

In 1902, a Chautauqua Association was formed in Columbus Junction--the pioneer assembly in southeastern Iowa. The chautauqua grounds, comprised of 20 acres, were purchased by the association in 1904. Until 1930, the

58 - LOUISA
(continued)

Louisa County Historical Society
(continued)

chautauqua programs provided family entertainment each summer, with such well-known personages as William Jennings Bryan (the "Prince of Chautauqua"), Booker T. Washington, Robert La Follette, and Carry A. Nation. Faced with increasing financial difficulties, the association turned the grounds over to the town of Columbus Junction (incorporated July 4, 1874) in 1923.

● **Swinging Bridge**
Columbus Junction, Iowa
just off Iowa 92

A swinging, wooden, suspension bridge was first built in 1886 on Elm Street as the thoroughfare between 3rd and 4th, across a deep wooded ravine, the area known locally as "Lover's Leap." The first bridge was built of barrel staves and wire. It was replaced by a wooden bridge supported on stilts, condemned in 1902. Another bridge was built in 1904; it collapsed around 1920. The present 262-foot-long bridge was then built to replace it. The bridge has been repaired and restored in recent years and is preserved as an unusual historic landmark.

● **Toolesboro Indian Mounds**
Toolesboro, Iowa

State Historical Society of Iowa
402 Iowa Avenue
Iowa City, Iowa 52240

Acquired by the State of Iowa: 1963
Admission: Free
Open: Daily except Tuesday, 1:00-5:00 p.m., Memorial Day through Labor Day

A 15.6-acre tract containing 2 conical ceremonial burial mounds preserved from a group of 9 on the bluffs overlooking the Iowa River in the Toolesboro area. Approximately 100 ancient Hopewell Indian mounds, from the Middle Woodland period (500 B.C. to 300 A.D.), have been located near the junction of the Iowa and Mississippi Rivers. Many mounds have been obliterated by cultivation of the land since the mounds were first explored in the 1870's by a party from the Davenport Academy of Science (W. H. Pratt, Reverend Jacob Gass, and others). Skeletons and artifacts have been found in the mounds, including pottery, sheets of mica, shell beads, shell dippers, effigy pipes, and some of the only copper artifacts (axes, celts, and awls) found in Iowa. Many of these specimens and relics were removed to the museum in Davenport (see Putnam Museum, Scott County). A demonstration prairie plot is being developed by transplanting and seeding grasses and flowering plants similar to those found in the area before white settlement. The property was formally dedicated as a National historic landmark on June 23, 1973.

A Visitor Center, containing displays and dioramas depicting the area's history, was opened to the public on June 1, 1971. It is located on a site overlooking the spot where Joliet and Marquette beached their canoes on June 25, 1673 for the first meeting between Indians and white men on Iowa soil. This is also the site of the Sac-Fox war council that started the Black Hawk War with an attack on Fort Armstrong in 1830.

COUNTY AND COUNTY SEAT; LOCATION ON MAP	NAME AND LOCATION	DESCRIPTION

9 - LUCAS

Chariton
H-7

● **Hillcrest Rock Museum**
West of Chariton, Iowa
on U.S. 34

Collection of minerals and unusual rocks, and a nature trail.

● **John L. Lewis Labor Memorial**
North of Bandstand
Lucas, Iowa

Marion D. Siglin, Chairman
R. R. 2
Lucas, Iowa 50151

Organized: 1970
Admission: Free

A memorial and museum pertaining to labor and mining. An old house is being reconditioned for a museum, surrounded by a park. Mining tools, pictures, papers, and items related to mining and miners have been collected. Lucas, Iowa was the birthplace of John Llewellyn Lewis (1880-1969). He began work in the coal mines at the age of 12, and left the Iowa coal fields to become one of America's stormiest and most powerful national labor leaders and President of the United Mine Workers of America (the world's largest trade union) from 1920 until his retirement in 1960.

● **Lucas County Historical Society**
123 17th Street
Chariton, Iowa 50049

Dale Burge, President
838 North Grand
Chariton, Iowa 50049
or
Mrs. Norma Pim, Curator
R. R. 1, Lucas, Iowa 50151

Organized: 1901
Incorporated: August 22, 1908 (expired 1922); June 22, 1965
Meetings: Third Friday in March
Number of Members: 325
Dues: $1.00 annual
Museum Opened to Public: September 22, 1968
Admission: $0.50; children $0.25
Open: Sunday and Wednesday, 1:00-5:00 p.m.

The first county historical society organized in Iowa, followed a few weeks later by Decatur County Historical Society.

A 1908 house has been acquired for a museum, and furnished with items related to the heritage of early settlers. A music room, parlor, kitchen, and child's bedroom are filled with appropriate objects and antiques. In the basement are stone jars, churns, iron pots, a hand loom, miner's tools, and a replica of an old-fashioned general store. An old schoolhouse is also on the 3½-acre plot. The 33 cemeteries in Lucas County are being surveyed, and a "Museum Musings" column is written for the local newspaper.

● **Mormon Trail**
Courthouse grounds
Chariton, Iowa

A huge boulder with bronze tablet marks the Mormon Trail which passed through here. The monument was erected by the Iowa Daughters of the American Revolution in 1917 in memory of the pioneers who followed this trail and its tributaries. The townsite of Chariton was located on the trail September 11, 1849.

● **Stephens State Forest**
Scattered areas northeast of Chariton and southwest of Lucas, Iowa

James Bulman, Area Forester
R. R. 3, Box 31
Chariton, Iowa 50049

A total of 8,625 acres of forest in Appanoose, Clarke, Davis, Lucas, and Monroe Counties, set aside for demonstrations and multiple use. Stephens State Forest, named for Dr. T. C. Stephens a prominent educator and native of Sioux City, is divided into 6 separate units: Lucas Unit (990 acres), Whitebreast Unit (3,075 acres), Cedar Creek Unit (817 acres), Chariton Unit (1,115 acres), 1000 Acres Unit (965 acres), and Unionville Unit (1,700 acres).

59 - LUCAS
(continued)

Stephens State Forest
(continued)

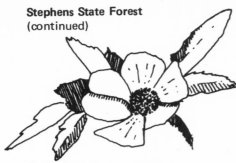

Since 1937, several hundred acres have been planted to evergreens and hardwood trees.

The forest is used as a place to camp, picnic, hunt (in season), fish (in lakes and ponds), hike, study nature, and enjoy the out-of-doors. White-tailed deer inhabit the area, and there are red and gray squirrels, raccoons, rabbits, woodchucks, muskrats, skunks, red and gray foxes, and a variety of both game and songbirds. Since 1968, the forest has been stocked with wild turkeys, and on spring mornings the woods resound with gobbling.

60 - LYON

Rock Rapids
A-1

● **Blood Run Indian Village Site**
2 miles south of Gitchie Manitou
State Preserve, at the confluence of
Blood Run Creek and the
Big Sioux River

A large and, for the most part, unexplored Indian village site, occupied into historic times. The village was known to early fur traders who explored the upper Missouri River and its tributaries. At least 100 mounds, possibly erected over burials, are said to exist on the site. These are the only known mound groups attributable to the Oneota Culture. The Oneota lived within parts of 8 midwestern states at one time or another and were the forerunners of such Indian tribes as the Ioway and Oto, who occupied this part of Iowa when the white man arrived. Most Oneota remains have been found along or near the Mississippi River. The artifacts recovered to date from the Blood Run Site suggest an Oneota occupation from about 1700 to 1750. In September 1970, this site was designated a National Historic Landmark by the National Parks Service.

● **First Reinforced Concrete Bridge
in the United States**
City Park, at east edge of
Rock Rapids, Iowa

Constructed: 1893
Dedication at New Location: August 31, 1964

First reinforced concrete arch bridge built in the United States. Designed by Joseph Melan, an Austrian who originated the Melan system of reinforcing concrete. Supervisor of construction was Frederick Von Emberger, and the builder was John Olson of Rock Rapids. The arch supporting the 30-foot span rises 6½ feet to the crown and is reinforced by railroad rails. Sioux Falls jasper was used for the stone facing. Lyon County paid $830 to construct the bridge, which included the cost of the Portland cement imported from Germany for $3.25 per barrel. Originally built across Dry Creek, the bridge was moved 3 miles north when road improvements made its removal necessary in order to save it from destruction. A campaign was launched to save the bridge and it is now preserved in a small park as a memorial to pioneers of the area. A scale model of the Bridge is in the Smithsonian Institute in Washington, D. C.

Possibly the first use of structural concrete in a U.S. bridge was in 1848, when the Starrucca Viaduct was engineered and built by James P. Kirkwood at Lanesboro, Pennsylvania. In 1848, Kirkwood was named the second president of the American Society of Civil Engineers. The 1040-foot-long span was the most expensive railroad bridge of its time, linking the Eastern Seaboard and the Midwest. It cost $320,000 and carries 2 tracks, 100 feet above the creek bed. The 19- x 40-foot pier footings of the viaduct are of plain concrete.

- LYON
(continued)

Gitchie Manitou State Preserve
9 miles northwest of Larchwood, Iowa

State Conservation Commission
State Office Building
300 Fourth Street
Des Moines, Iowa 50319

This portion of prairie and brushland in the extreme northwest corner of Iowa, covering 153 acres in the valley of the Big Sioux River, is one of the most unusual areas in the state. Gitchie Manitou is the Sioux Indian name for "Great Spirit" or "Great Force of Nature." French explorers called it Coteau des Prairies or "Hill of the Prairies" and English trappers referred to it as "Height of Land." The oldest known rock outcrop in Iowa is Sioux Quartzite, dating back to the Pre-Cambrian Era, at least 1.2 billion years ago. Sioux Quartzite was named in 1870 by Dr. C. A. White, an eminent State Geologist. Erosion has exposed this hard pink-colored rock only in this corner of Iowa. In other parts of the state, the Sioux Quartzite lies buried deep under the soil.

In the 1890's, prisoners quarried the quartzite and much of it was shipped out. Dimension stone from here was used in the construction of many buildings. The Sioux Quartzite has also been used in road construction. The area was rescued from further exploitation when it was made a geological monument in 1921, and is now a State Preserve. Jasper Pool is a deep-colored pool in the quartzite exposure.

The area is also of botanical interest. Desert plants, such as prickly pear cactus, and prairie grasses and wild flowers are found on the lush native unplowed prairie along the Big Sioux River. Western prairie birds are common. Old-timers in the area claim that Gitchie Manitou was one of the secret meeting places of Sitting Bull and his Sioux warriors when they were preparing for the Battle of the Little Big Horn where Custer's troops were wiped out. Artifacts found here give evidence of previous Indian occupation. A series of circular Indian burial mounds are located in the southern portion of the preserve.

A bronze plaque mounted on a rock was placed within the park to mark the site of Gibralter, the first post office in Lyon County, 1869-1871.

Kruger Mill
Klondike, Iowa

The shell of an old water-powered mill and the mill dam in the Big Sioux River. The dam is broken on the Iowa side. August Kruger platted the town of Klondike in 1900. The mill property is privately owned.

Lake Pahoja Recreation Area
5½ miles southwest of
Larchwood, Iowa

Lyon County Conservation Board
Steve Richardson, Executive Officer
505 South 10th Avenue, Apt. 3
Rock Rapids, Iowa 51246

A 235-acre area including a 72-acre artificial lake. The development provides picnic areas, camping sites, a swimming beach, and a boat ramp. Nature trails wind through native prairie and wildlife habitat areas along the lake, providing an opportunity for nature study.

60 - LYON
(continued)

● **Lyon County Historical Society**
Rock Rapids, Iowa

Ronald Schemmel, President
Alvord, Iowa
or
Mrs. Roscoe (Nadene) Pettengill,
Treasurer
R.R. 2
Rock Rapids, Iowa 51246

Incorporated: November 1, 1971
Meetings: Annual meeting in November
Number of Members: 300
Dues: $2.00 annual; $1.00 junior; $40.00 life or 20 consecutive years membership

Sponsors a pioneer craft fair, tours, and workshops. The Society has also helped inventory historic places, prepare a history of churches, and check cemeteries, and publishes a quarterly newsletter. In 1974, the 1873 *Historical Sketch of Lyon County, Iowa* by S. C. Hyde and *A Compendium of History, Reminiscence and Biography of Lyon County, Iowa*, originally published in 1904 by the Pioneer Association of Lyon County, were reprinted.

The former Rock Island depot in Rock Rapids is being restored for a museum and meeting place.

● **McGuire Log Cabin**
City Park at west edge of
Rock Rapids, Iowa

One of the first log cabins in Lyon County, originally built in the 1860's by James and Pat McGuire. The 1-room cabin has a stairway to an upper loft. The relocation and restoration of the cabin was sponsored by the local Kiwanis Club.

61 - MADISON

Winterset
G-5

● **Covered Bridges**
Located on rocked roads in
the Winterset, Iowa area

Chamber of Commerce
Winterset, Iowa 50273

Typical of bygone days are the dozen old wooden covered bridges still in existence in Iowa. Pennsylvania boasts 250 such structures——more than any other state. Iowa ranks 14th nationally in the number of covered bridges still standing. Madison County, "covered bridge capital of Iowa," has preserved 7 of its original 16 covered bridges, built between 1855 and 1884. The oldest of those remaining was completed in 1870. All of the Madison County covered bridges were built of white pine, probably shipped in from Oregon, and cost from $900 to $2,000 apiece. The roofs of all but 2 of the Madison County bridges are flat. The Cutler or Donahue and the Imes bridges have the conventional peaked roof. In 1872, the first wrought iron bridge was built in the county, marking the beginning of the end of the old wooden covered bridges, symbols of America's romantic past.

The names of the Madison County covered bridges are: Cedar Lake or Casper, Cutler or Donahue, Hogback, Holliwell (the longest span), Imes, McBride, and Roseman or Oak Grove. All are in use for light traffic (8-ton limit) or foot traffic. During the summer of 1970, the Cutler or Donahue covered bridge, built 100 years earlier, was moved to the west side of Winterset City Park and restored. A Covered Bridge Festival is held in Winterset in early October each year. Other original covered bridges in Iowa are located in Keokuk, Marion, and Polk Counties.

The wooden bridges were roofed to keep the rain, snow, and ice off the flooring and beams, thus preventing rotting of the wood and prolonging their life. Unprotected wooden bridges usually deteriorated in 15 or 20 years. The covered

- MADISON
(continued)

Covered Bridges
(continued)

bridges also protected the traveler and could even afford a place to camp under shelter at night. Built to look much like a barn, the covered bridges were less likely to frighten farm animals and prevented them from stampeding when driven through the bridge, as they could not see the rushing waters below. Such bridges also served as the site of political rallies and revival meetings, and as public bulletin boards. Children played inside the bridges on rainy days, and lovers found them a romantic place to slowly ride through in a buggy, which led to calling them "kissing bridges." The old bridges were also the scene of robberies, holdups, murders, and hangings. One of the Madison County covered bridges (Roseman) is haunted, according to local legend.

● **Earlham Historical Preservation Society**
Earlham, Iowa

Mrs. Ted Harris, President
Earlham, Iowa 50072

Meetings: Three times a year
Number of Members: 200
Dues: $1.00 annual
Museum Open: Sunday, 2:00-5:00 p.m. during summer
Admission: Free; donations accepted

Operates a museum located in the town's first permanent public school building. The limestone and brick structure dates back to 1871. The museum contains such items as an old horse-drawn fire hose cart, early Quaker clothing, old farm machinery, toys, an early Presbyterian church organ, old school books and religious volumes, bound copies of *The Breeder's Gazette* from the 1890's, and antiques. The Society is also interested in the preservation of other historic landmarks in the community.

● **John Wayne Birthplace**
Winterset, Iowa

John Wayne, whose real name is Marion Michael Morrison, and whose father was a druggist, was born on May 26, 1907 in Winterset, Iowa, although there is disagreement as to the exact location of his birthplace. While in Winterset, the family lived in several different homes. John Wayne's nickname, "Duke," is said to have come from the name of the family dog. The Morrisons moved to California where the future motion picture star was a star high school football player. John Wayne got his first job in the motion picture industry as fourth assistant property man under director John Ford. Wayne was named the top money making Hollywood star in 1950. In 1969, after 40 years in motion pictures, he was awarded a best actor Oscar for his role as the fat, one-eyed marshal in "True Grit."

● **Madison County Historical Society**
Winterset, Iowa

George Mueller, President
R. R. 1
Van Meter, Iowa 50261
or
Henry C. Miller
515 W. Fremont
Winterset, Iowa 50273

Organized: 1904
Meetings: As called
Number of Members: 70
Dues: $1.00 annual; $25.00 life

A library and collection of relics related to Madison County history are preserved in 6 rooms on the third floor of the Madison County Courthouse, built in 1876 on the foundations of the original courthouse, destroyed by fire in 1875. The dignified building was designed by architect

61 - MADISON
(continued)

**Madison County
Historical Society**
(continued)

Alfred H. Piquenard, who also designed the State Capitol in Des Moines (see Polk County). The courthouse is constructed of native limestone quarried in Madison County. The solid walnut stairs and other interior woodwork are noteworthy. The dome, which rises 136 feet above ground level, is a familiar landmark.

The Society also publishes material on Madison County history and has restored and is maintaining the old stone North River or Bennett School built in 1874 and located north of Winterset. The schoolhouse is being appropriately furnished and is open during the Covered Bridge Festival and at other times by appointment.

● **Original Delicious Apple Tree**
Near Peru, in Madison County, Iowa

In 1870 a chance seedling apple tree was found in an orchard planted in the 1860's by Jesse Hiatt, a Quaker who came to Madison County in 1856. Mr. Hiatt cut the seedling down, but it sprouted and made a larger growth during the year, so he decided to let it grow and see what kind of fruit it would produce. From this original tree the Stark Nurseries developed the Delicious Apple. Some 10,000,000 trees have since come from its branches. A sudden freeze on November 11, 1940 killed the original tree, but from the stump new shoots have grown and these are now bearing apples. The famous tree is protected by an iron fence, and is located on private property. A glacial boulder marker, placed at the east side of Winterset City Park, commemorates the discovery.

● **Pammel State Park**
5 miles southwest of Winterset, off Iowa 92 at Iowa 162

State Conservation Commission
State Office Building
300 Fourth Street
Des Moines, Iowa 50319

This picturesque region was once called Devil's Backbone Park because of an unusual limestone ridge extending the length of the park. Its present name honors the late Dr. Louis H. Pammel of Iowa State University, who was a distinguished botanist and an early supporter of the conservation movement in Iowa. One of Pammel's students was George Washington Carver (see Story and Warren Counties), who worked with Dr. Pammel as his assistant at Ames for a period of 2 years.

A branch of Middle River winds through the 281-acre park, over limestone beds. Iowa's only highway tunnel passes through the ridge. This was formerly the water tunnel for old Backbone Mill, built in 1855-58 by William Harmon. The burrstone from the old gristmill, abandoned in 1904 and demolished in 1913, is preserved in a marker at the entrance to the park. Activities such as hiking, fishing, picnicking, and camping are popular.

MAHASKA

aloosa
G-8

- **Chief Mahaska Statue**
  West side of the public square
  Oskaloosa, Iowa

A statue of Chief Mahaska of the Ioway Tribe, modeled in Paris by Iowa sculptor Sherry Edmundson Fry. Chief Mahaska, for whom this county is named, lived at peace with the white man. He was slain in 1834 at the age of 50 years by another Indian, in what is now Cass County. The statue was presented to the City of Oskaloosa by James Depew Edmundson in memory of his father William Edmundson, who settled in present-day Iowa in 1836. He was appointed sheriff by the Territorial Legislature and was in charge of the organization of Mahaska County, completed May 13, 1844.

- **Frederic Knight Logan Home**
  416 B Avenue East
  Oskaloosa, Iowa

The home of composer Frederic Knight Logan (1871-1928), identified by a stone marker erected in 1940 by the Oskaloosa Chapter of the Daughters of the American Revolution. The 1½-story, rough red brick house, trimmed with stone, is privately owned. Logan composed *Missouri Waltz* (lyrics by his mother, Virginia Knight Logan), *Pale Moon, Blue Rose Waltz, Over the Hills, E'en as the Flower*, and other songs. He also acted as accompanist to Caruso, Schumann-Heink, and Edith Mason, and traveled with Maude Adams on her coast to coast repertoire tour.

- **Mahaska County Historical Society**
  Oskaloosa, Iowa

  Henry Hackert, President
  Allied Gas and Chemical Co.
  U.S. 63 South
  Oskaloosa, Iowa 52577

Organized: January 31, 1942
Meetings: Annual meeting in November
Number of Members: 432
Dues: $2.00 annual; $25.00 life

Owns and maintains the Nelson Homestead Pioneer Farm and Craft Museum (see below).

- **Nelson Homestead Pioneer Farm and Craft Museum**
  R. R. 1, Glendale Road
  Oskaloosa, Iowa 52577

  Mr. and Mrs. Ambrose Doller,
  Director and Curator
  R.R. 1
  Oskaloosa, Iowa 52577

Acquired: 1958, from the late Roy Nelson and his sister, Lillian Nelson
Admission: Area other than musuem free; museum $0.75; children 8-16 years old, $0.25; children under 8 free when accompanied by adult
Open: Tuesday through Saturday, 10:00 a.m.-5:00 p.m.; Sunday, 1:00-5:00 p.m.; closed Monday; May 12 through October 12

The 2-story farm house dating back to 1852 was built of bricks from a local kiln, and native timber, by Daniel Nelson on a 320-acre farm. It has been restored and furnished in the style of the period. The museum building is patterned after a Pennsylvania Dutch barn. Exhibits include furniture, quilts, clocks, books, antique tools, agricultural implements, war relics, and arrowheads. A log cabin, built in 1867, has been moved from Bussey, Iowa to the site of the original log cabin occupied by the Nelson family from 1844 until the brick house was completed. The barn, built in 1856 from native lumber cut on the farm, contains pioneer farm equipment, vehicles, and machinery. The 1861 Prine School was moved in 1966 from its original location west of Oskaloosa to the museum area. This 1-room rural school has been restored and furnished with

62 - MAHASKA
(continued)

**Nelson Homestead Pioneer Farm
and Craft Museum**
(continued)

double desks, classroom equipment, and school records. The Mott Country Store has been moved here from its original location in Lacey, Iowa and was restored in 1972.

Daniel Nelson owned 2 white mules, Becky and Jenny, that served in the U. S. Artillery during the Civil War. They lived out their remaining days on the farm, and are buried in a special plot, near the Museum -- "the only mule cemetery in Iowa."

A Pioneer Crafts Festival is held in September, with demonstrations of wool carding and spinning, dyeing, rosemaling, quilting, loom rug-weaving, candle dipping and molding, butter churning, cheese making, bread making, soap making, shingle making and woodworking, chair caning, harness making, blacksmithing, cider making, and other pioneer activities. The Daniel Nelson Home and Barn have been entered on the National Register of Historic Places (1974).

Seminars on the early crafts of Iowa pioneers are offered with courses in spinning and weaving, rug making, rosemaling, natural stain dyeing, caning, and pioneer technology.

63 - MARION

Knoxville
G-7

● **Big Rock Park**
North side of Pella, Iowa

Board of Park Commissioners
City of Pella, Iowa

Established: 1957

An 83-acre natural woodland area, named for a large glacial boulder. Trees and wild flowers are identified for the study and appreciation of nature. The park includes a prairie area, a shrub-dominated area, and a fine hardwood forest. Many varieties of bird, animal, and insect life may be seen.

● **Marion County Historical Society**
Marion County Park, west edge of Knoxville, Iowa

Carl R. McConeghey, President
401 West Robinson
Knoxville, Iowa 50138
or
Mrs. Carolyn May, Curator
309 S. First
Knoxville, Iowa 50138

Organized: March 1955
Meetings: Third Monday of month, 7:30 p.m.
Number of Members: 350
Dues: $2.00 annual
Museum Open: Saturday and Sunday, 1:00-6:00 p.m., May 1 - October 1; other times by appointment

The Society's museum, now containing over 15,000 items, has previously been located in the Marion County Courthouse, Belknap's Jewelry Store, and the former milk house of the Veterans Administration Farm, in Marion County Park. Construction on a new museum building was begun during the summer of 1969 and opened in May 1970. A Red Schoolhouse (Pleasant Ridge School built in 1874), a rural church (Valley Church), a reconstructed log cabin from near Pleasantville, a small C.B. & Q. railway depot (Donnelly Station), and a wooden covered bridge (half of the old Marysville, Iowa covered bridge) have been moved to the park and restored. A garden with plants and shrubs native to Iowa is being developed. There is also a small lake, and a picnic and a camping area in the park.

COUNTY AND COUNTY SEAT; LOCATION ON MAP	NAME AND LOCATION	DESCRIPTION

- MARION
(continued)

Marion County Historical Society
(continued)

A botanical garden at the Veterans Administration Hospital, nearby, may also be visited.

- **Pella Historical Society**
507 Franklin Street
Pella, Iowa

Paul Farver, President
501 Lincoln Street
Pella, Iowa 50219
                or
Dennis H. Steenboek, Secretary
507 Franklin Street
Pella, Iowa 50219

Organized: August 24, 1965
Number of Members: 300
Dues: $5.00 annual
Admission to Museum: $0.50; students, $0.25; children under 12 free
Museum Open: Week days, 8:30 a.m.-noon and 1:00-5:00 p.m.

Sponsors the annual Tulip Time Festival in May, when there are conducted tours of the community, street scrubbing, folk dancing, parades, and stage presentations.

The Pella Historical Site includes tulip beds; a museum displaying antiques, farm machinery and equipment, Dutch artifacts, and Americana of the mid-1800's; the Van Spankeren Store in the Wynberg Dwelling; the Beeson-Blommers Mill (from near Lynnville); the Werksplatt (old-fashioned carpenter shop); and the boyhood home of frontiersman and Western law man, Wyatt Earp, who lived here from age 2 to 16. His part in the taming of the Old West has become legend and the subject of motion pictures and television programs.

In downtown Pella, there has been an extensive remodeling program by business firms to create an Old World atmosphere symbolic of the Netherlands.

- **Red Rock Lake**
Dam located 6 miles southwest of Pella, Iowa

Red Rock Lake Association
320 East Robinson
Knoxville, Iowa 50138

An $80 million project which includes a 9,000-acre reservoir, complete recreational facilities, natural areas including a large waterfowl preserve, and points of historic interest. The dam itself is 1¼ miles long, 100 feet high, 600 feet wide at the base, and 44 feet wide at the top, and supports a highway. The longest bridge in the Midwest crosses the Des Moines River (Iowa 14) over Red Rock Lake and overlooks the former pioneer village of Red Rock. Normal river flow passes through 14 concrete culverts in the base of the spillway, while 5 large gates on top control overflow water.

This area was a popular spot with Indian tribes who called the red and yellow bluffs Painted Rocks. Red Rock Lake is named for the remnants of red limestone still visible at the upper end of the lake, where 19th Century quarries were operated.

The Hiawatha-Pioneer Trail runs through the area. The migratory waterfowl refuge, a portion of the Red Rock Game Management Area, affords an opportunity to view the thousands of geese and ducks that stop here to feed and rest during migration. Large fields of goose browse are planted to attract the wild flocks. The refuge itself consists of 10,683 acres and is closed to hunting at all times. Except for the migration period, September 15 to December 15,

63 - MARION
(continued)

Red Rock Lake
(continued)

the refuge is open for such recreational activities as fishing, boating, and hiking.

Wilcox Wildlife Area includes irregularly-shaped lakes and badlands created by strip mining, and provides a popular spot for rock and fossil hunting. Forty feet of the original 80-foot-long Marysville, Iowa wooden covered bridge has been moved from its original site to a road over a small creek in the park.

Roberts Creek County Park, located on the north side of the reservoir, about 7 miles west of Pella, covers 1,535 acres centered around a 300-acre lake. Facilities are provided for swimming, picnicking, boating, and camping.

Elk Rock State Park (north and south units) includes about 900 rolling, wooded acres on the shores of Red Rock Lake, and is being developed for a variety of recreational activities--picnicking, hiking, fishing, boating, and camping.

64 - MARSHALL

Marshalltown
E-7

● **C. D. Coppock County Park**
3 miles west of Le Grand, Iowa,
off U. S. 30

Marshall County Conservation Board
Garry L. Brandenburg, Executive Officer
R. R. 2
Marshalltown, Iowa 50158

An area of 9 acres obtained from the U.S. Government by C. D. Coppock in 1855, together with adjacent land. Some time later, the timber was cleared and the logs were used for mine timbers. The present stand of second growth timber includes oak, maple, hickory, ironwood, black walnut, and elm. No pasturing has been done on the tract, so there is an abundance of wild flowers and a dense growth of underbrush, including gooseberries and blackberries. Recreational uses include picnicking and camping.

● **Central Iowa Genealogical Society**

Mrs. Barbara Price,
  Corresponding Secretary
406 New Castle Road
Marshalltown, Iowa 50158

Organized: 1965
Meetings: Third Sunday of month, 2:00 p.m., except July and August
Number of Members: 63
Dues: $1.00

A local chapter of the Iowa Genealogical Society (see Polk County). A surname index has been prepared; supplements are to be added. The Society also sponsored a facsimile reprint of the 1878 *History of Marshall County*, with the addition of a name index.

● **Historical Society of Marshall County**
Marshalltown, Iowa 50158

James R. Bradbury, President
R. R. 5
Marshalltown, Iowa 50158

Organized: 1908
Meetings: Quarterly
Number of Members: 75
Dues: $1.00 annual

Collects and preserves materials related to the history of Marshall County; erects historical markers; and publishes historical matter. Guided tours and educational programs for school children are offered.

A Memorial Log Cabin was built in Riverview Park at the end of North 3rd Avenue in 1936-37 to honor pioneers who came here prior to 1885. The project was financed by descendents of these early settlers.

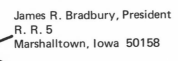

- MARSHALL
(continued)

● **Susie Sower Historical House**
129 East State Street
Marshalltown, Iowa 50158

Admission: Donations accepted
Open: By appointment; annual open house

Susie Sower Historical House is maintained by court appointed trustees as a historical museum for use of the Historical Society of Marshall County. Built in 1860, it was occupied by the George Sower family from 1870 until the death of Susie Sower, the last survivor, in March 1952. The frame house was restored and repaired in 1958 and dedicated May 10, 1959. The house contains hand-carved woodwork and parquet flooring. Original furniture and furnishings of the Civil War period afford a glimpse of gracious living of the past century. The front hall, parlor, music room, kitchen, and master bedroom are featured. One room in the house contains a collection of Indian relics, including unusual arrowhead arrangements; original paintings by artist Charles Pushetonequa, Mesquakie Indian of Tama; and crinoids from the Le Grand, Iowa quarries.

Wetherbee Rural Schoolhouse (Taylor Township No. 4) has been moved to the Sower property and restored. The country school is furnished with old double desks, pot-bellied stove, recitation bench, organ, ABC reading chart, water bucket and dipper, and school bell.

● **Three Bridges Park**
1½ miles northwest of
Le Grand, Iowa

Marshall County Conservation Board
Garry L. Brandenburg, Executive Officer
R. R. 2
Marshalltown, Iowa 50158

A 12-acre tract bordering the scenic Iowa River, and covered by wild shrubs and native trees——oak, walnut, basswood, butternut, and elm. Many songbirds and small animals inhabit the area. There are exposed limestone bluffs and small caves, and one of the first rock quarries in Marshall County is located on the site. Rock for the Marshall County Courthouse was quarried here. The foundations of an early gristmill and the remains of an old log cabin may still be seen. There are nature and hiking trails and facilities for fishing, picnicking, and camping.

● **Timmons Grove County Park**
1¾ miles southwest of
Albion, Iowa

Marshall County Conservation Board
Garry L. Brandenburg, Executive Officer
R. R. 2
Marshalltown, Iowa 50158

A tract of approximately 198 acres of timberland, bisected by the Iowa River. The changing of the river channel around 1914 has left a number of bayous. Some 25 varieties of native trees, in addition to an abundance of wild flowers, herbs, and shrubs, make this a suitable area for nature study. A wide variety of songbirds live here, together with squirrels, rabbits, muskrats, raccoons, fox, deer, wood ducks, mallards, quail, and pheasants. Recreational activities include fishing, picnicking, hiking, and camping.

- MILLS

nwood
H-2

● **Early Trails Monument**
Near Glenwood, Iowa,
along U. S. 275

A marker erected by the Glenwood Chapter of the D A R commemorates the early trails across Mills County--the Dragoons in 1835, the Mormons in 1846, and the stagecoach in 1850. The Indians frequently followed animal trails, which were later used by the explorers, military detachments, and the pioneers. These footpaths became the earliest roads, used by wagons and coaches, and many new trails appeared during the great westward movement of the 1800's.

65 - MILLS
(continued)

● **House of a Thousand Bottles**
Nishna Vale Farm

Otha D. and Lola B. Wearin
Hastings, Iowa 51540

Admission: $0.50; children free
Open: By appointment

An extensive collection of character and figure bottles, glassware, and art objects housed in a museum building.

● **Hoyt House**
½ mile south and 1 mile east
of Hastings, Iowa

Historic home which served as a station on the Underground Railroad in the 1850's. Privately owned, the house is not open to the public. A stagecoach station was located just across the road.

● **Mills County Caves**
Oak Township, in northwest
Mills County

Several caves used by early-day outlaws and horse thieves. Horses stolen from the early settlers of the vicinity were hidden in the caves and sold by the outlaws to Mormons, emigrant parties, and California gold-rushers.

● **Mills County Historical Society**
P.O. Box 170
Glenwood, Iowa 51534

Raymond H. Mintle
207 East Florence
Glenwood, Iowa 51534

Organized: August 1957
Meetings: Twice a year or as called
Number of Members: 150
Dues: $1.00 annual
Admission to Museum: $0.25
Museum Open: Weekends, June-October; other times by
appointment

The Society owns and operates Mills County Historical Museum (a gift of the Mintle family) in Glenwood Lake Park. Exhibits include Indian artifacts, pioneer items, early American glass, furniture, clothing, dolls, farm implements, musical instruments, paintings, fabrics, and historical documents. There is also a country store and a country school.

● **Pony Creek Park**
3½ miles northwest of
Glenwood, Iowa

Mills County Conservation Board
Kelly Bartles, Executive Officer
R. R. 1
Pacific Junction, Iowa 51561

An area of 50 acres having natural, geological, historical, and archeological significance. About 1/3 of the tract lies in the Pony Creek Basin or Watershed, east of the Missouri River, and is characterized by irregular, broken, narrow ridges, steep slopes and deep gullied valleys, and loess bluffs. Timber covers much of the area. From the ridge top are scenic views of the Missouri River bottoms and the bluffs across the river in Nebraska and within the Pony Creek valley in Iowa. There are hiking trails in the park, and picnicking and camping are permitted.

This region was settled by pioneers during the last half of the 19th Century, and Mormons camped here on their way to the West. At least 3 sawmills were in operation during this early period. One family cut and hauled cordwood from here to the Council Bluffs area. Many of these early settlers were skilled in locating bee trees and sold honey. Prehistoric Indian camps and burial mounds have attracted archeologists to the area. An estimated 150 to 200 earth lodges, dating from 1000-1350, are located here. The Pony Creek Indian site is on the National Register of Historic Places.

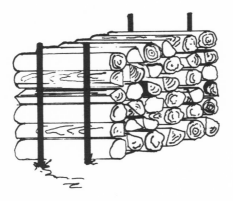

6 - MITCHELL

sage
A-8

● **Hamlin Garland Home**
Northeast of Osage, Iowa

Boyhood farm home of Iowa author Hamlin Garland (1860-1940). His *Son of the Middle Border* was autobiographical. Garland attended Cedar Valley Seminary in Osage from 1876 to 1881, and received his first literary inspiration while a student there. A marker honoring Garland was placed on the old Cedar Valley Seminary grounds on July 3, 1931.

● **Mitchell County Historical Museum**
North Sixth Street
Osage, Iowa

Dedicated: 1968
Admission: Free; donations accepted
Open: Friday, Saturday, and Sunday, 1:00-5:00 p.m., May to October

Old Central, on the former Cedar Valley Seminary campus, was leased by Mitchell County Historical Society (see below) in 1966 from Osage Community School District for use as a museum. The 2-story building was originally constructed by the people of Osage and financed by popular subscription. It was then presented to the Baptist Association, in August 1869, and used as an administration building for the newly established Seminary. Civil War and pioneer displays, old clothing, home furnishings, a doll collection, school and church records, tools, doctor's instruments, art by local painters, and a library are in the museum. In addition, there is a model sitting room, an old-time kitchen, and a bedroom. A music room contains many old musical instruments. Old conveyances include a covered wagon, an old 2-seated cutter made by the Case Automobile Company for its owner J. I. Case, and an old horse-drawn, enclosed rural mail delivery truck.

● **Mitchell County Historical Society**
North Sixth Street
Osage, Iowa

William H. Biedermann, President
R. R. 4
Osage, Iowa 50461

Organized: 1961
Meetings: Annual meeting second Wednesday in March
Number of Members: 260
Dues: $1.00 annual; $10.00 life

Activities include marking historic sites, conducting annual tours to historic areas, compiling histories of famous people and of Mitchell County, and preserving a rural school and a former log house. The Society operates the Mitchell County Historical Museum (see above).

● **New Haven Potholes**
2½ miles northwest of
New Haven, Iowa

Mitchell County Conservation Board
Roger W. Stevenson, Executive Director
East Main Street
Osage, Iowa 50461

A 168-acre wildlife area, largely marshland, near the Little Cedar River, with many small potholes. Vegetation includes marsh plants, wild flowers, and a stand of aspen trees. Plantings of prairie plants and conifers have been made. A nature trail winds through the area, for use of school groups and nature lovers. An information display is at the beginning of the trail.

66 - MITCHELL
(continued)

● **Otranto Community Park**
East edge of Otranto, Iowa

Mitchell County Conservation Board
Roger W. Stevenson,
Executive Officer
East Main Street
Osage, Iowa 50461

A recreational park of about 5 acres, located on the east bank of the Cedar River in northwest Mitchell County. At the park entrance is a 4-ton, cast-iron water wheel from the Otranto Mill, built in 1876 by E. A. Wilder and his 2 brothers, Nelson and Frank. The mill was operated by various owners until 1945 when it was torn down. The huge water wheel was recovered from the river in 1959 when a dam across the Cedar River was rebuilt. The wheel was placed at the park entrance in 1960.

● **St. Ansgar Mill**
1 mile southwest of St. Ansgar,
Iowa on blacktop road

A picturesque old water mill and dam on the Cedar River. The northern Iowa landmark was built in 1861. A cement dam was constructed in 1915 to replace the first dam made of brush and logs, and the tailrace has been filled in. The original source of power for the mill's operation was a water wheel; later, a water turbine was installed. Electricity was finally used to do custom grinding and manufacture livestock feeds. The town of St. Ansgar was settled in 1853 by Norwegians under the leadership of Reverend Claus L. Clausen.

67 - MONONA

Onawa
E-1

● **Ingeman Lutheran Church**
5 miles west of Moorhead, Iowa

Services have not been held in the white frame, steepled church since around 1952, but it is still kept up and is open to the public. Visitors may sign a guest book. Old residents of the area called this "the low church" to distinguish it from another Lutheran church that once stood about a mile away on a much higher elevation. Graves in the churchyard include 7 children of the John Johnson family who died of diphtheria in 1898.

- MONONA
(continued)

● **Lewis and Clark State Park**
2 miles west of Onawa on Iowa 175

State Conservation Commission
State Office Building
300 Fourth Street
Des Moines, Iowa 50319

Established: 1924

Named for Meriwether Lewis and William Clark, who were commissioned by President Thomas Jefferson in 1804 to head an expedition up the Missouri River and into the far Northwest, after the Louisiana Purchase. Members of the Lewis and Clark Expedition arrived in this area on August 9, 1804 and spent several days exploring the region and making observations on its geography and on the plant and animal life. The party camped at a spot opposite the present-day park, one of 9 different campsites in Iowa used between July 18 and August 21, 1804. The 286-acre park is situated on Blue Lake, an oxbow formed by the meandering of the Missouri River. When Lewis and Clark visited the region, the lake was part of the main channel of the river. Since then, the river has changed its course to the west, leaving the natural lake in the shape of an oxbow. Recreational facilities are available for fishing, swimming, water skiing, boating, snowmobiling, picnicking, and camping; nature trails crisscross the heavily wooded park; and there are flood plains and sandy areas adjacent to 982-acre Blue Lake.

● **Monona County Historical Society**

Wilson Gingles, President
Castana, Iowa 51010

Organized: January 21, 1973

● **Oldham Recreation Area**
1½ miles northwest of Soldier, Iowa

Monona County Conservation Board
Page W. Carlson, Chairman
P. O. Box 168
Soldier, Iowa 51572

A popular spot for fishing, boating, swimming, picnicking, camping, hiking, and bird watching. A 17-acre pond, created by an earthen dam, extends for over 1½ miles up a valley. Waterfowl, small animals, and other wildlife frequent the area. The park is used by schools and conservation groups for field instruction.

67 - MONONA
(continued)

- **Preparation Canyon State Park**
5 miles southwest of Moorhead, off Iowa 372

State Conservation Commission
State Office Building
300 Fourth Street
Des Moines, Iowa 50319

About 50 or 60 Mormon families, members of "Jehovah's Presbytery of Zion," settled at this point in 1853 and established the village of Preparation. Several thousand acres of choice land was acquired in the community and all property turned over to the head of the order as trustee. The colony was broken up because of dissension between Charles B. Thompson, the Mormon leader, known as "Father Ephraim" and Baneemy, and his followers. Most of the descendants of the colony at Preparation may be found today in the Reorganized Church of Latter Day Saints. The 187-acre park includes many small streams and springs, a variety of trees and wild flowers native to Iowa, canyons, and a commanding view of the rolling loess bluffs above the Missouri River flood plain. There are picnic facilities and trails for hiking and nature study.

- **Whiting Woods**
4 miles southwest of Mapleton, Iowa

Monona County Conservation Board
Page W. Carlson, Chairman
P. O. Box 168
Soldier, Iowa 51572

An 80-acre area covered with hardwood timber, many species of shrubs, and a variety of wild flowers. Foot trails through the forest preserve enable students and nature lovers to walk through the timbered areas to study and enjoy the wonders of nature. There is also a picnic area, and a pond provides fishing.

68 - MONROE

Albia
H-8

- **Albia Business District**
Albia, Iowa

Buildings around the town square and courthouse have been renovated and restored to their original Victorian charm. The colorful buildings, decorated with wrought iron and shutters, give a nostalgic look to the county seat town. This area was at one time among the chief coal fields in Iowa (see Coal Mining, below).

- **Coal Mining**
Various locations throughout Monroe County

Coal was discovered in Iowa in 1835, and was first mined in 1840. The coal found in Iowa is interlayed with shales, siltstones, sandstones, and limestones over an area of more than 20,000 square miles. The peak year in coal production in Iowa was 1917, when from 350 to 400 mines were in operation and 9,049,806 tons of coal were produced. Monroe County was once one of the important soft coal mining areas in the state. Many towns of 1,000 or more population were dependent upon the mines. In 1910, Iowa employed 18,005 coal miners, but by 1969 the number had declined to 176. With the decreased demand for soft coal following World War II, many of the mines closed and miners moved away, leaving ghost towns. Consol (northwest of Albia) once had the largest coal producing mine west of the Mississippi River. Bucknell (west of Consol) is an abandoned mining town, with houses and foundations remaining to outline the once busy streets.

Buxton (north of Albia, near the county line), once a community of 9,000 people, was the largest coal mining town in Monroe County. During its heyday, a large

- MONROE
(continued)

Coal Mining
(continued)

population of Negroes was brought here from the South to work in the mines. Several churches were established, and the town had a YMCA, baseball team, and a band. The town eventually faded into oblivion, but for many years former residents had an annual reunion, the Buxton Picnic.

Buxton

By 1975, only 1 coal mine was still operating in Monroe County--a shaft mine at Melrose. Three other Iowa counties still have operating coal mines--Lucas (Chariton), Mahaska (Oskaloosa), and Marion (Bussey, Pella and Otley). Lovilia Coal Mine No. 4 in Monroe County is now the largest underground coal mine in Iowa. In 1970 this mine produced 250,841 tons of coal and had 6 surface employees and 17 men working underground. Virtually all of the coal mined in Iowa is consumed within the state by electric power plants and in heating public buildings.

- **Georgetown Rest Area**
8 miles west of Albia, Iowa,
along U.S. 34

Monroe County Conservation Board
John Yenger, Executive Administrator
308 North 8th Street
Albia, Iowa 52531

Rev. Paul Donahue
St. Patrick's Catholic Church
R. R. 2, Albia, Iowa 52531

A 3-acre wooded area between old U.S. 34 and the relocated U.S. 34, near the historic St. Patrick's Catholic Church at the little settlement of Georgetown. The area is owned by the church and maintained under a lease agreement with Monroe County Conservation Board. Picnic facilities are provided.

St. Patrick's Church is open to visitors (north entrance) except when the pastor is away from the parish. At one time this was the Mother Church for a number of Catholic churches in the area. Construction was begun on St. Patrick's Church in 1860 and was completed after the Civil War. The building is 100 by 60 feet, and 50 feet high. It was built of native stone hauled by ox cart from a nearby quarry. A log cabin church preceded the present church whose interior, redecorated sometime after 1958, is considered one of the handsomest in southern Iowa. The settlement of Georgetown was originally called Staceyville.

- **Kendall Place**
209 Benton Avenue East
Albia, Iowa 52531

The home of Iowa Governor Nathan E. Kendall (1868-1936). The 2-story home was presented to the City of Albia in 1923 for use of the Albia Women's Club and as a community center. Kendall, a self-educated lawyer, who served as Iowa's Governor from 1921 to 1925, was a polished speaker, noted for his brilliant oratory. At his

68 - MONROE
(continued)

Kendall Place
(continued)

request, Governor Kendall's ashes were placed in an urn and buried under the flagstone walk, about 3 feet in front of a marble seat and memorial on the lawn of his former home in Albia.

● **Monroe County Historical Society**
Albia, Iowa

Charles W. Wever, President
315 South B Street
Albia, Iowa 52531

Organized: 1959
Meetings: Monthly
Number of Members: 125

After a period of inactivity, the Society now plans a local museum and library. Halfway Prairie School, originally located halfway between Albia and Eddyville, Iowa, on the old stagecoach road, was preserved for a time, but can no longer be seen.

● **Stephens State Forest**
Scattered areas in Appanoose, Davis, Lucas, and Monroe Counties

A forest preserve consisting of 6 separate units in south central Iowa. For additonal information, see Lucas County.

● **Trussell Cemetery**
5 miles southwest of
Blakesburg, Iowa

A small Mormon cemetery in Urbana Township. The Mormons reportedly camped on the farm of Aaron Stocker, one of several Mormon camps along the Old Southwest Trail, going West. Due to sickness and starvation many died and, at this particular camp, following the death of 3 Mormons, Trussell Cemetery was started with their graves. Mr. Stocker purchased his 160 acres of government land for $200 on June 2, 1847. The gravestones are of sandstone, buried deep in the earth. Bordering the little cemetery on 2 sides is prairie hay, used by early settlers for pasture.

Humakona House, located on the Old Southwest Trail, was once used as a post office and stagecoach stop.

69 - MONTGOMERY

Red Oak
H-3

● **Chautauqua Park Pavilion**
Red Oak, Iowa

Travis Tinsley, Chairman
Chautauqua Pavilion Restoration
  Committee
Red Oak, Iowa 51566

The round, steel and wood outdoor pavilion being preserved in memory of the Chautauqua Era in Iowa. (See Des Moines County, also.) Built in 1908, the pavilion cost $5,200 and seated nearly 5,000 persons. Actually, the first Chautauqua was held in Red Oak from June 29 to July 5, 1905. Large canvas tents were used for the first 3 seasons. Jane Addams, Irvin S. Cobb, William Jennings Bryan, Henry Wallace, Senator Robert LaFollette, and evangelists Billy Sunday and Gypsy Smith were among those appearing on programs. The pavilion was used until 1929 and is one of the few remaining. It was placed on the National Register of Historic Places in May 1972.

Chautauqua was founded at Chautauqua Lake, New York in 1874 as a system of summer school and correspondence school education for Sunday school teachers and workers. From this religious beginning, programs were broadened to include general education and popular entertainment. The tent Chautauquas were organized later and operated throughout the United States until well into the 20th Century. Iowa was among the first states to become identified with the Chautauqua movement. Traveling groups went from town to town giving programs of lectures, readings, concerts, and recitals in large tents or permanent pavilions. In the peak year of 1924, traveling or circuit Chautauquas visited some 10,000 communities and were attended by over 40 million persons. With the coming of the automobile, radio, motion pictures, and other forms

- MONTGOMERY
(continued)

Chautauqua Park Pavilion
(continued)

of entertainment, the popularity of chautauqua decreased after 1925.

● **Stanton Historical Society**
Stanton, Iowa

Donald A. Peterson, President
P. O. Box 215
Stanton, Iowa 51573

Incorporated: February 18, 1975
Number of Members: 100

The Society is restoring and furnishing a rural schoolhouse, moved from its original location to Main Street in Stanton.

● **Viking Lake State Park**
Off U.S. 34,
3 miles east and 1 mile south of
Stanton, Iowa

State Conservation Commission
State Office Building
300 Fourth Street
Des Moines, Iowa 50319

Established: 1957

Viking Lake is an artificial impoundment of 150 acres with 4½ miles of shoreline. The hills and valleys in this general area were once favored as campsites by the Indians. Many artifacts were discovered when the dam was built to form the lake, and at least one Indian burial site is now under water at the northeast corner of the lake. Part of the nearly 1,000 acres included in the park has been left undeveloped. Wild flowers common to the area may be seen, as well as beavers, muskrats, deer, ducks, shore birds, and song birds. There are foot trails for hiking, and facilities for picnicking, boating, swimming, fishing, and camping.

- MUSCATINE

scatine
-12

● **Alexander G. Clark House**
209 West 3rd Street
Muscatine, Iowa

A 2½-story brick double house built in 1878 by Alexander G. Clark (1826-1891), Iowa's most prominent black man of the post-Civil War period, who came to Muscatine in 1842. The house was saved from demolition in last minute efforts and moved to another lot nearby. It is being preserved as a repository for Iowa black history in recognition of Clark's many accomplishments. He was a successful businessman, lawyer, orator, editor, and civil rights advocate. In 1867, Clark's 12-year-old daughter Susan was denied admission to a Muscatine grammar school. Clark brought suit against the local school board and in a decision by the Iowa Supreme Court the following year, it was ruled that all children--regardless of race, religion, nationality, or any other distinctions which would deny equality of educational opportunity--could attend common school in Iowa--a landmark decision. Clark was also the guiding spirit of Iowa's first "Colored Convention," which urged the Legislature to pass a black suffrage amendment to the Iowa Constitution. This was done by striking the word "white" from the Constitution as it originally stood. The amendment was submitted to a vote of the people and adopted in 1868. Clark's son, Alexander, Jr., was the first black student admitted to The University of Iowa Law College, in 1878, and became its first black graduate. When Clark himself was 57, he entered the same school and became the second black graduate. He was admitted to the Muscatine Bar Association in 1884. He was active in the Republican Party during the reconstruction period, and was referred to as "the colored orator of the West." He was also a prominent Mason. Clark was appointed minister resident and consul-general to Liberia in 1890 by U. S. President Benjamin Harrison. Clark died of malaria in 1891 and lies buried in Greenwood Cemetery in Muscatine.

70 - MUSCATINE
(continued)

● **Laura Musser Art Gallery and Museum**
1314 Mulberry Avenue
Muscatine, Iowa 52761

Clifford J. Larson, Director

Opened to Public: May 15, 1966
Admission: Free
Open: 10:00 a.m.-noon and 2:00-5:00 p.m., Tuesday through Saturday; 2:00-5:00 p.m., Sunday; 7:00-9:00 p.m., Tuesday and Thursday; closed Monday

A gift of the Laura Musser McColm Atkins estate to the City of Muscatine, featuring displays of historic artifacts and works of art. The municipal museum is housed in a 24-room mansion built in 1908 by Peter Musser for his daughter Laura. Mr. Musser made his fortune in the lumber business. The formal parlor and dining room have been maintained essentially as they were when the Musser family used them.

The permanent collection on display includes silver, pewter, pottery, china, cut glass, ivories, carved teakwood, vases, paper weights, table linens, drawings, water colors, and oil paintings. The Muscatine Room houses a display representing old-fashioned rooms. Other rooms display relics used by Muscatine County soldiers during the Civil War, industrial exhibits of products of Iowa industries and businesses, and historical objects related to Muscatine and the old steamboating days on the Mississippi River. Traveling art exhibits, art classes, and lectures are also featured. The music room wing (1921) is used as an assembly room (capacity of 85) for meetings, programs, recitals, and musicales. An Estey player pipe organ made in Brattleboro, Vermont is played for museum visitors.

The museum is surrounded by 4 acres of landscaped grounds, including a formal garden and Japanese tea garden. The grounds are used for outdoor concerts, art shows, art classes, and landscape work.

● **Muscatine Area Heritage Association, Inc.**
705 West 4th Street
Muscatine, Iowa 52761

John J. Witmer, President
R.R. 1
Moscow, Iowa 52760

Incorporated: August 6, 1971
Meetings: Second Thursday of month, September through November and February through April; annual meeting first Monday in May
Number of Members: 70
Dues: $3.00 individual; $5.00 family; $25.00 individual life; $50.00 family life

Offers programs on local history, featuring then and now scenes in the Muscatine area, and publications. A museum is planned.

● **Muscatine Island**
South of Muscatine, Iowa

A 27,000-acre "island" of sand and gravel, formed by the Mississippi River when it changed channels. Once the site of a Union Army camp during the Civil War, the area is noted today for its production of watermelons, cantaloupes, cucumbers, potatoes, sweet potatoes, pumpkins, cabbage, sweet corn, squash, peppers, and tomatoes. Muscatine melons have been grown here in the sandy soils since about 1860 and have become famous for their good flavor.

Around 1914, Muscatine had some 35 button factories, and was known as the Pearl Button City of the United States. Button blanks and buttons of various sizes and kinds were made from fresh water clam shells and shipped all over the

0 - MUSCATINE
(continued)

Muscatine Island
(continued)

world. The shells were brought to Muscatine from the rivers to be manufactured into buttons--a multi-million dollar business. Muscatine was also the home of the largest button machinery manufacturing industry, had 2 of the largest sash and door plants in the world, and was noted for its seed and vegetable farms.

● **Nye Cemetery Historical Site**
¼ mile south of Wild Cat Den
State Park

Muscatine County Conservation Board
Daryl F. Kothenbeutel, Executive Officer
Muscatine, Iowa 52761

This 2-acre tract contains the grave of Benjamin Nye and other early settlers in the county. (See Wild Cat Den State Park, below.)

● **Pecan Grove**
2 miles southwest of
the city limits of Muscatine

State Conservation Commission
State Office Building
300 Fourth Street
Des Moines, Iowa 50319

The only natural stand of pecan trees in Iowa. The 25-acre tract is located along Muscatine Slough, which was formerly the channel of the Mississippi River. There are 47 mature trees and hundreds of smaller ones and seedlings, making this the largest stand of pecan trees in Iowa. There is presently no public access to the grove.

● **Salisbury Bridge Recreation Area**
10 miles northwest of Muscatine, Iowa
on county road

Muscatine County Conservation Board
Daryl F. Kothenbeutel, Executive Officer
Muscatine, Iowa 52761

A 74-acre general purpose recreation area adjacent to Salisbury Bridge over the Cedar River. Additional land is being acquired. Natural areas exist along the river banks, with open grassy meadows and several wooded sections containing a wide variety of native trees and dense underbrush. Chicken Creek merges with the Cedar River approximately 1 mile south of the recreation area. The park site is used for picnicking, camping, nature study, fishing, and boating.

● **Weed Park**
East edge of Muscatine, Iowa

A city park named for the donor. A total of 18 horseshoe-shaped Indian mounds, of which some 16 are undisturbed, are located within the park. The others have been excavated during construction activities. A zoo is located in the park which extends over wooded hills and bluffs overlooking the Mississippi River and its many islands and bayous.

● **Wild Cat Den State Park**
3 miles east of Fairport, Iowa,
off U.S. 22 on Iowa 389

State Conservation Commission
State Office Building
300 Fourth Street
Des Moines, Iowa 50319

Old Mill Open: Sunday, or by appointment for groups

The 322-acre area was donated to the state by the Brandt sisters, who lived here at one time. The heavily timbered terrain includes 100-foot cliffs, rock formations with such descriptive names as "Steamboat Rock," "Devil's Punch Bowl," "Fat Man's Squeeze," and "Horseshoe Bend." Names carved in the rocks over a century ago may be seen. Picturesque trails wind through the park. As many as 25 varieties of ferns have been identified, including walking leaf, polypody, and maidenhair, and wild flowers are here in abundance.

A mill built in 1850 on Pine Creek by Benjamin Nye, one of the first settlers in Muscatine County (he settled here in 1834), has been restored. The well-preserved mill is one of 3 built by Mr. Nye in this vicinity. (The first was built in 1839.) Although the mill ceased to operate in 1927, most of the machinery, grain chutes, and encased millstones are

70 - MUSCATINE
(continued)

Wild Cat Den State Park
(continued)

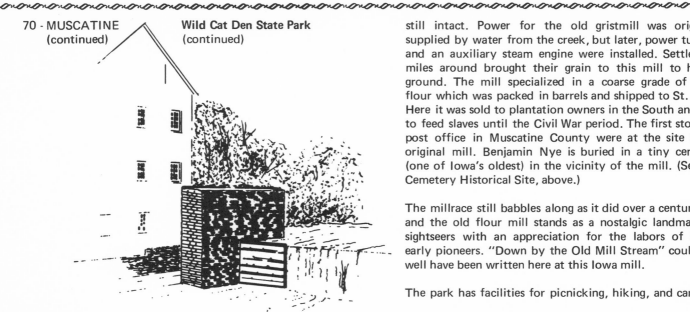

still intact. Power for the old gristmill was originally supplied by water from the creek, but later, power turbines and an auxiliary steam engine were installed. Settlers for miles around brought their grain to this mill to have it ground. The mill specialized in a coarse grade of wheat flour which was packed in barrels and shipped to St. Louis. Here it was sold to plantation owners in the South and used to feed slaves until the Civil War period. The first store and post office in Muscatine County were at the site of the original mill. Benjamin Nye is buried in a tiny cemetery (one of Iowa's oldest) in the vicinity of the mill. (See Nye Cemetery Historical Site, above.)

The millrace still babbles along as it did over a century ago, and the old flour mill stands as a nostalgic landmark for sightseers with an appreciation for the labors of Iowa's early pioneers. "Down by the Old Mill Stream" could very well have been written here at this Iowa mill.

The park has facilities for picnicking, hiking, and camping.

Acquired for Restoration: 1965

71 - O'BRIEN

Primghar
B-2

● **Covey Church Park**
7 miles south of Hartley, Iowa on blacktop road, or 8 miles northeast of Primghar, Iowa

O'Brien County Conservation Board
Jack Mau, Executive Officer
Paullina, Iowa 51046

A highway rest and picnic area adjacent to the first wooden frame church and the second church established in O'Brien County. The church was named for Reverend John Covey. Originally a Congregational Church, it was later a Methodist Church, and is now being preserved as a historic landmark. The old pews and other furnishings have been saved. The site is bordered on the west and north by large spruce trees. A cemetery is located across the road.

● **Litka Park**
6½ miles northeast of Sutherland, Iowa on county road

O'Brien County Conservation Board
Jack Mau, Executive Officer
Paullina, Iowa 51046

A wooded area along Waterman Creek, a tributary of the Little Sioux River, with various types of trees, shrubs, and wild flowers. The 4-acre park, half of which was acquired as a gift from Arnold and Verda Litka, is used as an outdoor classroom for nature study, and for picnicking.

● **O'Brien County Historical Society**
Primghar, Iowa

William B. Schwartz, President
Sheldon, Iowa 51201
or
Mrs. John (Caroline) Bohan,
Secretary-Treasurer
Primghar, Iowa 51245

Incorporated: November 19, 1941
Reactivated: November 1970
Meetings: Third Tuesday evening of each month
Number of Members: 230
Dues: $2.00 annual; $1.00 student

The first hotel in Primghar--the Grand--is being restored by the Society for use as a museum. The 2-story frame building was originally 3 times its present size. The other 2/3 of the hotel was removed and used for 2 dwellings, one of which is still standing. There will be rooms in the museum to represent a pioneer living room, dining room, kitchen, and bedroom. Displays of items related to O'Brien County history will include an oxbow that came across the prairie, farm machinery, trundle bed, and Indian artifacts. Each town in the county is compiling a scrapbook of pictures, clippings, and papers for display on a large table.

- O'BRIEN
(continued)

● **Sheldon Historical Society**
Wesley Hebrink, President
Sheldon, Iowa 51201

Organized: 1972
Meetings: Monthly
Dues: $1.00 annual

● **Wittrock Indian Village Site**
4 miles east of Sutherland on
blacktop county road, 3/4 mile
south on gravel, and 1/2 mile
west through a field

State Conservation Commission
State Office Building
300 Fourth Street
Des Moines, Iowa 50319
    or
Alfred Wittrock
Sutherland, Iowa 51058

Acquired: 1936

A 5-acre tract of prairie land preserved as the site of an
ancient village occupied by Indians of the Mill Creek
Culture. The fortified village covered about 1½ acres and
contained 17 houses inside a log stockade protected by a
rampart and moat. The village, which dates back to about
1200, was discovered by archeologists in the summer of
1965. The first fortified Indian village was found in Iowa,
near Lansing, in 1964. The Wittrock Indian Village Site was
dedicated as a National Historic Landmark in October
1965. The site is essentially undisturbed by cultivation or
relic-hunting, and is inaccessible except by foot.

- OSCEOLA

ley
-2

● **Johnson Wilderness Area**
1 mile southeast of Allendorf, Iowa

Osceola County Conservation Board
Joseph E. Clarey, Jr., Secretary
Box 182
Sibley, Iowa 51249

Six acres of timber and grassland located on both sides of
the Ocheyedan River, maintained as a wildlife habitat. A
majority of the trees, consisting of cottonwood, ash, aspen,
and willow, were planted in the early 1870's as a tree claim.

Tree claims were authorized to encourage the
establishment of shelterbelts and woodlots in areas barren
of trees. The 1873 *Code of Iowa* (in Title VI, Chapter 1,
Section 798) provided that "For every acre of forest trees
planted and cultivated for timber within the state, the trees
thereon not being more than twelve feet apart and kept in a
healthy condition, the sum of one hundred dollars shall be
exempted from taxation upon the owner's assessment, for
ten years after each acre is so planted. For every acre of
fruit trees planted and suitably cultivated within the state,
the trees thereon not being more than thirty-three feet
apart and kept in a healthy condition, the sum of fifty
dollars shall be exempted from taxation upon the owner's
assessment, for five years after each acre is planted. Such
exemption shall be made by the assessor at the time of the
annual assessment, upon satisfactory proof that the party
claiming the same has complied with this section; and the
assessor shall return to the board of equalization the name
of each person claiming exemption, the quantity of lands
planted to timber or fruit trees, and the amount deducted
from the valuation of his property."

Section 799 of the 1873 *Code* continues, "The board of
supervisors may exempt from taxation for any one year,
except for state purposes, an amount not exceeding five
hundred dollars for each acre of forest trees less than three
years old, planted and suitably cultivated for timber, or for
each one-fourth mile of hedge, or for each one-fourth mile
of shade trees along the public highway, or for each acre of
fruit trees not more than three years old, and also a
proportionate exemption for each one-fourth mile of
hedge, or one-fourth mile of shade trees along the public
highway ....But no person shall have any personal property

72 - OSCEOLA
(continued)

Johnson Wilderness Area
(continued)

more than one-half his real estate exempted under this and the foregoing section, nor shall there be any exemption on account of nursery trees grown for sale...."

The Johnson Wilderness Area may be used for primitive camping, hiking, and hunting.

● **Ocheyedan Mound**
Near Ocheyedan, Iowa,
off Iowa 237

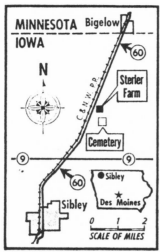

Copyright, 1974, Des Moines Register and Tribune Company

For many years this was considered the highest point in Iowa, 1,675 feet in altitude. However, in March 1971, a U.S. Government survey party found the mound to be only 1,613½ feet above sea level, and the highest point in Iowa was shifted to the northwest about 10 miles. The new high point--1669.85 feet above sea level--is northeast of Sibley at a point just below the Iowa-Minnesota border, in the hog lot on the Merrill Sterler farm. The long, flat ridge is not conspicuous, and there are other flat top ridges only 1 or 2 feet lower within a mile or so. One of these lies in Wilson Township Cemetery. The location (in Wilson Township) is NE ¼ of Section 29, Township 100 N, Range 41W. The lowest point in Iowa is at the confluence of the Des Moines and Mississippi Rivers, where the elevation is 478 feet above sea level.

The name Ocheyedan means "spot where they weep" and refers to the Indian custom of seeking elevations on which to mourn for their dead. This isolated glacial mound was formed during the recession of the Wisconsin Glacier, the last of 5 glaciers that invaded what is now Iowa. The mound rises 170 feet above the surrounding countryside, and served as a landmark to guide early travelers and settlers. The prairie, with its many small lakes and sloughs, afforded excellent hunting. On the surface of the mound are boulders of granite, limestone, and Sioux quartzite.

● **Osceola County Historical Society**
Sibley, Iowa

Ferd Jarrott, President
Ocheyedan, Iowa 51354

Miss Ferne Truckenmiller,
Museum Curator
Sibley, Iowa 51249
or
Mrs. Stella W. Fox
Sibley, Iowa 51249

Organized: 1936
Meetings: Annually, May 1
Number of Members: 65
Dues: $0.50 annually
Admission to Museum: Free
Museum Open: Sunday and holidays, 2:00-5:00 p.m.;
    other times by appointment

Maintains the Albert W. McCallum Museum, a protective, painted log building enclosing the H. K. Rogers House, located in Sibley City Park. The house is one of the first wooden dwellings built in the county, in 1871. Articles on display include Civil War guns, swords, and uniforms; china and glassware; farm and household equipment; manuscripts; and other items related to the history of the county.

Clarinda
I-3

- **Colonel W. P. Hepburn Home**
  321 West Lincoln Street
  Clarinda, Iowa 51632

  Dorothy Schwimmer , Owner

The home of William Peters Hepburn (November 4, 1833-February 7, 1916), who moved to Iowa at the age of 8 years with his parents. He served as U.S. Representative from Iowa for a total of 22 years, and was prominent in national affairs. He was the author of the Hepburn Law, which prohibits discrimination and rebates by railroads, and of the Pure Food and Public Health Act (59th Congress). Under a huge maple tree behind the home, President Theodore Roosevelt and Colonel Hepburn sat in 1903 and discussed plans for purchase of the Canal Zone and building the Panama Canal.

On the Clarinda High School grounds, a bronze tablet marks the site of the first schoolhouse in Clarinda, built in 1854, and commemorates the spot where President Roosevelt spoke on April 28, 1903.

Hepburn was editor and part owner of the *Clarinda Herald* and practiced law at various times in his life. The town of Hepburn, Iowa, located about 8 miles north of Clarinda, was named for him. During the Civil War, he organized and served as captain of Company B, 2nd Iowa Cavalry. He advanced to the rank of lieutenant colonel and served under the commands of Generals Sheridan and Rosecrans. When 8 companies of infantry and 1 of cavalry reported in 1878 for the Soldiers Reunion and Decoration Day Military Maneuvers and the election of field and staff officers, Hepburn was elected as colonel.

Colonel Hepburn died in Clarinda, where he had moved in 1867, and is buried in Clarinda Cemetery on North 16th Street.

The former Hepburn home is now privately owned, but arrangements may be made for tours. In the large frame house is a collection of original oil paintings, by a Polish artist, of the first 27 U.S. Presidents (through Woodrow Wilson).

- **Glenn Miller Home**
  South 16th and Clark
  on U.S. 71
  Clarinda, Iowa

Famous dance band leader, arranger, and trombonist Glenn Miller was born at Clarinda, March 1, 1904. This was his boyhood home. Miller formed his own band in 1936, and gained tremendous popularity which has continued long after his death in December 1944 in a mysterious airplane accident somewhere over the English Channel, toward the end of World War II. A marker has been erected by the Clarinda Lions Club near the Miller home.

- **Goldenrod School Museum**
  Page County 4-H Fairgrounds
  Clarinda, Iowa

Restored and Dedicated: August 5, 1965
Admission: Donations accepted
Open: First week in August, during 4-H Fair; other times by
    appointment.

A 1-room rural school built in 1873 and used until 1959 has been restored and furnished as it would have looked in

73 - PAGE
(continued)

Goldenrod School Museum
(continued)

the early 1900's. In this schoolhouse, Jessie Field Shambaugh began her work in 1901 with rural boys and girls in agriculture-- the beginnings of the 3-H and 4-H boys and girls clubs. She also served as Page County Superintendent of Schools, and was responsible for the first Boy's Farm Camp (1910). The old school was moved from Fremont Township through the efforts of Page County Historical Society (see below).

● **Nodaway Valley Park**
2 miles northeast of
Clarinda, Iowa, along U.S. 71

Page County Conservation Board
Dale C. Olson, Executive Officer
R. R. 1
Braddyville, Iowa 51631

A 72-acre tract preserved as a forest and wildlife area. The timber has existed since the earliest settlements in Page County. The land at first consisted of numerous small parcels of from 2 or 3 acres up to 10 or 15 acres, presumably for use as woodlots. The area is made up of a series of ridges and deep ravines, near the West Nodaway River. About 75 percent is in native second growth hardwood timber, notably burr oak. Glacial deposits are clearly visible throughout the area, particularly in the side slopes of the V-shaped ravines, which contain many boulders. The park abounds with wild flowers, songbirds, deer, and all of the small wild animals native to this area. The high ridges afford interesting scenic views of the entire valley. There are nature trails and facilities for picnicking and camping.

● **Page County Historical Society**
Clarinda, Iowa

Mrs. Anna Hausen, President
West Willow Street
Clarinda, Iowa 51632

Mrs. Wayne L. Whitmore, Secretary
620 South 16th Street
Clarinda, Iowa 51632
or
Ed. W. Fulk
1115 North 16th Street
Clarinda, Iowa 51632

Organized: 1963
Meetings: As called by Board
Number of Members: 152
Dues: $1.00 annual; $5.00 sustaining; $10.00 life; $10.00 business and professional

Sponsors or participates in antique shows, tours of historic homes, historical pageants, and showing of floats in holiday parades. A new county history is being written.

In Clarinda is the birthplace of Marilyn Maxwell (1922-72), noted singer, dancer, and motion picture and television actress.

Shenandoah is considered the nursery center of the United States. The oldest of the 6 nurseries located here dates back to 1870.

● **Pioneer Park**
8 miles east of
Shenandoah, Iowa, along Iowa 2

Page County Conservation Board
Dale C. Olson, Executive Officer
R. R. 1
Braddyville, Iowa 51631

A 22-acre naturally attractive site in the central part of Page County. Walnut Creek, bordered with a fringe of native trees and shrubs, flows through the area. The tract was a part of the original U.S. Department of Agriculture soil conservation experiment farms, and some of the improvements in the picnic area date back to the days of the Civilian Conservation Corps (C.C.C.). Camping and fishing are also permitted.

· PALO ALTO

metsburg
B-4

● **Grotto of the Redemption**
West Bend, Iowa 50597

Admission: Donations accepted
Open: Daily; conducted tours from June 1 to October 15

A monument in ornamental and semi-precious stones, covering 1 square block, depicts events in the life of Christ. Construction was begun in 1912 by Reverend Paul M. Dobberstein. Since his death in 1954, the work has been continued by Reverend L. H. Greving. There are 9 grottos and the 14 Stations of the Cross. Stones from every state in the Union and from nearly every country in the world make up one of the largest and most complete collections of minerals, fossils, shells, and petrifications in existence. The geological value is estimated at over $2,500,000.

● **Kearny State Park**
Emmetsburg, Iowa

State Conservation Commission
State Office Building
300 Fourth Street
Des Moines, Iowa 50319

Dedicated: July 4, 1944

A 40-acre tract of historical significance which includes a lake 5 miles long, dotted with 5 islands.

In 1820, Lieutenant Stephen Watts Kearny and his company of First U.S. Dragoons crossed the interior of Iowa on the first of 2 exploratory expeditions. One of their campsites, used in both journeys (1820 and 1835), was on the shore of Five Island Lake (formerly Medium Lake) near the present site of Emmetsburg. A large stone marker on the west shore of Five Island Lake shows the Dragoon Trail of 1835 across the State of Iowa. This park preserves the name of the leader of the military expedition--the first to explore northern and northwestern Iowa. Kearny, later to become a General, was one of the organizers of the U.S. Dragoons (soldiers on horseback), and, in 1835, was commandant of Fort Des Moines No. 1 near Montrose. He recommended against establishing a military post at Raccoon Forks (later Fort Des Moines No. 2). More than half of Kearny's military career was closely associated with Iowa, although, judging from his journals and writings, he was never much impressed with the land or climate of what is now the State of Iowa.

In 1871, some 50 years after Kearny's first exploratory expedition through this area, Alexander Peddie came here from Scotland. He bought a 40-acre tract on the west shore of the lake, planted many varieties of trees, including the seed of Scotch pine brought from his native land, and built a large mansion in a natural oak grove overlooking the lake. Peddie named the area Rutland Park after his ancestral home in Scotland. The house burned down in later years, but the trees remain in this area of natural beauty.

The park is operated by the City of Emmetsburg under a management agreement. Facilities are available for fishing, boating, golf (green fee), and picnicking.

74 - PALO ALTO
(continued)

● **Palo Alto County Historical Society**
Emmetsburg, Iowa

J. A. Graves, President
Emmetsburg, Iowa 50536

Organized: 1969
Meetings: Monthly
Number of Members: 62
Dues: $2.00 annual

The former Free Methodist Church has been acquired for a museum depicting pioneer life in Palo Alto County. Historic tours are also sponsored.

---

75 - PLYMOUTH

Le Mars
C-1

● **Kingsley Historical Society**
Kingsley, Iowa

Douglas T. Baker, President
P. O. Box 191
Kingsley, Iowa 51028

Organized: 1973
Meetings: Third Thursday of month
Number of Members: 15
Dues: $1.00 annual

Organized to preserve the history of the community. In 1974, the former land office in the now abandoned town of Quorn, in Elk Horn Township, was acquired under long-term lease, and is being restored. The Close Brothers, Englishmen, purchased and improved hundreds of acres of land in this area from 1878-80 for an English agricultural colony and as a speculative venture. Quorn (an English name), platted in October 1880, was located on the West Fork of Little Sioux River, but was later abandoned when the Chicago and North Western Railroad was built about 2 miles to the east, and the town of Kingsley, in Garfield Township, came into existence. A post office was in operation at Quorn from 1880 until 1883. The Society also maintains the old Quorn Cemetery and is researching burial records.

● **Plymouth County Historical Museum**
On U.S. 75, at entrance to Airport
P.O. Box 444
Le Mars, Iowa

Carol B. Parkinson, President
Lakeside Motel
Le Mars, Iowa 51031

Dr. Edwin C. Danner, Curator
Le Mars, Iowa 51031

Opened to Public: May 3, 1965
Admission: Free; donations accepted
Open: Daily, 1:00-5:00 p.m.; other times by appointment
Number of Members: 50
Membership: $10.00, plus annual dues of $2.50; $100.00 life

A historical complex of 4 buildings, including a 3-story museum building; an old school building, appropriately furnished; a 17-x 18-foot log cabin built in 1863 of hand-hewn oak logs, and completely furnished; and a building for antique cars and farm machinery.

The main building houses the famous Parkinson collection of ancient and historical musical instruments. Started in 1855 by G. W. Parkinson, the collection has remained in the family ever since.

- PLYMOUTH
(continued)

Plymouth County Historical Museum
(continued)

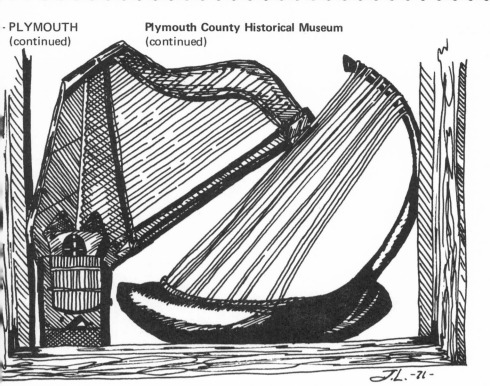

The more than 500 musical instruments include an Egyptian cradle harp from the King Tut Dynasty, dating back to 1450 B.C. (one of 5 priceless harps from the Miller Harp Collection, Bristol, England); an Irish battle harp; action harps (a foot pedal changes the tone); a Devil's harp (200 years old); an old pirate violin made of human and animal bones; violins from China, Hungary, India, Italy, Russia, and the Philippine Islands; jungle drums; an 1868 portable roller organ; music boxes; an organistrium (the official ecclesiastical musical instrument in England and France after the Reformation); an 1868 orchestrone; and an 1889 coin-operated music box. These instruments are played for concerts and demonstrations, and tape recordings of the music may also be heard during tours of the museum.

The Westmar College museum collection is also on display. There are Civil War items, guns, and historic small clay tablets of biblical times from Egypt. Plymouth County Historical Museum is jointly sponsored and financed by the Lions Club, City of Le Mars, Plymouth County Conservation Board, and other local organizations and business firms.

In 1969, a *History of Plymouth County* was published in recognition of its centennial, and, in 1974 the Museum sponsored the reprinting of *A. Warner & Company's 1891 History of the Counties of Woodbury and Plymouth, Iowa. Their early settlement and progress illustrated.*

● **Plymouth County Historical Society**
LeMars, Iowa

Mrs. Nelson (Esther) Brown, President
R. R. 2
Merrill, Iowa 51038

        or

J. Henry Lucken
317 6th Street, S.E.
LeMars, Iowa 51031

Organized: 1943
Meetings: As called; annual potluck picnic in July
Number of Members: 60
Dues: $0.50 annual

Organized to discuss and preserve local history and hear recollections of old-timers. Members provide articles for local newspapers.

76 - POCAHONTAS

Pocahontas
C-4

● **Kalsow Prairie**
1 mile west and 4½ miles north
of Manson, Iowa

State Conservation Commission
State Office Building
300 Fourth Street
Des Moines, Iowa 50319

Acquired: 1948

An example of original native Iowa prairie set aside as a
botanical monument. The 160-acre area includes flat
upland and lowland. A wide variety of prairie wild flowers
bloom through the seasons, with new faces almost every
week. A total of 230 species representing at least 35
different plant families have been identified here, including
oxeye daisy, compass plant, sunflowers, wild indigo, lead
plant, wild rose, golden Alexander, purple cone flower,
blazing star, and goldenrod. Prairies are able to survive
burning, but spraying is fatal. The plow was responsible for
the vanishing of most of our prairie flora.

● **Little Cedar Creek Game Farm**
Section Lane Road

Paul Mefford, Owner
526 North First
Laurens, Iowa 50554

Established: 1958; in present location since 1963
Admission: Free
Open: All year; tours on request

A 16-acre site devoted to the breeding of wild ducks, geese,
pheasants, partridge, quail, deer and other animals, all on
display. There are several ponds for waterfowl.

● **Little Clear Lake Park**
11½ miles west of Pocahontas, Iowa
1 mile off Iowa 3

Pocahontas County Conservation Board
E. I. Rosenberger, Executive Officer
1107 2nd Avenue, N.W.
Pocahontas, Iowa 50574

A 15-acre tract on the west shore of Little Clear Lake, an
excellent waterfowl marsh where migrating birds and small
game may be observed. The shallow natural lake covers
only 187 acres. The park may also be used for picnicking,
boating, fishing, hunting, and camping.

● **Lizard Lake Park**
6 miles southwest of
Gilmore City, Iowa

Pocahontas County Conservation Board
E. I. Rosenberger, Executive Officer
1107 2nd Avenue, N.W.
Pocahontas, Iowa 50574

The largest of the lakes in Pocahontas County, having
nearly 16,000 feet of shoreline, and covering approximately
280 acres. Many parts of the lake are quite shallow and
contain swampland grasses, which provide cover for
wildlife. Thousands of ducks, geese, and other game birds
stop to rest and feed here on their spring and fall flights.
Within the 67-acre park are Indian mounds, located in a
12-acre area on the east side of the lake. There are 4
separate areas which provide vantage points for viewing the
lake. Boating, fishing, hunting, picnicking, and camping are
permitted.

● **Pilot Creek Park**
3 miles east and 1 mile south
of Rolfe, Iowa on county road

Pocahontas County Conservation Board
E. I. Rosenberger, Executive Officer
1107 2nd Avenue, N.W.
Pocahontas, Iowa 50574

One of the few remaining primitive areas in Pocahontas
County, with rolling hills, and located about 1½ miles from
the Des Moines River. Pilot Creek crosses the park.
Vegetation includes native prairie grasses, wild gooseberries,
black raspberries, elderberries, strawberries, grapes, and
plums. Wild game, including deer and fox, frequent the
area. An acre of land on a hilltop west of the Youth
Recreation Area is in native virgin vegetation. Much of it is
similar to that found on Kalsow Prairie (see above).

- POCAHONTAS
(continued)

Pilot Creek Park
(continued)

The U.S. Government gave this and other lands to the Chicago and Northwestern Railway in the late 1800's to help finance construction of a railroad through sparsely settled prairie country.

An Indian battle, said to be the last fought on Iowa soil, took place within the boundaries of the park in 1853 or 1854. About 18 Sioux Indians made a moonlight attack on an encampment of around 30 Winnebago warriors. Ten Winnebagos lost their lives in the savage battle which followed. Things were going badly for them when a shot hit and killed the Sioux Chief Cou-sta-wa. One of the warriors serving under Cou-sta-wa was Inkpaduta (see Inkpaduta Trail, Clay County). The Sioux lost an estimated 7 warriors in the battle and finally withdrew, to return to the Dakotas. The Winnebagos returned to their reservation in Minnesota. The railway was later constructed directly through the battleground.

There are hiking trails in the park, and facilities for picnicking and camping.

● **Pocahontas County Historical Society**

Mrs. Arnold Schleusener, President
Laurens, Iowa 50554
or
Jessie Fae Schon
Rolfe, Iowa 50581

Organized: 1941
Reorganized: 1963
Meetings: Four times a year, including an Annual Dinner the third Monday in October
Number of Members: 135
Dues: $1.00 annual; $10.00 life

The Society has restored and furnished the last remaining log cabin in Pocahontas County, built in 1858 by Edward Tilley, near Old Rolfe. The present town of Rolfe is located about 2½ miles from Old Rolfe. The cabin is now located in Rolfe Memorial Park.

The 1867 Hait House, of classic Greek design, is to be restored as a museum. Other plans include the preparation of historical maps and uniform roadside markers at historic sites. A booth is maintained during the 4-H Fair, and the Society sponsored the reprinting of the 1904 *Pioneer History of Pocahontas County, Iowa.*

Three miles east of Rolfe is the site of one of the last Indian battles fought in Iowa (see Pilot Creek Park, above). A marker on the south side of the highway between Rolfe and Bradgate identifies the site.

● **Viking Mooring Stone**
near Rolfe, Iowa on farm
owned by James Martin

A glacial boulder, located in a pasture, is believed to be a Norse or Viking mooring stone. About 18 of the stones have been discovered in Canada, Minnesota, and Iowa. Each boulder has a nearly round hole, 1¼ inches in diameter, drilled to a depth of about 6 inches. A peg could have been inserted in the hole and used to anchor the boats of the Vikings at a time when this area was flooded. Others contend that the hole was drilled more recently for dynamite.

77 - POLK

Des Moines
F-6

● **Brown's Woods**
Southwest corner of
Des Moines, Iowa,
Just south of the
Raccoon River and
west of 63rd Street

Polk County Conservation Board
Wayne Bills, Executive Director
Jester Park
Granger, Iowa 50109

● **Chichaqua Wildlife Habitat**
5 miles east of Elkhart, Iowa

Polk County Conservation Board
Wayne Bills, Executive Director
Jester Park
Granger, Iowa 50109

Acquired: December 1972

A mature deciduous (oak-hickory) forest of 484 acres on the Raccoon River, between Walnut Woods and Water Works Park (see below). The tract was acquired at the beginning of this Century by Tallmadge E. Brown, and was deeded in 1922 to his son Louis P. Brown, who preserved it until his death in 1958 for future instructive or scientific purposes. The Brown estate sold the property to Polk County Conservation Board after lengthy negotiations. Such a large tract of woodland adjacent to a large metropolitan area makes it unique in Iowa. About 15 percent of the area is in the floodplain next to the Raccoon River. Uplands occur in the northeast part (1060 feet above mean sea level). Trees include white, bur, red, and black oak; basswood; shagbark hickory; ironwood; hackberry; black walnut; and elm. The woods provide habitat for a variety of wildlife, and such wildflowers as Dutchman's breeches, dog-toothed violet, wood anemone, rue anemone, jewelweed, Mayapple, violets, columbine, wild ginger, and wild geranium may be seen in season.

The timber is used for nature walks, bird watching, hiking, and photography.

A tract of over 1,166 acres in the flood plain of the Skunk River, straddling various parts of the river's meanderings. In 1920-21 a new channel was dug to carry the normal flow of the Skunk River, leaving the oxbows now included in the wildlife habitat. Ducks, geese, and pheasants are hatched here; crop and cover stations are provided for game.

The origin of the name Chichaqua is from the Algonquian word Checauque, meaning a rank, offensive odor, as of onions. Early survey records contained other variations in spelling, such as Chichaqua, Chacagua, or Shekagua. Another theory is that the Skunk River was so named because of the large number of skunks (Mephitis mephitis) living along its banks. Maps dating back to 1810 also refer to the stream as the Polecat River. In French, the name was Bête Puante, meaning stinking beast.

There are wildlife exhibits; and canoeing, ice skating, wilderness hiking and primitive camping, fishing and hunting are authorized within Polk County's largest park. A heavy timber area and duck marsh provide the habitat for observing geese, ducks, raccoon, deer, rabbits, possum, and other wildlife.

7 - POLK
(continued)

● **City Greenhouse**
Second and College
Des Moines, Iowa

Open: Easter weekend and continuing for 4 weeks, noon-5:00 p.m.; in early November for 2 weeks, noon-8:00 p.m.; other times by appointment from 8:00 a.m.-4:30 p.m.

Seasonal displays of flowers include a spring showing of wild flowers and an exhibit of chrysanthemums (90 varieties) in the fall to climax the growing season. Orchids, camelias, poinsettias, fig tree, lemon tree, orange tree, palm trees, rubber plants, banana plants, and colorful foliage may be seen growing throughout the year.

● **Des Moines Art Center**
Greenwood Park
Grand Avenue and Polk Boulevard
Des Moines, Iowa

Dedicated: June 2, 1948
Admission: Free
Open: Tuesday, Wednesday, Friday, Saturday, 11:00 a.m.-5:00 p.m.; Thursday, 11:00 a.m.-9:00 p.m.; Sunday, 1:00-6:00 p.m.; closed Monday
Membership Dues: $15.00 active; $5.00 student

The Des Moines Art Center, located in Greenwood Park (see below), was designed by Eliel Saarinen. It was founded by James D. Edmundson and presented to the City of Des Moines. An addition, designed by I.M. Pei, was opened in 1968. Included in the art collection are works by Goya, Daumier, Pissarro, Courbet, and many of the foremost American artists, including Gilbert Stuart. Classes in painting, drawing, sculpture, photography, jewelry, printmaking, and ceramics are offered for adults and children. A Junior Museum features exhibitions for children. Concerts, lectures, and studio demonstrations are scheduled.

● **Des Moines Center of Science and Industry**
Greenwood-Ashworth Park
Des Moines, Iowa

Robert L. Bridigum, Director

Dedicated: June 22, 1970; opened to public October 17, 1970
Admission: $1.00; children $0.50 ages 5-12.
Open: Tuesday through Saturday, 11:00 a.m.-5:00 p.m.;
Open: Sunday, 1:00-5:00 p.m.; Friday evening, 7:00-9:30; closed Monday
Membership Dues: $15.00 (individual or family); $25.00 contributing; $50.00 sustaining; $100.00 supporting; $250.00 sponsor; $500.00 benefactor

A privately financed educational facility designed to tell the story of the past, present, and future through exhibits, laboratory workshops, and study sessions. The brick and stone building of modern design is situated on a wooded bluff overlooking the Raccoon River Valley. Permanent and traveling exhibits on science and industry, classroom areas, laboratories, a lecture hall, and shops are in the main building.

The entrance lobby and 65-foot tower houses a Foucault pendulum. This instrument, designed in 1851 by Jean Leon

77 - POLK
(continued)

Des Moines Center of Science and Industry
(continued)

Foucault, consists of a brass ball suspended on a wire which swings over a frame, giving visible evidence of the Earth's rotation. At the latitude of Des Moines, about 41½ degrees north, the pendulum will make a complete rotation in 36 hours and 12 minutes. At the North or South Pole, the pendulum would show a complete rotation of the Earth in 24 hours.

In the domed theater of the 138-seat planetarium, the motions of the Sun, Moon, planets, and major stars are duplicated by a $27,000 Spitz A4 projector. The sky can be presented as it appears at any time of the day or night for any time in the past or the future and from any point on the Earth. An outdoor walkway and observation deck provides a place to set up telescopes and observe the heavens.

Privileges of membership include special classes, openings, and programs; field trips; planetarium shows; use of the library; publications; and discounts on merchandise and supplies.

● **Des Moines Children's Zoo**
7401 S.W. Ninth Street
Des Moines, Iowa 50315

Robert Elgin, Director

Dedicated: May 8, 1966
Admission: $0.50, age 16 and over; $0.25, age 2 through 15; free, under age 2
Open: Memorial Day through Labor Day, Tuesday-Friday, 11:00 a.m.-8:00 p.m.; Saturday, Sunday, and holiday noon-8:00 p.m.; closed Monday; from Labor Day October, weekends only

Owned and operated by the City Park Board, the Children's Zoo started from a gift of $150,000 contributed by Des Moines theatre owner and philanthropist, A. H. Blank. The zoo, located in Blank Park, includes MacDonald's Barn, with common domestic farm animals; deer; black bear; a monkey island; an Asian elephant; lions; leopard; wolves; small mammals; reptiles; birds of prey from the United States and South America; and a flight cage containing exotic birds from Florida and South America. There is a petting area for children, open from 1:00-4:00 p.m. Other features in the 138-acre park include a half-mile ride on a one-third scale model train; Noah's Ark, surrounded by a pool; Old Mill; and Birthday House.

● **Des Moines Zoological Association**
c/o Des Moines Children's Zoo
7401 S.W. Ninth Street
Des Moines, Iowa 50315

Mrs. Jesse Deets (Justine) Smith, President
7215 Washington Avenue
Des Moines, Iowa 50311
or
Mrs. Marlin A. (Marie) Steger
5315 Waterbury Road
Des Moines, Iowa 50312

Incorporated: 1967
Board Meetings: Second and fourth Tuesday of month
Number of Members: 350
Dues: $7.50 individual; $15.00 family; $25.00 contributing

Affiliated with the Des Moines Children's Zoo (see above), this private, non-profit association was organized to promote greater interest in the zoo, and to participate in zoo events. Lectures are given and motion pictures shown by noted zoologists. A newsletter outlines programs, exhibits, and events at the zoo.

- POLK
(continued)

Des Moines Zoological Association
(continued)

Mrs. Jack M. (Chris) Harmer
President, Docent Association
233-59th Street
Des Moines, Iowa 50312

The Docent Association gives presentations to schools, and offers lectures, slide programs, and zoo tours and birthday parties.

● **Ewing Park**
5100 S.E. Indianola Drive
Des Moines, Iowa 50320

Acquired: 1938
Flower Displays: Wild flowers, April and May; lilacs from May 1-20, depending upon the weather

The 357-acre farm of David Rittenhouse Ewing and his wife Lucinda was given to the City of Des Moines by their daughter, Mrs. Winnie Ewing Coffin, to be preserved as a recreational park. The Children's Forest contains some 4,000 trees native to Iowa and others which are not native to the state, such as the cork tree, gingko, and tulip tree. A small grove of quaking aspen, practically unknown in Iowa, is located in another area of the park. The Lilac Arboretum features over 200 varieties of the finest French lilacs and a few varieties of flowering wild crab apples, cherries, and plums, together with ornamental and native Iowa shrubs. An 11-acre area is devoted to wild flowers, with name markers. The park is popular with birds common to Iowa.

Fort Des Moines No. 2
S. W. First and Elm Streets
Des Moines, Iowa

City Parks Department
City Hall
400 East 1st Street
Des Moines, Iowa 50309

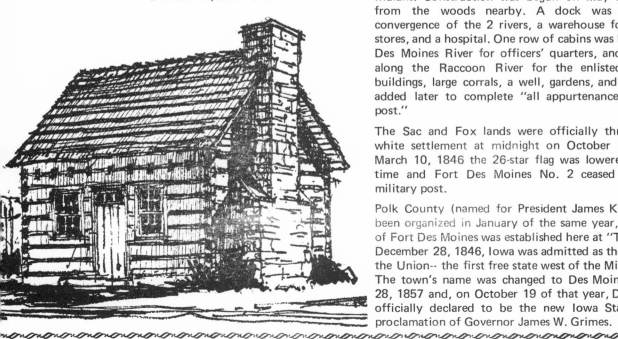

The site of the second of 3 early military establishments in Iowa named Fort Des Moines, and the birthplace of the City of Des Moines. Fort Des Moines No. 2 was established in 1843 at the junction of the Raccoon and Des Moines Rivers by Captain James Allen. It was built to protect the Sac and Fox Indians from unscrupulous white traders, land grabbers, and speculators, and from the warlike Sioux Indians. Construction was begun on May 20, using logs from the woods nearby. A dock was built at the convergence of the 2 rivers, a warehouse for commissary stores, and a hospital. One row of cabins was built along the Des Moines River for officers' quarters, and another row along the Raccoon River for the enlisted men. Other buildings, large corrals, a well, gardens, and flagstaff were added later to complete "all appurtenances to an army post."

The Sac and Fox lands were officially thrown open to white settlement at midnight on October 11, 1845. On March 10, 1846 the 26-star flag was lowered for the last time and Fort Des Moines No. 2 ceased to exist as a military post.

Polk County (named for President James Knox Polk) had been organized in January of the same year, and the town of Fort Des Moines was established here at "The Point." On December 28, 1846, Iowa was admitted as the 29th state of the Union-- the first free state west of the Mississippi River. The town's name was changed to Des Moines on January 28, 1857 and, on October 19 of that year, Des Moines was officially declared to be the new Iowa State Capital by proclamation of Governor James W. Grimes.

77 - POLK
(continued)

Fort Des Moines No. 2
(continued)

In time, all the original log buildings at the fort disappeared, but a bronze tablet was placed at the site in 1908 by Abigail Adams Chapter of the Daughters of the American Revolution. The course of the Raccoon River has been changed so that it enters the Des Moines River at a point farther downstream than when Fort Des Moines No. 2 was founded.

After several earlier attempts to restore the old fort, the Birthplace of Des Moines Association, an affiliate of Polk County Historical Society (see below), was successful in establishing a memorial at the original site. Since it would have been difficult to build an exact replica of the 1843 fort, old, well-preserved, hand-hewn log cabins of that period were located for removal to the fort site. The first log cabin reconstructed came from Washington County, and was dedicated on June 6, 1965. It is open on special occasions and may be visited by appointment. The restoration is located in the former West Riverside Park, which was renamed Des Moines Birthplace Park in 1970.

● **Fort Des Moines No. 3**
South of Army Post Road
Des Moines, Iowa

The last of 3 military installations in Iowa named Fort Des Moines, located about 4 miles south of the Raccoon forks, Fort Des Moines No. 3 was formally dedicated as a cavalry post on November 13, 1903. Local citizens raised $40,000 toward purchase of the land, and presented it to the U. S. Government. When completed, the claim was made that "there was no more beautiful Army Post in America." The 400-acre site was later used as a training center for Negro officers during World War I, and as an Army convalescent hospital.

During World War II, the installation served as the first training center for the Women's Army Auxiliary Corps (WAAC), later renamed the Women's Army Corps (WAC), and was known as "The Home of the WAC's." Over 100 buildings were added to the existing buildings of approximately the same number. Because of the WAC, Fort Des Moines No. 3 probably received more publicity than any other military post in the Nation. Following World War

7 - POLK
(continued)

Fort Des Moines No. 3
(continued)

II, Fort Des Moines No. 3 was used as a veterans' housing center for several years. Most of the original brick buildings have since disappeared by demolition, but a part of the old fort area is still used as a training center for Army, Navy, Marine, and Air Force reservists, and as an Army Recruiting and Induction Center, and headquarters for the Civil Air Patrol, Iowa Wing.

Approximately half of the original tract has been declared surplus by the General Services Administration, and will be devoted to conservation, environmental and nature study, and recreation.

● **Governor's Mansion**
2900 Grand Avenue
Des Moines, Iowa

Built by W. W. Witmer in 1903 and purchased by the State of Iowa in 1947 from Gerald S. Nollen, whose wife was a daughter of the builder. The cost of the Philadelphia Colonial house and lot was $27,200. Another $22,800 was spent on remodeling, and an additional $22,421 was spent on furnishing and decorating the mansion. Governor William S. Beardsley became the first Iowa governor to occupy the home, in January 1949.

● **Grand View Park**
East 32nd and Guthrie
Des Moines, Iowa

A natural woods with a larger variety of trees than any other park in the Middle West. The park includes nearly 76 acres; an 18-hole golf course covers an additional 100 acres.

● **Gray's Lake Park**
1535 Fleur Drive
Des Moines, Iowa

Dedicated: April 28, 1970

A 178-acre park including a lake of over 100 acres, formed in an old sand and gravel pit along the Raccoon River in the heart of the city. The lake is named for the family who dredged out the sand and gravel. There was talk over a period of several decades--as far back as 1936--of acquiring the property for a city park and recreational area. This was not actually accomplished until late in 1969. Sailboating, canoeing, swimming, fishing, and picnicking are popular activities.

● **Greenwood Park**
48th and Grand Avenue
Des Moines, Iowa

Nearly 81 acres of wooded hillsides, predominantly white oak. Ashworth Park (over 63 acres) is adjacent to the area. The formal Rose Garden, containing several thousand varieties, is one of 24 trail gardens recognized by the National Rose Society. Newly developed varieties are included and marked for public evaluation. The roses are in bloom from June until frost. Colorful day lilies bloom during the summer in flower gardens.

● **Horse Watering Trough**
S. E. Tenth and Scott Streets
Des Moines, Iowa

One of the last of 15 horse watering troughs installed around Des Moines by the Iowa Humane Society, formerly the Humane Alliance, established in 1883. One of the objects of the society was " . . . to erect and maintain fountains, tanks, troughs, and other receptacles of fresh water in eligible localities for gratuitous distribution to the dumb creation . . ."

77 - POLK
(continued)

Horse Watering Trough
(continued)

This is one of two Ensign fountains presented to the city in 1906. Another was formerly located at S.E. Sixth and Hartford Avenues, and later moved to near the entrance to the Owen Crist Farm, 3800 Park Avenue. The round, gray granite bowls were 6 feet in diameter, and rested on a base or pedestal, which contained 4 small water-filled bowls or cups to be used by dogs and cats. On each fountain was a bronze plaque stating that it was a gift of the National Humane Alliance honoring the founder Herman Lee Ensign.

For many years this fountain has also been used as the water supply for nearby residents who do not have wells, or running water in their homes. This neighborhood, the "Southeast Bottoms," was one of the earliest settled in the Des Moines area-- during the 1850's.

● **Hoyt Sherman Place**
15th and Woodland
Des Moines, Iowa

Des Moines Women's Club
15th and Woodland
Des Moines, Iowa 50309

Open: Tours by appointment, 8:00 a.m.-4:30 p.m., Monday through Friday

The central part of a 3-building complex was begun in 1877 as the home of Hoyt Sherman, the younger brother of General William Tecumseh Sherman, famous for his "March to the Sea" during the Civil War. Hoyt Sherman came to Fort Des Moines in 1848, and was appointed postmaster in 1850. He built the first 2 post offices here. During his career he was School Fund commissioner; a leader in establishing a bank, street railway, waterworks, public school, college, and insurance company; served in the Iowa Legislature; and held the rank of major in the U.S. Army. Original furnishings in the old mansion include the dining room furniture and a painting of early Des Moines at the forks of the Raccoon and Des Moines Rivers. Mrs. Sherman died in 1887, but Mr. Sherman lived in the house until his death on January 25, 1904. Some of the prominent guests entertained here were President and Mrs. U. S. Grant, General William T. Sherman, General Philip Sheridan, and Major William McKinley, who was then Governor of Ohio and later became U.S. President.

The property was acquired in 1907 from the heirs by the Des Moines Park Board Commissioners. Since then, the Des Moines Women's Club has leased Hoyt Sherman Place for its headquarters. In 1909 an Art Gallery was added, and in 1923 a 1,500-seat auditorium and a room adjacent to the Art Gallery were built. This room, named for Major H. S. M. Byers, a personal friend of the Shermans, houses a collection of paintings, statuary, antique carved chests, and art objects.

● **Iowa Genealogical Society**
6000 Douglas Avenue
P. O. Box 3815
Des Moines, Iowa 50322

William H. Lees, President
227 Clinton Street
Boone, Iowa 50036

Organized: 1965
Meetings: Second Tuesday of January, March, May and September; annual meeting in November; workshops as announced
Number of Members: 1,450
Dues: $5.00 annual

Activities are devoted to creating and fostering an interest

- POLK
(continued)

Iowa Genealogical Society
(continued)

in genealogy and preserving genealogical and historical data. A library of books and genealogical materials is maintained, and *Hawkeye Heritage,* an Iowa genealogy magazine, is published quarterly. Visitors are welcome at all meetings.

Seventeen local chapters affiliated with the Society are located in various parts of Iowa.

● **Iowa Local Historical and Museum Association**
c/o State Historical Building
East 12th and Grand Avenue
Des Moines, Iowa 50319

Melvin H. Goeldner, President
209 Pearl Street
Osceola, Iowa 50213

Founded: January 17, 1966
Incorporated: March 25, 1968
Meetings: Annual meeting in October; also spring meeting, and regional workshops during summer
Number of Members: 130
Dues: $2.00 annual

Organized to work cooperatively with existing organizations in promoting an interest in local, state, regional, and national history, and to exchange ideas and discuss common problems in the preservation of historic landmarks and sites and in the displaying of articles of historic value. Consultative services are available, regional workshops and meetings are conducted, and a newsletter is distributed to members.

● **Iowa Museum of Agriculture**
Iowa State Fairgrounds
Des Moines, Iowa

See **Iowa State Fairgrounds** below.

● **Iowa Society for the Preservation of Historic Landmarks**
Des Moines, Iowa

William J. Wagner, President
1106 High Street
Des Moines, Iowa 50309
or
Mrs. Lida Lisle Greene
Iowa State Historical Department
Historical Library
East 12th and Grand Avenue
Des Moines, Iowa 50319
or
LeRoy G. Pratt
317 Southwest 42nd Street
Des Moines, Iowa 50312

Founded: 1956
Incorporated: 1959
Meetings: Annual meeting in October; spring meeting or tour; field studies or tours during summer
Number of Members: 355
Dues: $3.00 annual; $5.00 family; $1.00 student

Organized to kindle and keep alive an active interest in the historical buildings, sites, and landmarks of Iowa, and to advise, aid, and encourage local groups and communities in their preservation. The Society does not own property, but seeks to cooperate with all existing organizations concerned with historic preservation. The Society sponsored the organization of the Iowa Local Historical and Museum Association (see above). Publications include an illustrated *Newsletter,* issued several times during the year; *The First Ten Years,* a history of the Society; a 2-color brochure and map of historic Iowa; note paper and correspondence cards with sketches of Iowa landmarks; and other historical materials. Speakers and color slide programs on historic preservation and Iowa landmarks are available for group meetings, upon request. An advisory staff assists and advises local groups in the identification, evaluation, and preservation of historic sites and buildings in Iowa. Meetings include tours to historic sites and landmarks.

| COUNTY AND COUNTY SEAT; LOCATION ON MAP | NAME AND LOCATION | DESCRIPTION |

77 - POLK
(continued)

● **Iowa State Capitol and Grounds**
1007 East Grand Avenue
Des Moines, Iowa

LINCOLN AND TAD

Open: Monday through Friday; tours by appointment

Situated on an eminence on the east side of the Des Moines River is this center of Iowa's government. Des Moines became the state capital by proclamation of Governor James W. Grimes on October 19, 1857. (The Grimes State Office Building, built on the Capitol Grounds in 1967-68, was named to honor Governor Grimes.)

The first capitol in Des Moines stood near where the Soldiers and Sailors Monument is today. Construction was begun on the present capitol in 1871, and the cornerstone, cut from an Iowa granite boulder, was laid by Governor Samuel Merrill on November 23. It was necessary to replace the original foundation stone, which proved defective, and the cornerstone was recut and relaid September 29, 1873. The capitol was dedicated in 1884, but was not completed until 1886. It was built on a "pay as you go" basis and cost the taxpayers $2,873,294.59. After an extensive fire in the north wing (House of Representatives) on January 4, 1904, the capitol was repaired and redecorated. Its commanding feature is the central dome, covered with 23-carat gold leaf. The dome itself is said to weigh 487,000 pounds, rises 275 feet above ground level, and is the largest gold dome in the country. The building includes many interesting architectural features, mural paintings, statues, displays of Civil War battle flags, and a pioneer suffragists plaque.

Monuments on the capitol grounds include the Civil War Soldiers and Sailors Monument (designed by Harriet A. Ketcham of Mt. Pleasant, and completed in 1896), the Senator William B. Allison Monument, the Pioneer group, the Christopher Columbus memorial, a replica of the Liberty Bell, a miniature of the Statue of Liberty, the Lincoln and Tad statue, historic cannons and mortars, and a Japanese Temple Bell and Bell House (a gift of the State of Yamanashi, Japan). Extensive exhibits of popular flowers may be seen blooming throughout the seasons in the flower beds surrounding the capitol.

On a high point southeast of the capitol is the grave of Willson Alexander (Alex) Scott, one of the first white settlers in the vicinity, who donated a tract of land (10.2 acres) on which to erect the capitol. Born in Crawford County, Indiana on November 20, 1818, Scott settled on this site in 1846 and eventually acquired some 500 acres of land. Overwhelmed in the financial crisis of 1857, he died on June 23, 1859 near Fort Kearny, Nebraska Territory enroute to Pike's Peak. He is buried here on his old homestead in accordance with his wishes.

The Court Avenue viaduct or underpass just south of the capitol spans 1 million years, geologically. The south abutment of the viaduct rests on the Kansas drift, second oldest of the 5 glaciers that touched Iowa, while the north end is situated on the Wisconsin drift sheet, youngest of the glaciers in Iowa. This glacial drift phenomena was discovered about 1870 when road cuttings were made during construction of the stone viaduct.

7 - POLK
(continued)

● **Iowa State Historical Department Division of Historical Museum and Archives**
State Historical Building
1112 East Grand Avenue
Des Moines, Iowa 50319

Jack W. Musgrove, Director

Admission: Free
Open: Every day of the year, 8:00 a.m.-4:00 p.m.; guided tours for groups

The Historical Memorial and Art Department was organized in 1892 and construction was begun in 1898 on the State Historical Building. An addition was built in 1908. In 1939, the Department was reorganized as the Iowa State Department of History and Archives, with its chief purpose to preserve Iowa history from the earliest geological time, through the days of the Indians and of the pioneers, to the present. The State Historical Department came into being July 1, 1974 by act of the 65th Iowa General Assembly, to include 3 Divisions--the Division of Historical Museum and Archives, the Division of State Historical Society (see Johnson County), and the Division of Historic Preservation (see Johnston County).

In the museum is a wide range of exhibits including rocks and fossils covering a billion years of geologic time, with an outstanding display of fossil crinoids from LeGrand, Iowa; mastodon bones; ancient Indian artifacts and modern Indian beadwork, canoes, and wickiup; mineral specimens and precious gemstones; firearms; tools, utensils, and implements used by Iowa pioneers; millstones from old Iowa mills; a prairie schooner; a stagecoach and other horse-drawn vehicles; early automobiles; pictures of Iowa's first automobile fatality; a 1909 Bleriot XI airplane (the first to fly in Des Moines, in 1911) built in France by Louis Bleriot; telephone equipment; early lamps; equipment used to explore outer space; sand paintings; early glassware; antique furniture; coins; animal and bird specimens; portraits of outstanding Iowans; and photographs. Also in the building are manuscripts, autographed letters and papers, historic maps, census records, enlistment and military service records, official reports, and newspaper files.

The Historical Library has approximately 50,000 volumes--books by Iowa authors or about Iowa, family records, and reference books. The Traveling Library, established by Governor Robert Lucas in 1839, now includes 290,000 volumes, phonodiscs, and films. The State Medical Library, located on the second floor of the Historical Building, contains over 61,000 volumes and more than 100,000 unbound medical and scientific periodicals. Doctors may request literature by mail, phone, or telegram. A small museum of old medical instruments is also located in the Medical Library. *The Annals of Iowa,* a historical magazine, is published quarterly by the Department. Lectures, slide programs, and consultative services are available.

Annals of Iowa

77 - POLK
(continued)

● **Iowa State Fairgrounds**
End of East Grand Avenue,
off S. E. 30th Street
Des Moines, Iowa

The Iowa State Agricultural Society first met in Fairfield on December 28, 1853, on the seventh anniversary of Iowa's statehood, and set the dates October 25-27, 1854 for the first fair. During the early years of its existence, the Iowa State Fair was held at different locations--Fairfield (1854-55), Muscatine (1856-57), Oskaloosa (1858-59), Iowa City (1860-61), Dubuque (1862-63), Burlington (1864-66), Clinton (1867-68), Keokuk (1869-70 and 1874-75), and Cedar Rapids (1871-73 and 1876-78). Since 1879, the Iowa State Fair has been held in Des Moines. The new grounds were dedicated September 7, 1886. This is the original "State Fair" of Phil Stong's best-selling novel which has twice been made into hit motion pictures.

From 1965 to 1969, different themes relating to eras of Iowa's heritage were used each year and replicas of historic buildings constructed in Heritage Village, spread over 10 acres up the hill from the Old Mill. These include an Indian village, with wickiups constructed by George Youngbear (1898-1971) and other Mesquakie Indians, and a 7-ton Northwest Indians totem pole carved by Richard Bordwell from an Idaho pine that was growing when Columbus arrived in America, representing the period before 1800; a replica of one of the blockhouses at Fort Madison, the first American fort constructed west of the Mississippi, typical of the period 1800-30; a replica of the first church in Iowa, built by the Methodists at Dubuque in 1834, and a sod house to represent the pioneer period, 1830-65; an appropriately furnished country schoolhouse (North Lincoln school from southeast of Indianola) of the Gay '90's period, 1865-1900; and displays of machinery and equipment related to the Roaring '20's, 1900-30. Grandfather's Barn was part of the original farm purchased in 1886 as a part of the Fairgrounds. The barn, filled with livestock, was opened to the public in 1973 as a classic example of an Iowa basement barn. The Douglass Pharmacy is a restoration of the pharmacy originally located in Postville, Iowa, dating back to 1872.

Near the sod house, a pioneer orchard has been planted with such old varieties of apples as Jennet, Rome Beauty, Ben Davis, Striped Delicious, and Jonathan. Sod houses were built by the pioneers where trees were scarce. The prairie soil was held together by the fibrous roots of the thick native grass. Foot-wide strips of sod were turned up with the plow; these strips were then cut in blocks and laid as bricks. Soil was tamped between the blocks. Hay and sod were also used for the roof, supported by ridgepoles. Often, native wild flowers bloomed on the roof. If heavy rains caused leaks, they were easily patched with soil and more sod blocks. Sod houses were inexpensive and provided the necessary shelter from violent storms, raging blizzards, and the sweltering summer sun, and they gave protection from prairie fires and Indian arrows.

- POLK
(continued)

Iowa State Fairgrounds
(continued)

Pioneer Hall houses the Iowa Museum of Agriculture, with exhibits and collections of items related to Iowa's past. On display are pieces of old farm machinery, tools and equipment, and early home furnishings. Other items to be seen include an early courtroom railing from Hardin County; a section of the old Green Mountain, Iowa post office; a re-created blacksmith shop complete with original tools; an early telephone switchboard; buggies and wagons; harness; a barbed wire collection; and a woven-wire maker.

Pioneer Hall itself is of historic interest. It was dedicated in 1886 as a poultry palace--one of the original buildings at the Fairgrounds. With declining interest in poultry exhibits, the big white-frame structure, topped with an old-fashioned cupola, was used for a utility building, dormitory, and a storage building before 1968 when it was repainted and renamed Pioneer Hall.

Outside Pioneer Hall is a display of some of the elaborately carved ornamental stone and pieces of columns salvaged from the Old Federal Building which stood for 100 years at Fifth and Court Avenues in Des Moines. Also included is the old cornerstone, showing the dates 1868, when the building was originally built, and 1886, when it was rebuilt with an addition. At the time the building was demolished by action of the Des Moines City Council in 1968, this largest Federal building built in Iowa, was the oldest public building in downtown Des Moines, and contained the first clock tower in the city. The huge bell, which is about 4 feet in diameter and 3 feet high, was stored in the City of Des Moines paint shop until the summer of 1971, when it was moved to the Fairgrounds. The lettering on the bell reads:

McShane Bell Foundry
Henry McShane & Co
Baltimore, Md.
Trade Mark
1889

The 378 acres included in the Fairgrounds are also used for various other activities throughout the year, such as auto races, polo matches, horse shows, contests, conventions, and outings, and, from May 1 to October 1, for camping.

77 - POLK
(continued)

● **Joseph B. Stewart Square**
East 14th Street and Grand Avenue
Des Moines, Iowa

This block-square park was dedicated to public use by Joseph Buffon Stewart September 8, 1857. It was formerly called Franklin Square or Block 40 Stewart's Addition.

A native of St. Charles, Missouri, Stewart, whose father was an Army surgeon, came to Fort Des Moines in 1853 as chief clerk in the Land Office. He remained here until 1856, handling receipts that sometimes reached $25,000 per day. He later ran a real estate and law office and helped settlers select and enter land for a fee. In September 1857, he laid out and platted 360 acres on the east side of the Des Moines River, northeast of Governor's Square. This became an addition to the city and is still known as Stewart's Addition. Mr. Stewart was one of the contributors and a factor in locating the State Capitol in Lee Township. He was also engaged in banking and railroading, and was active in civic, church, and school affairs. His home at 1200 Pleasant was purchased in 1879 by James Callanan (1822-1906) to use for a private school, and was remodelled and equipped for 250 students. Later, this became the main wing of the Iowa Methodist Hospital.

While a resident of Fort Madison, where he moved in 1835 at the age of 14, and before coming to Fort Des Moines, Stewart had the distinction of living in 3 territories and 2 counties without changing his place of residence. This came about as follows: Michigan Territory originally included what is now Iowa; from it was formed Wisconsin Territory, and, in 1838, the Territory of Iowa was established. Lee County was one of the counties formed from the original Demoine County. Mr. Stewart died in 1899 and is buried in Woodland Cemetery in Des Moines.

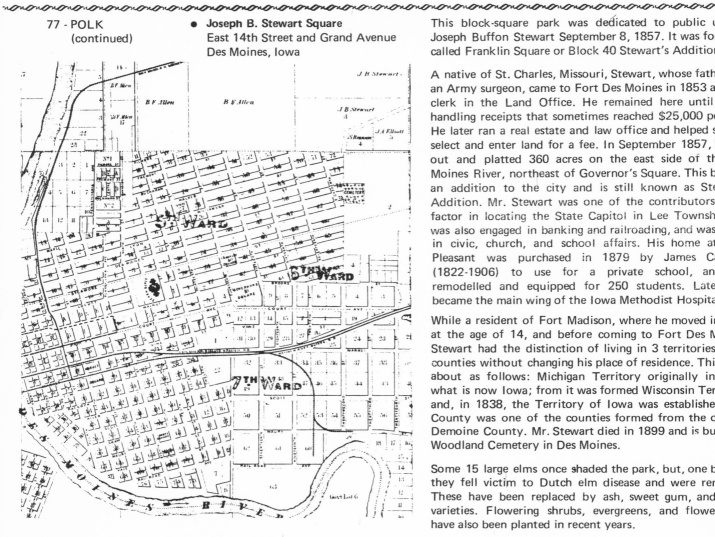

Some 15 large elms once shaded the park, but, one by one, they fell victim to Dutch elm disease and were removed. These have been replaced by ash, sweet gum, and other varieties. Flowering shrubs, evergreens, and flower beds have also been planted in recent years.

● **Lewis A. Jester County Park**
3 miles northwest of Polk City, Iowa

Polk County Conservation Board
Wayne Bills, Executive Director
Jester Park
Granger, Iowa 50109

Established: 1958
Open: During summer, 7:00 a.m.-10:30 p.m.; during winter, closed after 4:30 p.m.

The 866-acre recreational area includes nature trails, and a display of bison (buffalo), elk, and fallow (white) deer. Several ponds, as well as the Des Moines River, provide fishing. There are also facilities for boating, picnicking, camping, hiking, horseback riding, sledding, and golfing.

Nearly one-third of the park will be inundated during periods of high water since completion of the Saylorville Reservoir flood control project. (See Saylorville Dam and Reservoir, below.)

That woolly mammoths and other extinct animals roamed this area in glacial times is evidenced by the discovery of ancient tusks and other remains in gravel beds within the park. Such finds are quite common in glacial drifts throughout Iowa.

7 - POLK
(continued)

● **Living History Farms**
Along Interstate 80 and 35
Northwest edge of Des Moines, Iowa

H. Oliver Gillespie,
Executive Director
2600 N.W. 111th Street
(State Farm Road, north
of Hickman Road)
Des Moines, Iowa 50322
or
Dr. William G. Murray, President
3207 Oakland Street
Ames, Iowa 50010

Organized: August 1967
Membership Dues: $10.00 individual; $15.00 family; $5.00 student; $1,000.00 life
Admission: Non-members pay an admission fee for tours and various events

A nonprofit development designed to portray farming and agriculture in Iowa since the region was first settled. This will be done through 3 farms, where day-to-day operations will be carried on year-round--a Pioneer Farm of about 1840, a Horse and Steam Engine Farm of about 1900, and a Farm of the Future. Each of these farms will use the methods and equipment of its time. Demonstrations or special events through the growing season were begun in 1970. These include a Grain Harvest and Threshing Festival in mid-summer and a Corn Harvest Festival in the fall. Craft and art demonstrations are included, such as the production of sorghum molasses, and apple cider; making soap, candles, pottery, and bread; spinning, weaving, and dyeing; chair caning; and smoking meat.

The 500-acre tract acquired by Living History Farms was formerly a part of the Clive Honor Prison Farm, operated by the State of Iowa from 1915 until 1965. This land was first occupied by the Sac and Fox Indians prior to 1845. It was in 1867 that Martin Flynn purchased 600 acres from E. R. Clapp for $26.67 an acre. Flynn built a stately brick home, a large horse barn, and other buildings at Walnut Hill Farm; developed an outstanding herd of Shorthorn cattle; engaged in railroad contracting; operated a bank, a brickyard, and a business building (the former Flynn Building) in Des Moines; and owned a sheep ranch in Wyoming. Martin Flynn died in 1906, but the family maintained the farm (which had grown by 1880 to 1,320 acres) until 1915 when it was purchased by the State of Iowa.

At the site of the pioneer farm, located near the edge of the timber and near a small stream, a cabin and rail fence have been built of rough burr oak logs, cut nearby. A shelter for the oxen, corn crib, barn, smoke house, and a root cellar have also been constructed.

The Horton Log Cabin has been moved into the area from a farm south and east of the site of Moran, which is 3 miles southeast of Woodward. The 17-foot-square cabin was probably the original farm home, as a conventional frame house was built later enclosing the cabin. The old cabin was used as a kitchen until the farmhouse was torn down in 1970. Ruth's Mill, where logs could be sawed, was one of the earliest mills on the Des Moines River. It was located just east of present-day Woodward.

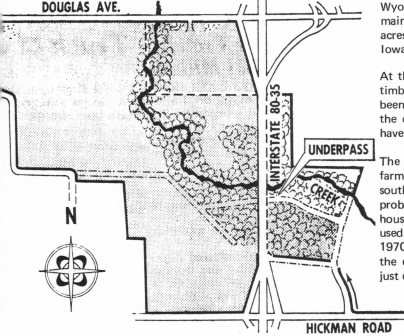

77 - POLK
(continued)

Living History Farms
(continued)

The Iowa farm of 1900 was opened to the public in the fall of 1974. The farm house was moved here from near Grimes, Iowa, and refurbished and appropriately furnished. An 1889 barn from near Stratford, Iowa has also been brought here and rebuilt as typical of its era. The red barn was originally built by Christian Carlson, who moved to Iowa from Sweden in 1869. It was used for horses, kept on one side, and milk cows, kept on the other. Hay was stored in the middle, and young animals occupied one end of the barn. With the increase in the size of farms and the decrease in farm population in the United States, farm buildings have become obsolete for present day agricultural operations and many have been abandoned and razed.

Other areas are being developed as funds become available.

The Flynn Mansion, horse barn, and other buildings are being preserved and maintained as a headquarters for Living History Farms. In 1974, the Flynn Mansion and Barn were placed on the National Register of Historic Places and were designated as the Meeting House for Iowa by the Iowa American Revolution Bicentennial Commission. In June 1975, Living History Farms was designated a National Bicentennial Celebration site.

Special tours of the Pioneer Farm and the 1900 Farm may be arranged for school children, adult groups, or individuals. Hay rides may be taken, and, in winter, bobsled rides, skating, and sledding may be enjoyed.

- POLK
(continued)

● **Mitchellville Historical Society**
Mitchellville, Iowa

John L. Carter
123 Center Avenue North
Mitchellville, Iowa 50169
or
C. C. Glenn
R. R., Mitchellville, Iowa 50169

Organized: August 1, 1954

Sponsored centennial celebration in 1956, and was active in marking, preserving, and developing historic sites in the area. The Society has been inactive in recent years.

● **Municipal Observatory**
Waveland Park
48th Street and University Avenue
Des Moines, Iowa

Established: 1921
Admission: Free
Open: Friday during academic year, 7:45-9:30 p.m., in clear weather; Monday night, by appointment, for groups and classes of 30 to 100

A cooperative enterprise of Drake University and the City of Des Moines. The land and building are provided by the city, while Drake University furnishes the scientific equipment, displays, and staff. The observatory is used for instruction in astronomy, and physical science classes; and public programs provide lectures and non-technical accounts of astronomy. A display of transparencies of astronomical subjects and the 20-piece Edgar Harlan collection of meteorite specimens are also in the observatory building. The instruments include an 8¼-inch refracting telescope, donated to the University by Francis Marion Drake, with optics by Brashear and mounting by Warner and Swasey Company.

● **Pioneer Park**
S. E. 16th and Pioneer Road
Des Moines, Iowa

Established: 1917

A 46-acre park, with an authentic split-rail fence bordering the entrance roadway. A panoramic view of Des Moines may be seen from a high promontory overlooking the Des Moines River Valley. This land, purchased by the city for a park, was formerly the Barlow Granger Homestead. Granger was the first printer and newspaper publisher in Fort Des Moines. *The Iowa Star* began publication on June 26, 1846 on a press installed in a former barracks at Fort Des Moines No. 2. Granger had previously set type beside Horace Greeley and took his often repeated advice, "Go West, young man. Go West."

● **Polk County Historical Society**
Des Moines, Iowa

Mrs. LeRoy G. (Louise) Pratt,
President
317 Southwest 42nd Street
Des Moines, Iowa 50312

Incorporated: 1938; reorganized in 1961 after a period of inactivity
Meetings: Monthly, except July and August, on the second Sunday of the month, or at special announced times
Number of Members: 185
Dues: $3.00 annual; $5.00 family; $10.00 sustaining; $100.00 life
Sponsor of the Des Moines Birthplace memorial--a reconstruction of historic log cabins on the original site of Fort Des Moines No. 2 (see above), established in 1843 at

77 - POLK
(continued)

Polk County Historical Society
(continued)

the junction of the Raccoon and Des Moines Rivers. The Society has co-sponsored "Highlights of Iowa History" programs at the State Historical Building, Des Moines, and Iowa and Polk County history programs on KDIN-TV (formerly KDPS). Meetings are held at various locations in Polk County. Publications include a monthly illustrated *Newsletter, Highlights of Polk County History, Polk County Coal Mines,* and other materials on Polk County history; a history of the Society and reprints of early Polk County histories are in preparation. The Society has also produced commemorative plates in limited editions.

● **Railroad Park**
Railroad Street, between Fourth and Fifth Streets
West Des Moines, Iowa

City of West Des Moines
City Hall
318 Fifth Street
West Des Moines, Iowa 50265

Dedicated: 1971

A landscaped park devoted to recapturing the rich railroad heritage of the community of West Des Moines (Valley Junction). A water tower and a watch tower have been built, and an open pavilion will have 6- x 8-foot display panels with pictures of early railroading. A caboose dating back to the beginning of the 20th Century was donated by the Burlington Northern Railroad and has been placed on display. Railroad signals and switching devices are to be added, and a museum is planned.

In August 1970, during the construction of Railroad Park, an old concrete-walled tar pit was "discovered." This pit was used by the railroad for dipping ties in tar to prolong their life. The pit was abandoned about 1933, filled with debris, and covered with dirt. Old buckets, lumber, and junk were found in the pit.

The project has been co-sponsored by the West Des Moines Kiwanis Club, the West Des Moines Chamber of Commerce, and the City of West Des Moines, with the cooperation of the Central Iowa Railroad Club.

● **Salisbury House**
4025 Tonawanda Drive
Des Moines, Iowa 50312

Built: 1923-1928
Admission: $1.00 guided tour, $0.50 4-room tour
Open: Four rooms are open Monday through Friday, 8:00 a.m.-4:30 p.m.; Saturday, 9:00 a.m.-12 noon, except summer; pre-arranged guided tours are available for groups of 10 or more

This 42-room reconstruction of King's House in Salisbury, England, built by Carl Weeks who was a drug and cosmetics manufacturer, is now the headquarters of the Iowa State Education Association. Salisbury House stands amid 11 acres of natural woodland and flower gardens. Flooring, ceiling beams, stained-glass windows, fireplaces, and other materials were obtained from England. To be seen within the house are paintings (including Cardinal Domenico Rivarola (1624) by Van Dyck and The Brothers (1809) by Sir Thomas Lawrence), sculptures, tapestries (including a huge 16th century Brussells), oriental rugs, stained glass, art objects, elaborate furnishings of the Tudor period, 16th

77 - POLK
(continued)

Salisbury House
(continued)

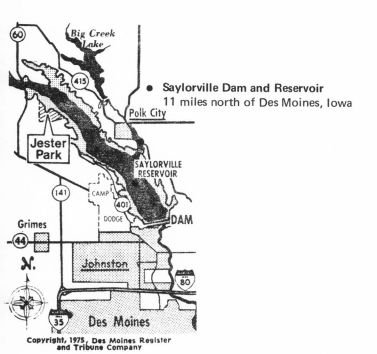

Copyright, 1975, Des Moines Register and Tribune Company

● **Saylorville Dam and Reservoir**
11 miles north of Des Moines, Iowa

● **Site of Camp Burnside**
Redhead Park
East 18th Street and Dean Avenue
Des Moines, Iowa

● **Site of First Public School**
in Des Moines
Northeast corner of Ninth and
Locust Streets
Des Moines, Iowa

● **Straight Mineral Collection**
Second floor of Administration
Building (Old Main)
Drake University
25th and University Avenue
Des Moines, Iowa

Century paneling, and a library containing many valuable manuscripts, documents, and rare books (including a page from the original Gutenberg Bible, the Oxford Lectern Bible, and an illustrated edition of Charles Dickens by John Forster, the only one of its kind). A large music box plays 12 different tunes, and a Welte-Mignon 3600 pipe organ was especially designed for the mansion. The Indian Room, representative of American culture, contains relics and artifacts.

Construction Authorized: 1958

A flood control reservoir behind a rolled earth-fill dam which extends 6,750 feet from bluff to bluff, across the Des Moines River Valley. When filled, the reservoir, which impounds the water of the Des Moines River (largest stream within the borders of the State of Iowa), will lie in parts of Polk, Dallas, and Boone Counties. Construction on the project was begun in 1965 and is scheduled for completion by 1976. A multitude of recreational activities will be available, including boating, picnicking, camping, hiking, and fishing.

A barrier dam across Big Creek below Polk City prevented the 17-mile-long reservoir from flooding the town. North of Polk City 1½ miles, the Big Creek diversion project created an 850-acre lake that forms the nucleus of Big Creek Recreation Area, a part of the Des Moines River corridor extending north from the Capital City.

A granite boulder with bronze tablet marks the site of Camp Burnside (1862). This was a rendezvous for volunteers from Iowa to the Union Army during the Civil War, 1861-65.

Redhead Park was presented to the city by Wesley Redhead whose residence was located nearby. He served as postmaster from February 10, 1853 to May 16, 1861 and owned South Park Coal Mine. His grave is in Woodland Cemetery, Des Moines.

The site of the first public school in Des Moines is marked by a plaque on the front of the buiding located on the northeast corner of Ninth and Locust Streets. The school was completed in 1855, at a cost of about $8,000. It was under construction for nearly 2 years. The school was known as Third Ward School or Brick School House and was abandoned in 1869.

Open: Monday through Friday, 8:00 a.m.-5:00 p.m.

The Halver R. Straight Mineral Collection was willed to Central Iowa Mineral Society in 1956, and display space has been provided at Drake University. Approximately 300 different varieties of rocks, minerals, semi-precious stones, and fossils are included in this outstanding collection, with each specimen identified.

77 - POLK
(continued)

● **Terrace Hill**
2300 Grand Avenue
Des Moines, Iowa

● **Thomas Mitchell Park**
1 mile south and 1½ miles
west of Mitchellville, Iowa

Polk County Conservation Board
Wayne Bills, Executive Director
Jester Park
Granger, Iowa 50109
          or
Pete Butler, Chief Park Ranger
R. R., Mitchellville, Iowa 50169

A mansion, including a 90-foot tower, considered one of America's finest remaining examples of Victorian architecture. The home was built in 1869 by Benjamin Franklin Allen, one of Iowa's first great financiers, at a cost of $250,000, including furnishings. On October 13, 1866, Allen announced that the grounds on the summit of the bluffs in the western part of Des Moines, "between the Adel road and the 'Coon River," were being prepared for a home for himself and family. The 29-acre tract was then covered with a dense growth of hazel brush, scrub oak, and heavy timber. J. T. Elletson was retained to landscape the grounds, saving as much of the original forest as was possible. He laid out the estate with grass plots, flower beds, vineyards, orchards, winding drives and walks, and a reservoir tapping the river for water for the fountains and pools. Allen, a nephew of Captain James Allen who established Fort Des Moines No. 2, was the first president of Capital City State Bank, organized on November 3, 1869. When Des Moines was a frontier town with a population of only 7,500, Allen's home was known as the "Prairie Palace of the West."

Following B. F. Allen's bankruptcy, in Chicago, the property was purchased by Frederick Marion Hubbell in 1884 for $55,000. It was owned and maintained by the Hubbell estate until 1971. The 63rd General Assembly authorized the Iowa Executive Council to negotiate to acquire the property for the State of Iowa. On August 24, 1971, the mansion, now located on an 8-acre tract, was formally presented to the State by 5 heirs of the Hubbell estate. Under the terms of the agreement, the State of Iowa is to maintain and preserve Terrace Hill as a historic landmark for at least 25 years. A special Terrace Hill Planning Commission, appointed to determine the future use of the familiar landmark, has recommended it for a Governor's Mansion and it is now being restored for this use.

Established: 1962

The 154-acre park was formerly the farm of Thomas Mitchell, pioneer settler, and founder of Mitchellville. He operated a tavern or stagecoach stop 13 miles east of Fort Des Moines No. 2 (see above), and founded the Universalist Church (see below) and a seminary in Mitchellville.

Camp Creek flows in a southerly direction through the area, with many boulders exposed in the stream bed, and there is a 7-acre pond. About half the land within the park is covered with hardwood timber. There are facilities for picnicking, hiking, sledding, ice skating, fishing, and camping. A replica of the old Thomas Mitchell log cabin is included in the park development plans.

- POLK
(continued)

Tree Shakers Genealogical Society
West Des Moines, Iowa

Mrs. Harry W. (Mary F.) Kelley,
Secretary
548 29th Street
West Des Moines, Iowa 50265

Organized: February 1974
Meetings: First Monday of month
Number of Members: 20
Dues: $3.00 annual; $5.00 husband and wife

A local chapter of the Iowa Genealogical Society (see above), organized to do genealogical, biographical, and historical research and compile statistics for Polk County. Cemetery burials are being recorded and marriage and death records for Polk County are being copied.

Universalist Church
205 N. W. Fourth Street
Mitchellville, Iowa

Polk County Conservation Board
Wayne Bills, Executive Director
Jester Park
Granger, Iowa 50109

A spired, white-frame church, surrounded by pines, and reminiscent of New England. Thomas Mitchell (1816-94), who founded the town of Mitchellville in 1856, donated the ground for the church, built in 1868. He served as its first moderator. In addition, he founded a seminary whose buildings were later acquired by the State of Iowa for the Iowa State Training School for Girls (10-18 years of age). The first girls were received there in 1880.

Thomas Mitchell was born in New Hampshire and settled on Camp Creek in 1844 when this was still Indian country (see Thomas Mitchell Park, above). His cabin was one of the first built in what is now Polk County, which he helped organize in 1846. He was the county's first sheriff, serving from 1846 until 1848, and made the county's first arrest. He served in the Iowa Legislature, first as a Representative, then as Senator. He also held office as Polk County supervisor. In addition to his career as a public servant, he operated an inn and acquired a great deal of land in the eastern part of Polk County.

When Mitchell died, more than 1,000 persons crowded into and around the church for his funeral services. Some of those attending the funeral came on a special chartered train from Des Moines. On October 14, 1970, the Iowa Universalist Convention donated the church to Polk County Conservation Board, as a historic shrine to be used as a museum and meeting place. In 1971, the Mitchell family Bible, containing family records and mementoes, was acquired by gift.

Walnut Woods State Park
6 miles southwest of Des Moines, Iowa, on county road off Iowa 5; or may be reached from Iowa 5 (Airport) Exit off I-35
State Conservation Commission
State Office Building
300 Fourth Street
Des Moines, Iowa 50319

Formerly the B. F. Elbert farm, the 260-acre preserve lies along the Raccoon River and is named for the thick grove of native black walnut trees, one of the largest stands in Iowa. Facilities are available for the picnicker, angler, and camper.

Water Works Park
Off Fleur Drive
Des Moines, Iowa

Open: Sunrise to sunset

A natural park of about 1,500 acres along both sides of the Raccoon River, including Denman Woods and Arie den Boer Arboretum. There are large areas of river bottom

77 - POLK
(continued)

Water Works Park
(continued)

woodlands, grassy meadows, several bodies of water, and roadways and trails for hiking, bicycling, and horseback riding. A great variety of wildlife may be seen, and the area is considered "a bird watcher's paradise." Wild flowers, trees, and shrubs of nearly every kind native to the area are in the park.

Charles S. Denman Woods is a memorial to the general manager of the Water Works when the property was acquired by the city. The chemical laboratory and water treatment plant, greenhouse, ornamental sunken pool with water lilies and goldfish, fountains, and flower beds are other attractions.

The Arie den Boer Arboretum is one of the world's finest collections of flowering crab apple trees, which bloom in early May. Some 350 varieties are represented in this 1,500-tree collection acquired from all states and many foreign countries. There are also specimen shade trees, lilacs, ornamental shrubs, and evergreens.

- **West Des Moines Historical Society**
West Des Moines, Iowa

Mrs. Robert A. (Bonnie) McFadden,
President
517 9th Street
West Des Moines, Iowa 50265

Organized: February 1970
Meetings: 3 times a year; board meetings monthly, except November and December
Number of Members: 102
Dues: $2.00 annual; $5.00 family; $10.00 supporting; $25.00 sustaining; $50.00 life

A Society organized following the Valley Junction Diamond Jubilee to promote and maintain an active interest in the history of West Des Moines (formerly Valley Junction), and to preserve articles and materials related to the heritage and growth of the community. A West Des Moines Heritage Day is sponsored each year in recognition of the city's incorporation in October 1893. Newspaper clippings, genealogy records, and photographs of historic interest are being collected. A history of the city is in preparation.

- **Yeader Creek Park**
1 mile south of Des Moines, Iowa
adjacent to Ewing Park

Polk County Conservation Board
Wayne Bills, Executive Director
Jester Park
Granger, Iowa 50109

Dedicated: June 9, 1968

A 454-acre recreational area which includes Easter Lake, located on the site of an old coal mine. Fishing, boating, and picnicking are permitted.

In 1968, the Owens Covered Bridge, Iowa's most historic and Polk County's only remaining covered bridge, was moved to a new location spanning one arm of the lake. The old bridge was originally located at the site of the first covered bridge in Iowa, built in 1844. It was at this spot, near present-day Carlisle, that Captain James Allen made a ford across North River to bring in lumber used to construct Fort Des Moines No. 2 in 1843. In those days, this road was known as the Dragoon Trail. The old covered

POLK
(continued)

Yeader Creek Park
(continued)

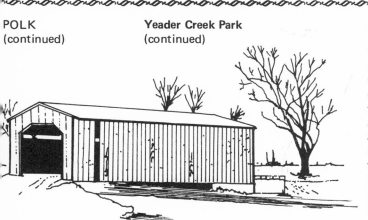

bridge, now restored in its new setting, was originally built in 1887-88 and was used until 1940 when it was abandoned for a new road. The bridge is nearly 100 feet long and has unusual wings at the openings to keep the truss from weathering. It is a Howe type bridge, named for the uncle of the inventor of the sewing machine. A later model than the other existing covered bridges in Iowa, it uses iron rods and angle blocks to prevent sagging. After the old road was abandoned and the course of North River was changed, the bridge was left almost forgotten, high and dry in dense timberland until acquired by Polk County Conservation Board. The original location is in the flood plain of Red Rock Reservoir, which necessitated its removal to the new location.

POTTAWATTAMIE

ncil Bluffs and Avoca
G-2

● **Arrowhead Park**
1½ miles southeast of Neola, Iowa

Pottawattamie County Conservation Board
H. L. Borwick, Executive Director
Pottawattamie County Courthouse
Council Bluffs, Iowa 51501

This 147-acre area was settled in the 1850's, and was a popular camping ground for the Pottawattamie Indians before the pioneers arrived. Many arrowheads have been recovered from the ravines. In pioneer times, hazelnut shrubs, cottonwood, box elder, ash, and maple covered the land. There are picnicking and camping areas, a fishing pond, and hiking trails left in their natural state.

● **Bayliss Park**
First Avenue and Pearl Street
Council Bluffs, Iowa

A 1-block-square park featuring several monuments, including a memorial to those who crossed Iowa in advance of the early settlements. Here, thousands of pioneers encamped to await pasturage on the plains and a turn at the ferries across the Missouri River, as they pressed on to the Golden West. A 20-ton boulder stands on the old Mormon Trail which passed through Kanesville, settled in 1824 (see Mormon Camp, below).

Black squirrels may be seen in the park. Their unusual color is due to melanism or over-pigmentation of their fur.

In the Chieftain Hotel, which once stood directly across the street from the park, were several original Grant Wood murals. These were salvaged in 1970 and restored, but are no longer located in Iowa.

● **Botna Bend Park**
Edge of Hancock, Iowa

Pottawattamie County Conservation Board
H. L. Borwick, Executive Director
Pottawattamie County Courthouse
Council Bluffs, Iowa 51501

Established: 1963

Contains 119 acres along the West Nishnabotna River, including timber and native shrubs, pasture land, and fishing access. A small buffalo herd has been established in a fenced-in 7-acre range. In pioneer times, one of the largest buffalo herds in Iowa ranged in this area. Songbirds, deer, and other wildlife are common. Activities include hiking, picnicking, and camping.

The Town of Hancock was laid out in 1880 by F. H. Hancock, and it became an important grain-shipping center. At one time, the river made a bend through what is now the town park, but the channel changed around 1889. The area along the river has been a popular place for picnics, 4th of July celebrations, old Army reunions, and the old settlers' picnic since early days.

78 - POTTAWATTAMIE
(continued)

● **Dodge Park**
Council Bluffs, Iowa

The 100-acre park was a gift to the City of Council Bluffs from Nathan P. Dodge, Jr., in memory of his parents. His father was a younger brother of General Grenville Mellen Dodge. A steam locomotive contributed by the Union Pacific Railroad stands in the park as a memorial to the railroad industry. Future plans include a Museum of Transportation.

● **General Dodge House**
Third Street and Story
Council Bluffs, Iowa

Open: Tuesday through Saturday, 10:00 a.m.-5:00 p.m.; Sunday, 2:00-5:00 p.m.; closed Mondays, Thanksgiving and Christmas, and during January
Admission: $1.00; children $0.50

Mrs. John A. Whittaker, Chairman
Board of Trustees
605 Third Street
Council Bluffs, Iowa 51501

Built by Grenville Mellen Dodge in 1869 at a cost of $35,000, the 3-story, 14-room brick mansion was designed by Chicago architect William Boyington, who also designed Terrace Hill in Des Moines (see Polk County). The home has been restored and furnished as accurately as possible to the 1870 period. The interior is notable for the walnut woodwork, Italian marble fireplaces, bronze door hinges with silver plates, plaster ceiling medallions, parquet floors, and many relics of historic significance. The red exterior brick was brought upriver from St. Louis.

The Victorian house with American mansard roof and large French windows is situated on a high rock-walled terrace. It was designated a National Historic Landmark by the U.S. Department of Interior on October 20, 1963. The property was completely air conditioned in 1969 for the comfort of visitors.

During the holiday season, the house is appropriately decorated and a Christmas Tea is held in December when Christmas music is played.

General Dodge was one of Iowa's foremost citizens--statesman, soldier, merchant, financier, railroad builder (Illinois Central, Rock Island, Texas and Pacific, and Union Pacific), and counselor of presidents. Prominent persons who were guests in the house include Presidents Grant, McKinley, and Theodore Roosevelt, and Generals Sherman and Sheridan. Indians called Dodge "Long Eye" because of his ability to see long distances with his surveying instruments.

General Dodge came to Council Bluffs in 1853 and returned the following year with his wife to embark in the freight and mercantile business. He interrupted his business career to join the Union Army during the Civil War, and soon rose to the rank of General. For his skill in building bridges and equipping railroads for the U.S. Army, he was highly commended by General U. S. Grant. During his lifetime, Dodge served as president of 7 railroads and 9 railroad construction companies, amassing a fortune in the millions. He died in Council Bluffs in 1916, and is buried in a tomb in Walnut Hill Cemetery.

- POTTAWATTAMIE
(continued)

General Dodge House
(continued)

The Ruth Anne Dodge Memorial ("The Black Angel" or "Angel of Death") is in Fairview Cemetery, at Lafayette Avenue and North Second Street. The Monument, erected in 1918, is considered one of the finest works of art by Daniel Chester French, who did the Minute Man at Concord, Massachusetts in 1875. The bronze statue is a translation of a dream Mrs. Dodge had on 3 nights preceding her death in 1916. Ruth Anne Dodge was the wife of General Dodge.

● **Golden Spike**
21st Street and Ninth Avenue
Council Bluffs, Iowa

Erected: 1939

A 56-foot concrete replica of the famed golden railroad spike driven at Promontory Point, Utah in 1869, to link the Union Pacific with the Central Pacific, thus spanning the continent with rails. The monument stands at the approximate site designated by President Abraham Lincoln as the eastern terminus of the Union Pacific Railroad. It was erected at the time of the world premiere of the motion picture, *Union Pacific*.

● **Grave of Amelia Jenks Bloomer**
Fairview Cemetery
East end of Lafayette Avenue
Council Bluffs, Iowa

Mrs. Dexter (Amelia Jenks) Bloomer (1818-94), a pioneer in the women's rights, female suffrage, and temperance movements, is buried in Fairview Cemetery. She was the founder and editor of *The Lily* (1849-55), probably the first American magazine edited by and for women. A native of New York State, she and her family moved to Ohio in 1854, and the following year settled in Council Bluffs, where she died December 30, 1894. She was an ardent advocate of dress reform and became famous for the baggy Turkish pantaloons or bloomers, gathered at the ankles, which she wore with a skirt when she lectured in favor of equal rights for women.

New York newspapers are credited with naming the women's undergarments for her, although she protested. While she was neither the designer of bloomers nor the first to wear them, she has been immortalized in history as "the original bloomer girl." Mrs. Bloomer was a vigorous speaker, although she was of small stature, and has been described as being "as delicate as Dresden china."

Mr. Bloomer was president of the Council Bluffs Board of Education in 1859, and of the State Board of Education in 1860. An elementary and junior high school in Council Bluffs have been named for him.

78 - POTTAWATTAMIE
(continued)

● **Historical Society of Pottawattamie County**
Council Bluffs, Iowa

Stephen L. Purington, President
209 South 28th Street
Council Bluffs, Iowa 51501
or
Mrs. Abbott (Elizabeth) Dean
231 Park Avenue
Council Bluffs, Iowa 51501
or
Arthur J. Rogers
130 Park Avenue
Council Bluffs, Iowa 51501

Organized: March 13, 1961
Meetings: January, March, April, May, September, October, and November
Number of Members: 110
Dues: $5.00 annual; $1.00 student

The Society has restored and furnished the General Dodge House (see above) in cooperation with the Council Bluffs Park Board. Guide service is provided for tours. A joint meeting is held annually with the Greater Omaha Historical Society.

Two historical plaques were restored and rededicated by the Society in 1973 at Pierce Street between Union Street and Franklin Avenue. One marks the sight of the old log Block House built in 1837 by U. S. troops stationed among the Pottawattamie Indians to protect them and the whites from hostile Indians. This was the first building in Council Bluffs. After the troops moved out, it was used as a Catholic Mission for 3 years and also served as a schoolhouse. The second monument is in memory of Father Pierre-Jean De Smet, Jesuit missionary who ministered to the Pottawattamie Indians at the Block House from 1838 to 1841. The monuments were originally erected in 1934.

The Society has placed materials in the Historical Reference Room of the Council Bluffs Public Library. These include books and papers of General Dodge, early editions, maps, pictures, scrapbooks, family histories, and other materials on early Council Bluffs and Pottawattamie County.

● **Horse Watering Trough**
Council Bluffs, Iowa

A 14,000-pound granite monument was presented to the city by the National Humane Alliance, founded by Hermon Lee Ensign in 1907. The trough was originally located at the junction of Broadway and Fourth Street, when horse-drawn buggies drove on the cobblestone streets alongside street cars. As horse traffic declined on Broadway, the watering trough was moved to Main and Pearl Streets. At various other times, the old trough has been located in Dodge Park and Fairmount Park. After the trough was re-erected by the City Park Department in December 1970, it was run into twice by cars and suffered considerable damage. It has been repaired and is to be placed near the Pottawattamie County Rotary Jail (see below). Originally, 4 brass lion heads spouted out the water into the circular trough, but these have been lost or stolen over the years. Above the base, smaller troughs are carved in the granite to hold water for thirsty dogs and cats.

COUNTY AND COUNTY SEAT; LOCATION ON MAP	NAME AND LOCATION	DESCRIPTION

- POTTAWATTAMIE
(continued)

● **Lake Manawa State Park**
1 mile south of
Council Bluffs,
Iowa, off Iowa 92

State Conservation Commission
State Office Building
300 Fourth Street
Des Moines, Iowa 50319

A 660-acre natural lake formed when the flooding Missouri River changed its course in 1881. Manawa is an Indian name meaning rest, peace, and contentment. Park facilities are available for boating, fishing, swimming, and picnicking.

● **Lee de Forest Birthplace Site**
523 Fourth Street
Council Bluffs, Iowa

U.S. Inventor and radio pioneer, Dr. Lee de Forest (1873-1961), was born and lived for 3 years in a house which was located on Fourth Street, between Story and Fifth Avenue in Council Bluffs. (The city directory of that period showed the location as "es S. Bancroft, bet. Dodge and Story.") His father, Henry Swift de Forest, was minister of the First Congregational Church. The "father of radio," who invented the 3-element electron tube in 1906, making possible modern radio, television, and electronics, had more than 300 inventions to his credit, devoted chiefly to the transmission of sound. The first demonstration of voice transmission over the air was by his radio telephone call from Arlington, Virginia to the receiving station on top of the Eiffel Tower in Paris, France in 1915. An elementary school at Twenty-Ninth Street and Ninth Avenue in Council Bluffs has been named for him. A De Forest Museum collection is in progress.

● **Lewis and Clark Monument**
North of Council Bluffs, Iowa
on Rainbow Drive

A monument erected in November 1935 on Rainbow Point, a high, wind-swept bluff above a loop in the Missouri River, commemorates the council Lewis and Clark held with Indians during the expedition to the Far West in 1804. The monument, constructed of native stone from Folsom Quarry, is the work of sculptor Harry E. Stinson and architect George L. Horner. The meeting place was called Council Point, Council Hill, or Council Bluffs and this name was later applied to the area and finally to the settlement on the Missouri River, which had first been called Hart's Bluff. When the Mormons arrived in 1846, they changed the name to Miller's Hollow and then to Kanesville for Army officer Col. Thomas L. Kane, who aided the Mormons in their migrations. After the Mormons left here, the name was changed to Council Bluffs by the Iowa Legislature in 1853. Sculpturing on the monument depicts Lewis and Clark meeting with the Otoe and Missouri Indians.

● **Lincoln Park and Monument**
Oakland and Lafayette Avenues
Council Bluffs, Iowa

A tall granite shaft commemorates the visit of Abraham Lincoln to Council Bluffs, August 12-14, 1859. The monument was erected in 1911 by the Council Bluffs Chapter of the D A R at Lookout Point, where Lincoln stood to observe the valley of the Missouri River. He later (November 17, 1863) designated the City of Council Bluffs as the eastern terminus of the Union Pacific Railroad. General Grenville M. Dodge was the chief construction engineer for the building of the railroad.

78 - POTTAWATTAMIE
(continued)

● **Long's Landing**
South of Council Bluffs, Iowa,
1 mile south of Lake Manawa

Pottawattamie County
Conservation Board
H. L. Borwick, Executive Director
Pottawattamie County Courthouse
Council Bluffs, Iowa 51501

This 24-acre tract includes the landing site of the first steamboat to come up the Missouri River to the Council Bluffs area. This took place in 1819 when Army Major Stephen H. Long (1784-1864) brought the *Western Engineer* to this point and terrified the Indians when he let steam escape from the ship's serpent-shaped bow.

Major Long also established Fort Smith, Arkansas in 1817, to keep peace between the Osage and Cherokee Indians. He called the site Belle Point, while the fort was named to honor General Thomas A. Smith, who was Long's superior officer and commander of the military district. The settlement became an important supply base during the California gold rush in 1849.

Long's Landing provides access to the Missouri River and there are facilities for boat launching, picnicking, and camping.

● **Mormon Camp**
Bayliss Park
First Avenue and Pearl Street
Council Bluffs, Iowa

After leaving Nauvoo, Illinois in 1846, Brigham Young and the Mormons established one of their many camps at this point on their way to the Great Salt Lake in Utah. Here the harassed people gathered supplies in preparation for their journey across the Great Plains. A huge boulder bearing two bronze tablets commemorates their historic trek. It was here at Kanesville (Council Bluffs) that Brigham Young was elected president of the Mormon Church, December 29, 1847.

● **North Council Bluffs Marsh**
North edge of Council Bluffs, Iowa; 16th Street Exit off Interstate 29

Pottawattamie County
 Conservation Board
Harold Borwick, Executive Director
Pottawattamie County Courthouse
Council Bluffs, Iowa 51501

A 14-acre marsh near the Missouri River. Nature trails are being constructed to provide an outdoor classroom and offer an opportunity for nature study. Missouri River Access, nearby, may be reached from the 24th Street turnoff.

● **Oakland Historical Society**
Oakland, Iowa

Mrs. W. L. (Sadie) White, President
P. O. Box 117
Oakland, Iowa 51560

Organized: October 1969
Incorporated: July 20, 1972
Meetings: Fourth Wednesday of month
Number of Members: 80
Dues: $2.00 annual

An organization established to collect and preserve materials of local historical interest. Pictures, books, and antiques related to Oakland have been collected and are on display in a former general store and grocery store acquired in 1975 and located on Main Street. Some items are displayed in an early living room, a dining room, and a kitchen. Museum news and a weekly column, "Historical Facts and Fancies," appears in *The Oakland Acorn*. A commemorative plate with Oakland scenes was produced to promote the town's centennial in 1982 and to raise funds for the museum building.

- POTTAWATTAMIE
(continued)

● **Old Towne Park**
1 mile west of Macedonia, Iowa

Pottawattamie County
Conservation Board
H. L. Borwick, Executive Director
Pottawattamie County Courthouse
Council Bluffs, Iowa 51501

An 8-acre tract along the West Nishnabotna River consisting of timberland (elm, maple, ash, cottonwood, hackberry, wild plum, sumac, hickory, and walnut) as well as areas covered with native shrubs and wild flowers. The river access provides wildlife habitat, and is suitable for camping, picnicking, and fishing.

The first settler in this area was Thomas Jefferson Ring, who arrived here in the spring of 1848, followed by the Myer and Hawes families. Sawmills and gristmills were built; this was the location of Stutsman's Mill, the first mill in Pottawattamie County. Floods caused considerable damage through the years. In 1850, during the height of the overland migration of the Mormons to the Far West, the river was flooded for about 3 months, preventing the Mormons from crossing with their belongings. It was at this site that they waited for the waters to subside, following which a crude wooden bridge was constructed, to become known as Mormon Trail Crossing. Old Macedonia never grew to more than a hamlet, but had a post office, 2 stores, 2 blacksmith shops, a hotel, drug store, saddler shop, and a wagon factory. On July 4, 1880, the Chicago, Burlington and Quincy Railroad completed a road from Hastings, Iowa, on north along the east side of the river. This was about ¾ of a mile east of Old Macedonia, so a new town was laid out at the present site of Macedonia. The former townsite on the river has since been known as Old Towne.

● **Plymouth Rock Replica**
Ridgewood Memorial Park Cemetery
Council Bluffs, Iowa

A 4¼-ton, hand-carved granite replica of historic Plymouth Rock. This duplicate "Cornerstone of America" is in a setting similar to that of the original, which is located near the Atlantic Ocean in Waterfront State Reservation, at Plymouth, Massachusetts. It was there that, according to tradition, the Pilgrims landed from the *Mayflower,* December 21, 1620, and established the second permanent English colony in America.

● **Pottawattamie County Rotary Jail**
228 Pearl Street
Council Bluffs, Iowa

Completed: September 10, 1885

The unique Pottawattamie County Jail, built in a circular design. Constructed in 1885, it is one of the last remaining examples of 6 jails of this type built in the Midwest, and sometimes referred to as The Human Squirrel Cage, The Lazy Susan Jail, or The Jail in the Round. The rotary jail was invented by W. H. Brown and designed by Haugh, Ketcham Company of Indianapolis, Indiana; letters patent were issued July 12, 1881. The architects were Eckel and Aldrich of St. Joseph, Missouri and the contractor was Wickham Brothers of Council Bluffs, Iowa. Other rotary

78 - POTTAWATTAMIE
(continued)

Pottawattamie County Rotary Jail
(continued)

jails built in the 1880's were located at Crawfordsville, Indiana; Gallatin, Missouri; Maryville, Missouri; Maysville, Missouri; and Wichita, Kansas.

The building housing the Pottawattamie County Rotary Jail is a 3-story brick structure, providing quarters for the jailer and his family, a kitchen to prepare food for the prisoners, individual cells for women and juveniles, and storage rooms.

The rotary jail is basically a 3-story metal drum surrounded by a gridded, stationary cage, bolted to the flagstone floor and iron plates in the ceiling. The inner drum is divided into 3 levels or decks, each containing 10 pie-shaped cells with double bunk beds. There is only one door at each level in the outer cage. Entrance or exit to the individual cells is gained by rotating the entire "squirrel cage," by a geared hand-cranking device. This arrangement provided good security and prisoners could not see inmates in the other radial cells, but a jailer could inspect all cells from a single vantage point while the cylinder revolved. The bars of the jail are said to be "heavier than bars used in cages for African lions or Kodiak Alaskan bears."

Within 2 years after construction, the huge rotary jail was not revolving properly. In addition to the mechanical difficulties, the rotating jail was considered a human fire trap, and also proved hazardous for prisoners, who received broken arms, legs, feet, and hands when they were caught between the bars during the revolving of the cylinder. Condemned many times, the Pottawattamie County Rotary Jail was finally closed in 1970. The jail is being restored and preserved as a historic landmark.

● **Stempel Bird Collection**
Pottawattamie County Courthouse
Council Bluffs, Iowa

Pottawattamie County
Conservation Board
H. L. Borwick, Executive Director
Pottawattamie County Courthouse
Council Bluffs, Iowa 51501

Admission: Free

An outstanding display of 600 birds collected and mounted by Dr. Guido Stempel of Macedonia, who gave them to the County Conservation Board. Included in the display are such rare species as the whooping crane, bald eagle, and golden eagle.

● **Thomas Hart Benton, Jr. House**
231 Park Avenue (formerly
Market Street)
Council Bluffs, Iowa

Dr. & Mrs. Abbott (Elizabeth) Dean,
Owners
231 Park Avenue
Council Bluffs, Iowa 51501

A 3-story red brick house completed in 1857 by Thomas Hart Benton, Jr. (1816-1879) a nephew of the famous Senator Thomas Hart Benton (1782-1858) of Missouri. Artist Thomas Hart Benton (1889-1975) was also named for the Missouri statesman, who was his granduncle. Thomas Hart Benton, Jr. located in Dubuque in 1837, and served as Iowa State Superintendent of Public Instruction (1848-1854). He was one of the first bankers in Council Bluffs, where he arrived in 1854, and was commissioned in August 1862 by Governor Kirkwood as a Colonel of the 29th Iowa Infantry. After 3 years service in the Civil War, he was mustered out in October 1865 and brevitted

8 - POTTAWATTAMIE (continued)	**Thomas Hart Benton, Jr. House** (continued)	Brigadier General. That same year, he was the Democratic candidate for Governor.

The home, of Georgian architecture, is much as it was when built by Benton--massive doors, high ceilinged rooms, wide-planked flooring, and expansive windows. Fireplaces are located throughout the house.

● **Walnut Heritage House Museum**
Walnut Public Library
Walnut, Iowa 51577

Mrs. John (Wilma) DeBerg
Walnut, Iowa 51577
or
Mrs. Walter Rieck, Librarian
Walnut, Iowa 51577

Admission: Free
Open: Monday, Wednesday, Friday, and Saturday afternoons; hours vary according to season

Over 1,000 items are on display, featuring pioneer, Indian, and wartime relics belonging to early residents. Included are an 1884 advertising stage curtain from German Hall, the town's first entertainment hall; furnishings from old local business houses, including a desk from the first grocery store and a chair from the first barber shop; a large clock from the early post office; Victorian glassware and china; clothing of early residents; toys; handmade farm implements; early valentines; and a collection of old pictures, photographs, and tintypes.

9 - POWESHIEK

Montezuma
F-8

● **Arbor Lake County Park**
Southwest edge of Grinnell, Iowa
off Iowa 146
or ¼ miles south of I 80 between exits 45 and 46.

Poweshiek County Conservation Board
Roger L. Reed, Executive Officer
P. O. Box 389
Montezuma, Iowa 50171
or
Grinnell Park Commission
Grinnell, Iowa

A 15-acre, boot-shaped lake, surrounded by heavily wooded hills, making up a 37-acre recreational area for picnicking, hiking, fishing, camping, and nature study. The western shore of the lake is to be preserved in its natural state, and used as an outdoor classroom.

In 1902, the Grinnell Soft Water Company contracted with Isham Randolph, who was consulting engineer for the Panama Canal and chief engineer of the Chicago drainage canal, to design a lake storage reservoir. The 20-foot deep lake supplied soft water to the City of Grinnell, until drilled wells were installed in later years, and to Grinnell Electric and Heating Company. Between 1902 and 1920, improvements were made to the lake and recreational area. A clubhouse, beaches, bathhouse, bandstand, and playground were added, and hundreds of trees were set out by public-spirited citizens. Band concerts and fireworks provided entertainment for those who came here to picnic, swim, boat, fish, and camp. Beginning in 1922, the lake and park facilities were operated by private persons or civic clubs, then leased by the city until 1964 when the area was purchased by the city from Grinnell Soft Water Company.

● **Conard Environmental Research Area**
9 miles southwest of Grinnell, Iowa

Grinnell College
Biology Department
1202 Park Street
Grinnell, Iowa 50112

Acquired: 1968

A 365-acre tract of rolling prairie and sloping woodland on the North Skunk River, used as an outdoor laboratory and classroom, and as an environmental research area. The timber includes white oak, basswood, shagbark and pignut hickory, walnut, ash, cutleaf maple, and willow. Larch, spruce, and red pine have been set out as a conservation planting and for research. Wild flowers cover the wooded

79 - POWESHIEK
(continued)

Conard Environmental Research Area
(continued)

hillsides in the spring. The area includes a segment of the North Skunk River, a 14-acre lake with a marshy portion, and a 10-acre arboretum.

The tract was named in honor of Dr. Henry S. Conard, internationally recognized botanist, who retired from the faculty of Grinnell College in 1944 after 39 years of teaching there. He was an expert authority on bryology (mosses) and water lilies, and was noted for his intense interest in preserving the natural environment. Dr. Conard died in 1971 at Haines City, Florida at the age of 97.

● **Diamond Lake**
½ mile west of Montezuma, Iowa along U. S. 63

Poweshiek County Conservation Board
Roger L. Reed, Executive Officer
P. O. Box 389
Montezuma, Iowa 50171

A tract of 176 acres surrounds part of Diamond Lake, the Montezuma city reservoir (110 acres). The area consists of rolling hills covered with timber and grasses. Small game and songbirds are numerous. The park is used for picnicking, boating, fishing, camping, and as an outdoor classroom for nature study.

● **Grinnell Historical Museum**
1125 Broad Street
(near downtown area, just off old U.S. 6)
Grinnell, Iowa 50112

Admission: Free; donations welcome
Open: Tuesday through Sunday during summer, 2:00-5:00 p.m.; Friday and Saturday during winter, 2:00-5:00 p.m.; closed Monday; other times by appointment

A collection of articles of historical or cultural value related to the Grinnell community, housed in the former residence of J. H. McMurray, Jr., a local businessman. The late Victorian, 10-room home, built about 1896, with its ornate light oak woodwork and floors, provides an appropriate setting for the museum. On display is a unique desk--an "office in itself"-- used by J. B. Grinnell, founder of the city; an airplane engine made by pioneer Grinnell aviator William C. (Billy) Robinson, the "Bird Man;" homemade toys; old-time kitchen furnishings; and fancy wearing apparel of the 1890's.

● **Grinnell Historical Museum Society**
P. O. Box 22
Grinnell, Iowa 50112

Judge Michael Enich, President
Spring Street
Grinnell, Iowa 50112

Organized: 1950
Incorporated: 1958
Meetings: Museum Auxiliary Board meets last Thursday of month, except June and July
Number of Members: 275
Dues: $1.00 annual

Owns and maintains the Grinnell Historical Museum (see above).

The Society was organized by representatives of 4 women's clubs seeking a project for a community improvement contest. The objective of the Society was to collect Grinnell-related articles of historic and cultural value or antiques from the earliest days of the city to the turn of the century. In 1951, the Society displayed these treasures from the past in rooms above the old Cunningham Drug

— POWESHIEK
(continued)

Grinnell Historical Museum Society
(continued)

Store. A fire in 1954 destroyed the entire building and nearly everything in it. Additional articles were collected and, in 1965, the museum was moved to its present quarters.

Markers indicate the site of the J. B. Grinnell home and the communal Long House, a log structure built by the city founders. Mr. Grinnell was an ardent abolitionist and aided John Brown in maintaining the Underground Railroad.

— RINGGOLD

- **Caledonia, Iowa**
  Lotts Creek Township
  Southeast of Mount Ayr, Iowa

Settled in 1855 by the Walter, Swigart, and Stuck families, and named Caledonia for a name used in Sir Walter Scott's *Lady of the Lake*. A historical marker was erected in 1972 by Ringgold County Historical Society at the site. The town, perched on a narrow ridge between Lotts Creek and East Fork, was a thriving community with a population of 270 by 1880, and promise of a brilliant future. It was the only town in that part of the county except for Ringgold City, which then consisted of a store and trading post. Caledonia had several churches, a school, post office, hotel, lodges, general stores, harness shop, blacksmith shops, stockyards, broom factory, dressmakers, and doctors. When the railroad was not built through the town, it started to decline. Today the population of Lotts Creek Township is about 130.

ount Ayr
-5

In 1934, Bonnie and Clyde and their gang of desperados stopped briefly in Caledonia. In their flight from the law they parked their car in the church yard and members of the gang bought gasoline and supplies at the store. Leaving the town, they attempted to burn blood-soaked clothing worn by a wounded member of the gang on the Frank Marsh farm.

- **Ringgold County Historical Society**
  Mount Ayr, Iowa

  Charles P. Bennett, President
  R. R. 1
  Mount Ayr, Iowa 50854

Organized: 1939
Incorporated: 1942
Meetings: Annual--late July or early August; others as called.
Number of Members: 175
Dues: $1.00 annual
Courthouse Open: Monday through Friday, 8:00 a.m.-5:00 p.m.
Pioneer Center Open: Sundays and holidays 1:00-5:00 p.m., May 1-October 15; other times by appointment

Lincoln	Jefferson	Tingley	Union
Grant	Washington	Liberty	Monroe
Waubonsie			
Benton	Rice	Poe	Athens
Clinton	Middle Fork	Lotts Creek	Riley

Maintains a small historical museum located on the second floor of the Ringgold County Courthouse, in Mount Ayr, displaying items of local interest, and the Ringgold County Pioneer Center in Ellston, Iowa.

A pioneer cottage, built in 1864 by Elihue and Emeline Lucas Cornwall, and restored and furnished by their great-grandson, Cecil Cornwall. The home was presented to the Society by members of the family and moved to the town park in Ellston. A collection of pictures, papers, books, and articles pertaining to Ringgold County is

80 - RINGGOLD
(continued)

Ringgold County Historical Society
(continued)

maintained. On the grounds are plants and articles found in a farmyard of the 1860-1900 period. A collection of horse-drawn vehicles and early tractor farm equipment is located in the 50- x 100-foot Old Telephone Factory Farm Machinery and Rural Life Museum, which adjoins the park and cottage. The factory, was built in 1914 by promoters and no telephones were ever made there. The building was presented to the Society in 1970. The museum also contains the southern Iowa Old Time Thresherman's Hall of Fame.

The Society has marked the 1855 site of old Marshalltown, Caledonia (see above), and Ringgold City, all abandoned pioneer towns. What is said to be the largest buffalo wallow in the present State of Iowa has been identified with an explanatory sign. Located between Beaconsfield and Kellerton, the wallow covers about 3 acres, is about 20 feet deep, and has seldom been dry.

Also sponsored by the Society are Ringgold County historical tours, an annual "Old Timers Day," educational tours for school children, and a weekly newspaper column, "History Highlights." Assistance is given to members doing family and genealogical research.

● **South Central Chapter,**
Iowa Archeological Society
Mount Ayr, Iowa

Herburt Sovereign, President
906 North Taylor
Mount Ayr, Iowa 50854

Organized: August 20, 1969
Meetings: Fourth Wednesday of month, 7:30 p.m.
Number of Members: 12

A regional chapter of the Iowa Archeological Society (see Cherokee County). Activities include listing and reporting archeological sites, checking new construction areas, and studying Indian life.

81 - SAC

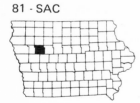

Sac City
D-3

● **Grant Park**
1½ miles northwest of
Auburn, Iowa

Sac County Conservation Board
Muriel Minglin, Secretary
Auburn, Iowa 51433

Established: 1963

A 98-acre parcel of land, bordering both sides of the Raccoon River, including a low flood plain area and a ridge, about 50 feet high, covered with hardwood timber and underbrush native to the region. In the spring, there is an excellent display of wild flowers.

The tract is part of the section in which Grant City was located--the first town founded in Sac County. The Indians first called the settlement Big Grove. This name was changed to Grant City when Ulysses S. Grant was elected President. A dam and mill was once located just above the park area, and just east of here was a pit that furnished clay for the brick and tile plant. Houses built of these bricks may still be seen in Grant City and Auburn, Iowa. When the Chicago and North Western Railway was built, it bypassed Grant City, and, in the late 1800's, a disastrous cyclone swept through here destroying most of the town's business district. Very little of the town was ever rebuilt.

The park is used for picnicking, river fishing, individual and group camping, hiking, and winter sports. The entire area serves as an outdoor classroom for the study of natural sciences.

- SAC
(continued)

- **Hagge Park**
2½ miles south of Sac City, Iowa

  Sac County Conservation Board
  Muriel Minglin, Secretary
  Auburn, Iowa 51433

Established: 1965

A scenic area of 85 acres, straddling the Raccoon River, and consisting of rolling bluegrass pasture and hardwood timber, primarily hickory and oak. The land was acquired from Emma Hagge. There are facilities for picnickers, campers, fishermen, hikers, and winter sportsmen. The area is also ideal for outdoor classroom activities.

- **Lake View Historical Society**
257 Crescent Park Drive (summer)
511 Harrison (winter)
Lake View, Iowa 51450

  Mrs. Frances Rogers, President
  Lake View, Iowa 51450

Organized: 1965
Meetings: As called
Number of Members: 50
Dues: $0.50
Admission to Cabin: Free
Cabin Open: Sunday, 2:00-5:00 p.m., June to September

The Society has restored and furnished an old log cabin, located 1 block east of Crescent Campground along Black Hawk Lake in Lake View. Hostesses in old-fashioned costumes are present during the summer to tell about the cabin and its contents.

In 1870, David Belt built the cabin along the Raccoon River 5 miles east of Lake View. It took 2 years to complete, during which time the family lived in a dugout. The walnut logs used in the cabin were obtained from around Sac City, where larger trees were to be found. The 1½-story building was moved to its present location in the 1920's.

- **Lubeck Forest**
½ mile north of Sac City, Iowa

  Sac County Conservation Board
  Muriel Minglin, Secretary
  Auburn, Iowa 51433

A heavily wooded area of 28 acres, located on a high bluff near the Raccoon River, acquired from Kenneth and Doris Lubeck. There are horseback and foot trails through the area, providing an opportunity for nature study. Picnicking and fishing are other activities permitted, and, during the winter months, the many hills provide an opportunity for skiing and sledding.

- **Reiff Park and Wildlife Area**
1½ miles south of Early, Iowa,
along U.S. 20-71

  Sac County Conservation Board
  Muriel Minglin, Secretary
  Auburn, Iowa 51433

Rolling hills, a small pond, river fishing access, a wildlife refuge, nature trails, campsites, and a picnic area are included in this 80-acre tract along the Boyer River. The park, utilized by educational and study groups, is named for the former owner, Margaret Reiff.

- **Sac County Historical Society**
Sac City, Iowa

  Mrs. Reuben (Mildred) Griffith
  812 Main Street
  Sac City, Iowa 50583

Incorporated: April 29, 1942

82 - SCOTT

Davenport
F-13

● **Allens Grove**
Allens Grove Township,
near Donahue, Iowa

A campsite occupied by Indians and containing virgin soil and timber of the original Black Hawk Purchase of 1832. It is maintained at the Camp Fire Girls campsite.

● **A Little Bit O'Heaven**
Palmer College of Chiropractic
808 Brady Street
Davenport, Iowa 52803

Opened to Public: July 1, 1924
Admission: $1.00; children under 12, $0.50
Open: Daily, 10:00 a.m.-5:00 p.m., Memorial Day through Labor Day

An exotic garden with statues, shrines, idols, bells, a small chapel, waterfalls, and mementoes collected by Dr. B. J. Palmer (the developer of chiropractic) during his world travels.

● **Bix Beiderbecke Memorial Society**
2225 West 17th Street
Davenport, Iowa 52804

Don O'Dette, President

Incorporated: December 8, 1971
Number of Members: 700
Dues: $5.00 annual

A non-profit organization formed to perpetuate the memory of Leon Bismarck (Bix) Beiderbecke (1903-31). The annual Bix Beiderbecke Memorial Jazz Festival in Davenport was initiated in 1972, and draws fans from all over the country. Plans include a Beiderbecke Memorial on the Mississippi riverfront, a scholarship fund for deserving young jazz musicians, and purchase of the Beiderbecke home at 1934 Grand Avenue to use as a museum for Bix memorabilia and mementos of the jazz age. The boyhood home of the legendary jazz cornet player, pianist, and composer is a 2-story frame house.

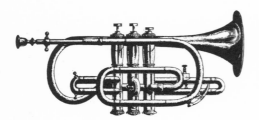

Although Bix didn't study music formally, he came from a musical family, and was fascinated by jazz. He was undoubtedly influenced by jazz bands he heard on Mississippi riverboats that docked at Davenport, and by Dixieland bands he heard in Chicago while attending high school there. Bix quit school and played with many of the early jazz bands during the 1920's including the Wolverines, Charlie Straight, Frankie Trumbauer, Jean Goldkette and Paul Whiteman. He is probably best known for his own composition, *In a Mist*, which he recorded as a piano solo, and his improvised solo of *Singin' the Blues*. A talented, sensitive, and imaginative musician, Bix has had a profound influence on the world of jazz. Paul Whiteman said that "Bix was not only the greatest musician I have ever known, he was also the greatest gentleman," and added that "he had a sure instinct for musical perfection . . ." Beiderbecke died of pneumonia in New York City after a year of illness. His grave is in Oakdale Cemetery in Davenport.

- SCOTT
(continued)

● **Buffalo Bill Cody Homestead**
3 miles southwest of McCausland, Iowa

Scott County Conservation Board
Daniel L. Nagle, Executive Officer
Scott County Courthouse
Davenport, Iowa 52801

Dedicated: May 28, 1967
Open: Saturday and Sunday, Noon-5:00 p.m.

LeClaire is the birthplace of William F. "Buffalo Bill" Cody (1846-1917). As a boy, he lived in at least 3 homes. One of these was moved from LeClaire, Iowa to Cody, Wyoming in 1933 and restored there on the grounds of the Buffalo Bill Museum. This home was made of hewn oak with mortised joints, and had walls covered with split oak lathe. It was purchased by Ralph Budd, president of the Chicago, Burlington, and Quincy Railroad from its owner, Captain Isaac Spinsby, for $150, dismantled and moved to Cody.

The Cody Homestead, located on a 4-acre tract near McCausland, is another of Buffalo Bill's boyhood homes, built of stone in 1847 by his father Isaac Cody, when Bill was only 1½ years old. His younger sister was born here. This is the only one of Buffalo Bill's boyhood homes still standing on an original site. A frame section (now painted white) was added later by the McCausland family, who came from West Virginia. The house is unusual with its large closets, walnut door panels, rock fireplace with walnut mantel, and a spout made of walnut running through one wall for the purpose of draining waste water. As a boy, Buffalo Bill played in the yard and over the surrounding hills and timber. Isaac Cody managed the 7,000 acre farm, which was owned by the Breckenridge family, for about 3 years. The Cody family left Iowa when Bill was only 8 years old. In later years, he was a messenger boy, Pony Express rider, scout and soldier for the Union, buffalo hunter, and owner of a Wild West Show. He died, almost penniless, in Colorado and is buried there on Lookout Mountain. A brother, Samuel Cody, is buried in the Christian Church Cemetery at Long Grove, Iowa. The house near McCausland was donated to Save Our Landmarks, Inc. (see Scott County Historical Society below) by Roy Curtis, and partially restored and furnished. Later, the property was deeded to Scott County Conservation Board and has been further improved, more furnishings added, and the grounds improved and restored to appear as they did when the Cody family lived here. A stagecoach, covered wagon, and buffalo (bison) may be seen. Picnicking is permitted on the grounds.

● **Buffalo Bill Museum**
River Drive
LeClaire, Iowa 52753

Mrs. Harold Kennedy, Curator
P.O. Box 1
LeClaire, Iowa 52753

Established: June 1957
Admission: $0.50; children under 12, free
Open: Daily, 9:00 a.m.-5:00 p.m., May 1 to November 1; Saturday and Sunday only during winter months, 10:00 a.m.-5:00 p.m.
Museum Membership: 140
Membership Dues: $1.00 annual

A memorial to Indians, pioneers, and steamboat days, operated by a nonprofit organization. The museum was formerly located in the old City Hall, but moved to a new 60-x 40-foot brick building opened on June 10, 1971. The new museum is adjacent to the *Lone Star,* a wooden hull

82 - SCOTT
(continued)

Buffalo Bill Museum
(continued)

stern-wheeler in dry dock along the Mississippi River. The boat was originally built in 1868 at Lyons, Iowa as a 27-ton side-wheel, geared boat for general towing purposes. It was rebuilt in 1890 as a stern-wheeler, and increased in size and tonnage. The old riverboat was decommissioned and taken out of service April 21, 1968. This last working steamboat on the Upper Mississippi has been kept just as it was when it operated on the river. The museum displays preserve documents and mementoes related to the history of the town of LeClaire--a rafting town, the home of river pilots, and the birthplace of William F. "Buffalo Bill" Cody (February 26, 1846-January 10, 1917). (See Buffalo Bill Cody Homestead, above.)

The new museum building was made possible largely through a donation from James Ryan, a former resident of LeClaire who gained fame and fortune as an inventor. Included in the museum displays are airplane flight recorders, one of his many inventions. Also to be seen are articles associated with Buffalo Bill (Wild West Show color posters, rifles owned by Cody, and photographs), Indian arrowheads and stone axes found in the Crow Creek area near Middle Road, beaded bags made by Indians held captive at Camp McClellan (see below), models of early steamboats, old photographs of LeClaire, Civil War mementoes, early farming and blacksmithing equipment, antique dishes, doll furniture, and riverboat memorabilia.

The Green Tree, a huge elm with a spread of about 200 feet, formerly stood along the banks of the Mississippi at LeClaire. Antoine LeClaire met with Indians and early settlers under the tree, for which the old Green Tree Inn was named. A victim of Dutch elm disease, the tree was cut down in 1964. A bronze plaque marks the spot where the elm once stood. On display in the museum is a huge slab of wood cut from the base of the famed tree.

LeClaire was also the home of Captain James Buchanan Eads, the engineer who erected the bridge at St. Louis bearing his name. His father, Thomas Eads, who was the inventor of a diving bell, built a frame house here in 1836.

● **Camp McClellan**
Lindsay Park
Davenport, Iowa

Established: August 1861

A boulder and tablet mark the site of Camp McClellan, a rendezvious for Iowa Volunteer Regiments during the War of the Rebellion. Located opposite the island of Rock Island, the 1,000-acre military establishment was where most of the recruits from Iowa were trained and drilled during the Civil War, prior to assignment to companies and regiments in the field. There were 48,000 Union soldiers quartered here in some 30 barracks, each 22 x 24 feet and equipped with 52 double berths. In 1862, some 400 Sioux Indians were imprisoned here following the massacre in Minnesota. At the close of the Civil War, during 1865 and 1866, approximately 45 out of the 60 Iowa Volunteer Regimental and Battery organizations were paid off and disbanded at Camp McClellan.

- SCOTT
(continued)

● **Claim House**
1329 College Avenue
Davenport, Iowa

A wooden house, said to be the first frame house in Wisconsin Territory, and the oldest remaining in Davenport. It was built in 1833 by George L. Davenport, a son of Colonel George Davenport (see Rock Island, below). Materials for the home were not available locally, so were brought from Cincinnati by steamboat. The Claim House was originally located nearer the river, on land given by the Indians to the young white son of their friend, Colonel Davenport, in 1832. The wooden structure was originally 16 x 16 feet. It has been moved several times and greatly changed. The original beams of rough-hewn lumber may still be seen in the attic. The home is privately owned.

● **Credit Island**
West River Drive
Davenport, Iowa

Acquired by City: 1918

An island park, the location of one of the earliest trading posts west of the Mississippi, and the site of the Battle of Credit Island during the War of 1812. Chief Black Hawk and 1,000 of his Indian braves, aided by a detachment of British soldiers, were victorious over 334 American soldiers under the command of Major Zachary Taylor (later President of the United States) on September 5, 1814. The British had previously been informed by the Indians that a large expedition of American troops had left St. Louis for the Upper Mississippi River on August 21.

● **Davenport Municipal Art Gallery**
1737 West 12th Street
Davenport, Iowa 52804

Lawrence Hoffman, Director

Organized: 1925
Admission: Free
Open: Tuesday through Friday, noon-4:30 p.m.; Saturday, 10:00 a.m.-4:30 p.m.; Sunday, 1:00-4:30 p.m.; closed Monday and holidays

Contains collections of paintings, sculptures, and decorative art. On display are works of European and contemporary American artists, including Grant Wood, and a Mexican-Colonial exhibit.

● **Fejervary Park**
West end of 12th Street
Davenport, Iowa

Admission to Zoo: $0.15
Zoo Open: Daily during summer; weekends from mid-May to June 10 and from Labor Day to end of September

The 75-acre park, on wooded bluffs, features a children's zoo built around Mother Goose characters. About 50 monkeys live on Monkey Island during the summer. The park includes the 21-acre estate formerly owned by Count Nicholas Fejervary, who came to Davenport from his native Hungary in 1853, and died here in 1895.

● **First Mississippi River Bridge**
Davenport, Iowa

The first bridge to span the Mississippi River was built in 1853-56. The site is now identified by markers. One of these is made of stone from an original bridge pier and is located on the north shore at the western end of the island of Rock Island. The north abutment of the bridge is marked by a boulder at the junction of 3rd and 4th Streets in Davenport. The first train to cross this railroad bridge

82 - SCOTT
(continued)

First Mississippi River Bridge
(continued)

was on April 22, 1856 and consisted of a locomotive and 8 cars.

Within a month of its opening, this bridge was badly damaged by the steamboat *Effie Afton* which struck one of the bridge piers and caught fire. The rivermen had tried to stop the building of the bridge and after this disaster the case was brought to court in Hurd et al vs Railroad Bridge Company. The river interests hired lawyer Stephen Douglas. Representing the railroad company in the case was a young attorney, Abraham Lincoln, who won the suit. This decision set a precedent giving the legal right to construct bridges across navigable streams.

This bridge was destroyed by fire and replaced in 1894 by the Government Rail-Auto Bridge at Second and Le Claire Streets. The draw span is constructed to make a 360-degree turn to let large riverboats and barges through Lock and Dam No. 15.

● **Fort Armstrong**
End of Government Bridge
on Rock Island, between
Davenport, Iowa and
Rock Island, Illinois

The "Guardian of the Mississippi," built in 1816 on Rock Island, opposite Davenport, on a high bluff above the rapids that began at this point. Its purpose was to control access to the Upper Mississippi from St. Louis, Missouri to the lead mines at Galena, Illinois. The fort was occupied from 1816-36. During the War of 1812, 4 years before the fort was built, the British and their Indian allies had a cannon mounted on the bluff. Most of the activity of the Black Hawk War of 1832 centered around this fort. The conflict ended in Black Hawk's defeat. Vandals set fire to the old fort in 1855, destroying the barracks and a blockhouse. In 1916, a replica of one of the 3 blockhouses constituting the original fort was built.

John Emerson, post surgeon at Fort Armstrong, was the owner of the famous slave, Dred Scott, subject of the bitterly contested issue of slavery in the Federal territories. The site of the home in which master and slave lived is at 217 East Second Street in Davenport. Dr. Emerson died at the LeClaire house in Davenport in 1843 before the public became aware of Dred Scott and the famous Supreme Court decision. Dr. Emerson is buried in the Old City Cemetery in Davenport.

● **Grave of Antoine LeClaire**
Mt. Calvary Cemetery
(formerly St. Marguerite's Cemetery)
803 East 39th Street
Davenport, Iowa

A white marble monument just inside the cemetery entrance marks the burial place of Antoine LeClaire (December 15, 1797- September 25, 1861) and his wife Marguerite (October 16, 1802-October 18, 1876). LeClaire, the son of a French Canadian and of the granddaughter of a Pottawattamie Indian chief, founded the town of Davenport in 1836. At the site of the house he built in 1832, LeClaire, as a friend and interpreter for the Indians, consummated the early treaties between the United States Government and the Sac and Fox Tribes. These treaties served as the basis for rights of title to much of the land now included in the State of Iowa. Some time after

SCOTT
(continued)

Grave of Antoine LeClaire
(continued)

LeClaire abandoned the house as a residence in 1854, it served as the first railroad depot west of the Mississippi on the Mississippi and Missouri Railroad, which became part of the Chicago, Rock Island, and Pacific Railway. LeClaire sold the land he was given by the government, together with other land he had acquired, to a group of men including Colonel George Davenport, an Englishman who had settled in the area, and for whom the town of Davenport was named. It was to Antoine LeClaire that Chief Black Hawk dictated his autobiography. Many of the papers and belongings of Antoine and Marguerite Le Claire may be seen at Putnam Museum (see below).

● **John M. Browning Memorial Museum**
Rock Island Arsenal

Dorrell E. Garrison, Curator
Rock Island, Illinois 61201

Established: July 1905; rededicated in 1959
Admission: Free
Open: Wednesday through Sunday, 11:00 a.m.-4:00 p.m.; closed Monday and Tuesday; open holidays except Thanksgiving and Christmas

Originally the Rock Island Museum, containing one of the largest military arms collections in the Mississippi Valley. This is now a memorial to the "father" of automatic weapons, which include the U.S. Automatic Pistol, Model 1911 (Colt); the Browning U.S. Machine Gun, Model 1917; and the B.A.R., U.S. Automatic Rifle, Model 1918. In the museum are weapons dating from pre-Revolutionary War times to the present, including weapons captured from Indian battles, the Civil War, Spanish-American War, the Boxer Rebellion, World Wars I and II, and the Korean Conflict. Both U.S. and foreign small arms and artillery and accessories are on display, especially equipment produced at Rock Island Arsenal. Many other items of historic interest to this area are also on display.

● **Phebe W. Sudlow Marker**
Sudlow Junior High School
1414 East Locust Street
Davenport, Iowa

A bronze marker dedicated October 1, 1936 to Phebe (Phoebe) W. Sudlow (1831-1922), who served as superintendent of the Davenport Public Schools (1874-78). She first taught school in Scott County in the Round Grove School when she moved to Iowa from Ohio in 1856. Miss Sudlow was the first woman to serve as a principal and as a city superintendent of public schools in the United States and was the first woman to serve as president of the Iowa State Teachers Association (1876-77). In 1878, she was elected to a professorship at The State University of Iowa, where she taught until 1881. Miss Sudlow was a vigorous exponent of women's rights and expressed herself pointedly on the subject. Her arguments for equal pay for men and women influenced not only the Davenport School Board, but other boards throughout the Middle West. She was over 90 years old when it was voted to change the name of East Intermediate School to the Phoebe W. Sudlow Intermediate School as a befitting memorial to her character and influence.

82 - SCOTT
(continued)

● **Putnam Museum**
(Formerly **Davenport Museum**)
1717 West 12th Street
Davenport, Iowa 52804

Joseph L. Cartwright, Director

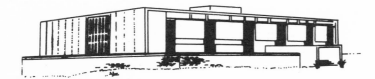

Established: December 14, 1867; present building completed in 1964

Admission: $0.75; children $0.25; school classes free

Open: Monday through Saturday, 9:00 a.m.-5:00 p.m.; Sunday, 1:00-5:00 p.m.

Museum Membership: 2000

Membership Dues: $10.00 annual; $15.00 joint; $5.00 student; $3.00 junior; $50.00 contributing; $100.00 sustaining; $500.00 life

This third oldest museum west of the Mississippi contains outstanding exhibits of local, regional, and river history; tools; household furnishings; textiles; costumes; 10,000 coins and stamps; military and transportation items; old pictures; and manuscripts and documents. Among the items on display is the original Black Hawk Treaty, signed in 1832 at what is now Fifth and Pershing Streets, following negotiations between Chief Black Hawk and General Winfield Scott. This treaty opened up the area to white settlement. Here also are the papers of Judge James Grant, an early settler who was said to be the highest paid lawyer in the United States during his era. The natural science collections include minerals, rocks, and fossils; shells; insects; mammals; birds; displays on archeology, anthropology, and ethnology of the Americas, Europe, Asia, Africa, Egypt, and the Pacific area; and a herbarium. The art collection includes primitive art, water colors, oils, prints, and sculptures. The B. J. and Mabel H. Palmer Memorial Collection is located in a separate wing. There are also changing and traveling exhibits. The library includes 50,000 volumes on history, science, and art. A World Adventure Series (motion picture travelogues with lecturers) and other film showings, lectures by outstanding authorities, environmental workshops, and field trips are sponsored. The museum was renamed in 1974 to honor the Putnam family, the primary benefactors.

● **Quad City Area Archeological Society**
Davenport Museum
1717 West 12th Street
Davenport, Iowa 52804

Ferrell Anderson, President
1530 West Kimberly Road
Davenport, Iowa 52806
or
Darrell Doss, Treasurer
2131 Myrtle
Davenport, Iowa 52804

Organized: 1969

Meetings: Last Tuesday of every other month, 7:30 p.m., September through May

Number of Members: 35

Dues: $2.00 annual; $3.00 family; $1.00 student

A regional chapter of the Iowa Archeological Society (see Cherokee County) and the Illinois Association for Advancement of Archaeology. Field trips and salvage excavations are held during the summer. Indoor meetings feature speakers on some aspect of archeology. The chapter actively engages in programs devoted to the preservation of archeological sites and materials. Artifacts are displayed at Davenport Museum (see above).

● **Rock Island**
In Mississippi River,
south of Davenport, Iowa

The island of Rock Island is situated in the Mississippi River between the cities of Davenport, Iowa and Rock Island, Illinois. The island is about 3 miles long and up to 3/4 of a mile wide, and contains 945 acres. This was a popular spot with the Indians and many of their ancient mounds are

2 - SCOTT
(continued)

Rock Island
(continued)

located on the island. In 1804, the island was acquired from the Indians by treaty. This treaty was never recognized by Chief Black Hawk and subsequent events finally led to the Black Hawk War of 1832.

Colonel George Davenport, for whom the town of Davenport was named, first settled on the island in 1816. Although Davenport was an Englishman, he fought for the Americans in the War of 1812, and served in the U.S. Army before coming to Fort Armstrong, where he had the agency for supplying government troops with provisions. He built a double log cabin in 1817 and began trading with the Indians, finally selling out to the American Fur Company. In 1833 he replaced his log cabin with a large 2-story Colonial home, which has been partially restored. It was in this home that Colonel Davenport was murdered by bandits on July 4, 1845 while his family was attending a picnic celebration. The 7 robbers were apprehended and convicted.

Also on the arsenal grounds are the National Cemetery established in 1865, the site of a Confederate Prison established in 1863, and a Confederate Cemetery where the bodies of 1,961 prisoners who died while confined here during the Civil War have been buried; 11 bodies have since been removed to their home states.

● **St. Anthony's Church**
417 Main Street
Davenport, Iowa 52801

The original church was erected in 1837 and was Davenport's first church. This church was designed by Father Samuel Mazzuchelli, while Antoine LeClaire was responsible for the construction and a major part of the financing. The 1837 church is now used for the parish school. In 1853, a rough-cut stone church of modified Georgian architecture was built; it has become a landmark in the city.

● **St. Mary's Chapel**
901 Tremont Street
Davenport, Iowa

A plaque placed in the entry to St. Mary's Chapel at St. Katharine's-St. Mark's School is dedicated to Marion Crandell (1873-1918), who was the first American woman killed in World War I while in active service. The inscription on the memorial plaque reads: "Marion Crandell...First American Woman Killed in World War at St. Menehould...March 27, 1918." Miss Crandell was born in Cedar Rapids, Iowa. She taught French for 2 years at St. Katharine's School in Davenport, Iowa before enlisting through the Y.M.C.A. on January 19, 1918 for assignment in canteen work in France. As a young girl she had studied in France and spoke the language fluently. Miss Crandell was killed by a German bomb in the village of St. Menehould while leaving the French soldiers' canteen where she worked as a volunteer. She was buried overseas in a military cemetery, the only woman's grave among 6,000 French soldiers.

A house in Davenport was purchased as a memorial and opened for faculty housing in 1923. The home was named

82 - SCOTT
(continued)

St. Mary's Chapel
(continued)

Crandell House and was occupied by teachers until 1969 when it was sold by the school. Located just off the campus, the house is now used as a private residence.

St. Katharine's-St. Mark's is now a co-educational school, with pupils enrolled from preschool age through high school. It was founded by the Episcopal Church in 1884.

On May 30, 1921, trees were planted on the Statehouse grounds in Des Moines in memory of Miss Crandell and 9 other women (Red Cross workers and nurses) who died during World War I, or in military camps or while on foreign duty.

● **Scott County Genealogical Society**
Davenport, Iowa

Mrs. MaryLou Hall,
Corresponding Secretary
2623 North Zenith Avenue
Davenport, Iowa 52804

A local chapter of the Iowa Genealogical Society (see Polk County). The 1882 *History of Scott County* was reproduced with a new name index in 1975.

● **Scott County Historical Society**
(Formerly **Save Our Landmarks, Inc.**)
Davenport, Iowa

Mrs. Edna C. Untiedt, President
2812 Marquette
Davenport, Iowa 52804
or
Mrs. Walter P. Keller, Secretary
R. R. 1
Davenport, Iowa 52804

Organized: September 1969
Incorporated: October 1969
Meetings: Third Tuesday of month, 7:30 p.m., at various locations
Number of Members: 101
Dues: $3.00 annual

A Society concerned with promoting and maintaining an interest in local history, erecting historical markers, participating in historical observances, collecting historical materials, and preserving historic landmarks in Scott County. The Cody Homestead (see Buffalo Bill Cody Homestead, above) near McCausland is one of the properties on which much work has been done. A log cabin, originally built in 1837 by a Mr. Arbel, 1 mile west of Long Grove, has also been moved to Walnut Grove Village in Scott County Park (see below), and restored and furnished. The village also includes a rural school, old blacksmith shop, depot, and general store. The Summit Presbyterian Church, built in 1859 in Lincoln Township at the corner of Utica Ridge Road and the Black Hawk Trail, north of Davenport, is owned by the Society and is used as a museum and meeting place. Summit Cemetery is adjacent to the church. The depot at Donahue, Iowa is being restored. The Society also catalogues, maps, and renovates cemeteries; sponsors county tours, presents displays and historic programs, and conducts genealogical research.

A sun-dried brick or adobe house, unusual for this part of the country, is located at Long Grove. A wooden frame house has been built over the original home, preserving the old walls. The property is privately owned (contact Mrs. Robert Lage, Long Grove, Iowa 52756).

- SCOTT
(continued)

● **Scott County Park**
3 miles east of Long Grove, Iowa, or
9 miles north of Davenport, Iowa,
off U. S. 61.

Scott County Conservation Board
Daniel L. Nagle, Executive Officer
Scott County Courthouse
Davenport, Iowa 52801

Dedicated: June 19, 1965

A 1,270-acre park in the northeastern part of Scott County, offering an opportunity for outdoor recreation, picnicking, camping, horseback riding, hiking, fishing, and swimming. The area includes lakes, grassy meadows, and rugged wilderness, and abounds in wildlife — birds, fox, deer, raccoons, beavers, rabbits, woodchucks, muskrats, mink, and weasels. The nature trails have signs identifying trees, shrubs, and other native plants. Many of the areas in the park have been given names to describe the surroundings, or are derived from the Sac and Fox Indians who once roamed over this land.

Walnut Grove Pioneer Village, near the north boundary of the park, includes a pioneer log cabin, rural school, blacksmith shop, depot, and general store, all appropriately furnished. The log cabin, schoolhouse, and blacksmith shop are original buildings, moved from other locations.

Stones from the old Scott County Courthouse have been erected as a memorial by the Scott County Pioneer Settlers Association.

- SHELBY

arlan
F-2

● **Elk Horn Creek Recreation Area**
1 mile west and 1½ miles south
of Elk Horn, Iowa

Shelby County Conservation Board
John Goeser, Executive Director
Defiance, Iowa 51527

A 60-acre multi-purpose outdoor recreation area providing opportunities for picnicking, camping, hiking, fishing, hunting, and nature study. The area is about 50 percent forested with a variety of hardwood trees. During the spring, mushrooms may be found in the moist humus of the north-facing slopes. Elk Horn Creek flows continuously through the area. Foundations made of hand-cut limestone blocks may still be seen on the ridge top along the southeastern boundaries of the site. The buildings have long since been moved away.

● **Manteno Park**
8 miles northwest of
Defiance, Iowa

Shelby County Conservation Board
John Goeser, Executive Director
Defiance, Iowa 51527

A 75-acre park in which are located Manteno Cemetery and Manteno Hall. The town of Manteno existed from 1856 to around 1900. The church, originally Methodist, was subsequently used by the Latter Day Saints. There are facilities in the park for boating, fishing, horseback riding, picnicking, and camping.

● **Nishna Valley Genealogical Society**
Harlan, Iowa

Mrs. Raymond Petersen,
Corresponding Secretary
R. R. 2, Box 186
Harlan, Iowa 51537

Organized: 1973
Meetings: Second Sunday in February, April, June, and October.

A local chapter of the Iowa Genealogical Society (see Polk County). Members have recorded cemetery inscriptions and early marriage records of Shelby County.

● **Shelby County Historical Society**
Harlan, Iowa

Mrs. Gaillard R. Heflin, President
R.R. 4
Harlan, Iowa 51537

Organized: January 24, 1965
Meetings: Fourth Sunday of each month, except August and December
Number of Members: 130
Dues: $2.00 annual

83 - SHELBY
(continued)

Shelby County Historical Society
(continued)

Promotes interest in local history, in cooperation with other civic groups. In January 1970, a log cabin built in 1857 was purchased, and restored as a museum. The cabin was located in Grove Township on land obtained on a swampland grant to John A. McIntosh from the State of Iowa. McIntosh, one of the first settlers in Shelby County, played an active part in its development, and was a trusted friend of the Indians. When the Indian, Yellow Smoke, was mortally wounded by other Indians, he crawled to the old cabin door and requested that "Uncle McIntosh" give him a white man's burial. This rite was carefully carried out and Yellow Smoke was buried on a knoll not far from the cabin's original location. In September 1970, the McIntosh log cabin was moved from its original site in Galland's Grove (settled in 1848 by Abraham Galland), to Potter's Park in Harlan and first opened to visitors in 1971, by appointment. A second log cabin (c. 1857), built by the Leland family, was added later, together with a museum. Society publications include the reporting of the 1915 Ed White *Shelby County History*, to which an index has been added.

Other historic sites in Shelby County include the first church in the county at Manteno (see Manteno Park, above), the old Stagecoach Trail at Portsmouth, a 17-acre virgin prairie located on the farm of Derald W. Dinesen (2½ miles north and 2 miles east of Harlan), and a meteorite (1865) in the Harlan Cemetery at the grave of William Wyland.

84 - SIOUX

Orange City
B-1

● **Big Sioux Park**
6 miles northeast of
Hawarden, Iowa

Sioux County Conservation Board
Gerald Schiefen, Executive Officer
R. R. 1
P. O. Box 39
Hawarden, Iowa 51023

A 147-acre area typical of Missouri River bottomland, with elevations ranging from 1,180 to 1,320 feet above sea level. The park, which slopes toward the Big Sioux River, is adjacent to Oak Grove Park (see below). A variety of indigenous trees, shrubs, grasses, and wild flowers may be seen here. Wildlife includes deer, badgers, opossums, raccoons, skunks, rabbits, squirrels, birds, and snakes. The general area, like most of Sioux County, was predominantly settled by the Dutch in the 1800's.

There are bridle trails, hiking trails, campsites, picnic areas, a toboggan and ski run, and a sledding area in the park.

- SIOUX
(continued)

Heritage Room and Hoeven Room
Northwestern College Library
101 Seventh Street, S.W.
Orange City, Iowa 51041

Professor Nelson Nieuwenhuis

Admission: Free
Open: Daily except Sunday; evenings Monday through Thursday

The Heritage Room contains books, pictures, and articles pertaining to the Dutch background of the college and the community. The Hoeven Room features mementoes of Charles B. Hoeven, Congressman from Iowa's Sixth District for 22 years.

Oak Grove Park
6 miles northeast of
Hawarden, Iowa

Sioux County Conservation Board
Gerald Schiefen, Executive Officer
R. R. 1, P. O. Box 39
Hawarden, Iowa 51023
or
State Conservation Commission
State Office Building
300 Fourth Street
Des Moines, Iowa 50319

Established: 1924

A scenic area of 102 acres, next to Big Sioux Park (see above). It is now operated under a management lease agreement between the State of Iowa and Sioux County. Most of the grove was originally owned by John Feikema, an early settler in the region, and it was used for several generations as a recreational area even before the land was purchased by the State. Present facilities include picnic areas, hiking and fishing access trails, and a camping area.

Sioux County Historical Society
Orange City, Iowa

Alan Hofland, President
322 - 1st Street N.E.
Orange City, Iowa 51041
or
Mrs. James Doornink, Secretary
323 Third NE
Orange City, Iowa 51041

Incorporated: July 1969
Meetings: Annually in April; board meetings monthly
Number of Members: 205
Dues: $5.00 annual; $100.00 life

In observance of the Centennial of Orange City in 1970, an old country schoolhouse of 1870 vintage was restored and furnished by the Society with items typical of that early day. A museum is to be built.

- STORY

ada
6

Ames High School Prairie
West of Ames High School
20th and Ridgewood
Ames, Iowa 50010

Richard Trump
1511 - 13th Street
Ames, Iowa 50010
or
Roger O. Landers, Jr.
3522 Ontario Road
Ames, Iowa 50010

Acquired: 1956

A 7½-acre portion of a 22-acre natural area adjacent to Ames High School. As an outdoor classroom for high school and university students, researchers, and nature lovers, the prairie provides an opportunity to evaluate and appreciate the natural environment and observe biological processes in the field. A wide variety of wild flowers and grasses may be seen through the seasons. More than 130 plant species have been identified. It is a living community of interdependent plants and animals that have evolved over the centuries.

Under the leadership of the Ames Conservation Council, efforts to preserve this unplowed tract of prairie and woodland were successful. A proposal to lease the tract to the Iowa Chapter of The Nature Conservancy (see below) for a period of 49 years at $1.00 per year was approved at a school election on September 14, 1970 by more than 80 percent of the voters. The area is managed by a 6-member committee including representatives from Ames Community School District, The Nature Conservancy, and the Ames Park Commission.

85 - STORY
(continued)

● **Carver Hall**
Campus of Iowa State University
Ames, Iowa

Dedicated: September 27, 1970

A $3.1 million building named for George Washington Carver (1864-1943) the distinguished alumnus of Iowa State University who won fame as a scientist, teacher, and accomplished painter. The frail son of slave parents was born in Missouri and orphaned in infancy by Civil War marauders. Carver developed interests in music, painting, flowers, and the sciences--a man of many talents. He enrolled at Simpson College in Indianola, Iowa (see Carver Hall, Warren County) at the age of 26 years, transferring to the Ames campus in 1891. He was the first black student to enroll at Iowa State, receiving his baccalaureate degree in 1894. He completed his work for a master's degree in 1896. While at Iowa State University he became a lifetime friend of "Tama Jim" Wilson, dean of agriculture, and Louis H. Pammel, head of the botany department. Carver was also a great friend of Henry A. Wallace, later U.S. Secretary of Agriculture and Vice-President. Carver loved nature, was dedicated to his work, and never married.

Carver Hall includes 42 classrooms, 2 large lecture halls, and the administrative offices of the College of Sciences and Humanities, the Department of Mathematics, and the Department of Industrial Administration.

● **Community Historical Society**
Main Street
Maxwell, Iowa 50161

Mrs. Basil (Charlotte) Caple, President
R. R. 1, Maxwell, Iowa 50161
or
Mrs. J. Harper White, Historian
R. R. 1, Maxwell, Iowa 50161
or
Miss Belva Swalwell, George Cook, and Jesse Parr, Curators
Maxwell, Iowa 50161

Organized: January 1964
Incorporated: February 7, 1964
Meetings: Second Monday of month, 8:00 p.m.
Number of Members: 175
Dues: $1.00 annual; $25.00 life
Admission to Museum: Free; donations welcome
Museum Open: Sunday and holidays, 2:00-5:00 p.m. from Memorial Day through Labor Day; other times by appointment

Operates a museum containing pioneer tools and machinery, old wearing apparel, toys, dishes, photographs, mementoes from various wars (including a sword used at Custer's Last Stand), and natural history displays -- a total of 3,300 articles donated or loaned for exhibit. In August, the Society sponsors the Annual Old Settlers Days, with special displays of pioneer items.

● **Cory Burying Ground**
South of Ames, Iowa, east of U.S. 169, or 200 yards north of the Ames Sewage Disposal Plant

A small family cemetery containing the graves of Mary Jane Cory, the mother of evangelist Billy Sunday, and other relatives.

STORY
(continued)

Cory Burying Ground
(continued)

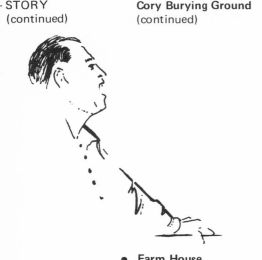

William Ashley (Billy) Sunday was born November 19, 1862 on a Story County farm. His father died in the Civil War and, at the age of 9, Billy was sent to a soldiers' orphans' home. He later lived with his grandfather, near Nevada, Iowa. In 1884, at the age of 22, Billy Sunday became center fielder for the Chicago White Stockings. He followed his career of professional baseball player until he became interested in missions and church work. He is said to have conducted his first revival meeting at Garner, Iowa. From then on, he and his wife, "Ma," were in constant demand for revival meetings. Services were usually held in tents with plank seats and sawdust on the ground or floor. From this the expression, "hittin' the sawdust trail," developed. Dishpans were used to collect offerings. The world-famed evangelist died of a heart attack November 6, 1935 and was buried at Forest Hill Cemetery in Chicago, Illinois.

● **Farm House**
Campus of Iowa State University
Ames, Iowa

A farm home considered typical of the second half of the 19th Century. Completed in 1861, this was the first construction on the 648-acre site of the Iowa State Agricultural College and Model Farm, which was chartered 3 years earlier by the Iowa General Assembly--one of the earliest land-grant institutions to be formally authorized. The house was built by the Board of Trustees without any formal plans "by rule of thumb." There was no architect and no contractor. With labor and materials furnished by residents of surrounding communities, the initial cost was $4,000.

The house was first occupied by W. H. Fitzpatrick, who rented the place for 2 years. This was later the home of Seaman A. Knapp (born 1833), noted agriculturist and teacher, who lived here from 1880 to 1885. Knapp was the originator of the county farm agent system used in Iowa, and gained national recognition for his contributions to agriculture in Louisiana and the South. From 1891 to 1896, this was the home of James (Tama Jim) Wilson (born 1836). After holding a number of local and state offices, Tama Jim (who farmed in Tama County, Iowa) served 3 terms in Congress and became U.S. Secretary of Agriculture in 1897, a post he held until 1913--the longest term of service for anyone to hold this office. The house has had various other occupants, serving in more recent years (until 1970) as the home of the Dean of Agriculture at the University. Dean C. F. Curtiss lived there longer than anyone else--from 1896 to 1946.

The 14-room, 2-story brick house has walls 18 inches thick, floor to ceiling windows, pegged beams, and a fireplace. The soft red brick exterior was coated with cement or stucco in 1909 to arrest deterioration. Farm House was designated a National Historic Landmark in 1964. It is to be restored to about the 1900 period.

85 - STORY
(continued)

● **Hickory Grove Park**
2 miles west and 2 miles south
of Colo, Iowa

Story County Conservation Board
Robert Ray Pinneke, Executive Director
Hickory Grove Park
Colo, Iowa 50056

A picturesque area of 368 acres, including a 98.4-acre artificial lake. East Indian Creek runs along the west edge of the park. To be seen are deer, beaver, squirrels, rabbits, quail, pheasants, and ducks and geese during migration. This is a place to picnic, swim, boat, camp, hike, fish, and hunt in season. A natural area and wildlife refuge afford an opportunity for nature study and conservation education. During the winter, the park is used for ice skating, and there are marked snowmobile trails and a flood-lighted toboggan slope.

● **Iowa Center**
North of Maxwell, Iowa

A former settlement, established in 1853, which reached its peak in 1856. Iowa Center had the second post office in Story County, and was one of the contenders for the state capital. After Des Moines was selected as the capital in 1856, Iowa Center's population began to decline. In 1882, when the Chicago, Milwaukee, and St. Paul Railroad bypassed the town, the population was further decreased when many of the local residents moved to Maxwell.

● **Iowa Chapter, The Nature Conservancy**

Roger Q. Landers, Jr., Chairman
3522 Ontario Road
Ames, Iowa 50010
or
John Brayton, Treasurer
R.R. 2
Sumner, Iowa 50674

Organized: 1963
Meetings: Annual meeting in Spring; board meetings as called; field trips as announced to members
Number of Members: 230
Dues: $10.00 annual; $15.00 family

A national, nonprofit, membership corporation dedicated to the preservation of outstanding natural areas for their aesthetic, scientific, and educational values. The work of The Nature Conservancy began in 1917 as a national committee of the Ecological Society of America. This committee was organized as an independent group in 1946 and, in 1950, the present name was adopted. Preserved areas vary in size from less than an acre to over 220,000 acres and include forest, prairies, swamps, bogs, marshes, seashores, and islands——all maintained essentially in their natural state. Land is acquired by gift, bequest, easement, or purchase. Loans may be provided to local organizations to protect outstanding natural areas through purchase. Financial and legal responsibilities are assumed for the permanent protection of natural areas acquired by the Conservancy.

The Iowa Chapter promotes and coordinates natural area acquisitions in the state. Membership is open to anyone interested in nature and the preservation of a green legacy for future generations. Those areas already acquired or in the process of being acquired include 42-acre Berry Woods in Warren County, 49-acre Retz Memorial Forest in Clayton County, 12-acre Savage Memorial Woods in Henry County, 16-acre Hanging Bog in Linn County, a 7-acre woodland tract (The Diggings) in Fort Dodge, Webster County, Iowa, 110-acre Freda Haffner Preserve (Arend's Kettlehole) in Dickinson County, and 21-acre William's Prairie in Johnson County. Field trips are made to areas being preserved or under consideration for acquisition. A *Newsletter* is published periodically. Speakers and programs on nature and conservation are available for meetings.

5 - STORY
(continued)

● **Robison's Acres**
3 miles west of
Iowa Center, Iowa

Story County Conservation Board
Robert Ray Pinneke, Executive Director
Hickory Grove Park
Colo, Iowa 50056

A wildlife sanctuary of 58 acres, bequeathed to Story County by Clay Robison of Maxwell, Iowa, who was a member of Story County Conservation Board until his death in 1966. An additional 21.5 acres is under easement. The forested area includes white oak, walnut, cherry, box elder, and elm, in addition to shrubs and wild flowers, including bergamot, blazing star, wild parsnip, and yellow coneflower. There is evidence of Indian mounds along West Indian Creek, which eventually joins the Skunk River, and numerous arrowheads have been found in the area. A 1-acre pond is stocked from Hickory Grove Lake. Hiking and nature trails have been constructed through the tract. In the winter, these trails are open for snowmobile traffic.

● **Schweringen Family Monument**
Sheffield Cemetery
5 miles southeast of Story City, Iowa
(May be reached from Interstate 35 by going east at the Roland exit and proceeding to the first road going south. This road leads into the cemetery.)

Dedicated: May 29, 1938

A large boulder with a bronze tablet erected by a group of 42 persons in memory of the pioneer family of Daniel and Mary Ann Schweringen and their 3 children, who met a tragic death on the prairie. In October 1860, 5 members of the Schweringen family were enroute from Ohio to stake a claim near Fort Dodge, Iowa. They were traveling in a covered wagon when a prairie fire trapped them about 5 or 6 miles northwest of Nevada, Iowa. The fire came up from behind the party and caught the cover on the wagon. The horses became frightened while Mr. Schweringen was removing the burning cover. He was kicked in the head and knocked unconscious. By the time he regained his senses, his family was dead. The father, barely alive, was able to reach the Hoover Home and report the tragedy. The charred remains of his wife and two children were found and buried here. Mr. Schweringen died soon after, from burns, and was also interred here. The skull of the third child was later found and buried on the burned-over prairie.

The ground for Sheffield Cemetery was donated by N.N. Sheffield in 1858. A plaque in his memory was donated by the Sheffield Cemetery Association and placed in the burial grounds.

● **Soper's Mill Area**
3½ miles east of Gilbert, Iowa

Story County Conservation Board
Robert Ray Pinneke, Executive Director
Hickory Grove Park
Colo, Iowa 50056

An 18-acre scenic area on the Skunk River, used today for picnicking, hiking, and fishing. This was originally the site of a dam and water-powered sawmill. It was rebuilt as a flour mill in 1871 by T. K. Soper.

North of the county road bridge is an old "bow-string" trussed arch bridge built before the turn of the century. Sedimentary bedrock formations are exposed in this part of the valley and may be inspected at this site.

COUNTY AND COUNTY SEAT; LOCATION ON MAP	NAME AND LOCATION	DESCRIPTION

85 - STORY
(continued)

● **Story County Chapter, Iowa Genealogical Society**
Ames, Iowa

Mrs. Vivian Jennings,
Corresponding Secretary
2226 Northwestern
Ames, Iowa 50010

Organized: April 4, 1968
Meetings: Second Monday of each month except December
8:00 p.m.
Number of Members: 32
Dues: $2.00 annual

Organized to create and foster an interest in genealogy, aid members in compiling family genealogies, preserve genealogical and historical data, cooperate with any group or individual interested in furthering genealogical work, and furnish Story County data for *Hawkeye Heritage,* the quarterly publication of the Iowa Genealogical Society (see Polk County). Genealogical research experiences are shared through programs or workshops. A reproduction of the 1887 *History of Story County* by William G. Allen was published in 1975.

● **Story County Historical Society**
Ames, Iowa

Mrs. John (Maggie) Hilgerson,
Chairperson
3009 Duff Avenue
Ames, Iowa 50010

Organized: February 1971
Incorporated: June 20, 1972
Meetings: As announced
Number of Members: 35

Organized to preserve historic sites and relics of the past and encourage their preservation. Tours are conducted to historic places in Story County. An educational program is sponsored.

86 - TAMA

Toledo
D-8

● **Dysart Historical Museum**
317 Main Street
Dysart, Iowa 52224

Robert Schlotterback
315 Main Street
Dysart, Iowa 52224

Established: 1964
Admission: Donations accepted
Open: Week days, April 1 to October 1; other times by appointment

Features historical items from central Iowa, rock specimens, war relics, old guns dating back to 1770, antique household items, early business machines, and a large collection of odd and curious money of the world.

On Seven Hills Road, 2 miles north of Dysart and extending into Benton County, is a series of scenic hills cut by nature, often referred to as the "Little Ozarks of Iowa."

● **Otter Creek Marsh**
2 miles northwest of Chelsea, Iowa

State Conservation Commission
State Office Building
300 Fourth Street
Des Moines, Iowa 50319

A game management area, comprising 3,284 acres of marsh and bottomland within the flood plains of Otter Creek and the Iowa River, popular with outdoor enthusiasts. During the annual spring migration, thousands of ducks, geese, and shorebirds congregate here on their way north. Bird watchers can observe and study a great variety of birds throughout the year, including cormorants, turkey vultures, and bald eagles. The partially developed area is also popular with hikers, fishermen, and hunters.

● **Otter Creek Park**
3 miles northeast of Toledo, Iowa

Tama County Conservation Board
Doug Danielsen, Executive Officer
R. R. 2
Toledo, Iowa 52342

A 277-acre area of rolling prairie and wooded slopes, located midway between the valleys of the Iowa River and Wolf Creek. Water lilies, arrowhead, pickerel weed, and cattails grow in the 69-acre artificial lake. Facilities for camping, picnicking, and swimming have been developed.

- TAMA
(continued)

● **Tama County Historical Society**
Toledo, Iowa

George Wilson, President
Elberon, Iowa 52225

Organized: April 9, 1942
Meetings: First Saturday in April, 2:00 p.m.
Number of Members: 165 (150 honorary)
Dues: $0.50 annual
Museum Dedicated: July 4, 1974
Admission to Museum: Free
Museum Open: Daily, except Sunday, 8:00 a.m.-5:00 p.m.

Articles of historic interest, collected by the Society, are on display in a museum located in the former Tama County Jail, built in 1869 and closed by the state jail inspector in 1970 after prisoners escaped by digging through the walls. The remodeled jail houses the collection formerly displayed in the Tama County Courthouse. Included are books; letters; a wildlife exhibit; pioneer, Indian, and war relics; antique tools; flags; and items of general interest.

● **Tama Indian Settlement**
West of Tama, Iowa

Approximately 1,500 Mesquakie Indians live on a settlement--not a reservation--comprising some 3,600 acres of timberland and river bottom along the Iowa River. The land is owned by the Indians, who are descendents of members of the once great Sac and Fox tribes. After being moved from their hunting grounds in Iowa to the bare plains of Kansas, following the Black Hawk Purchase, the Indians became dissatisfied with their new home. Appealing to Governor James Grimes, the Indians were permitted to purchase land in Iowa and returned to their beloved Iowaland. Some farming is done, and many of the Indians are employed in Tama and neighboring towns. Others do beadwork, or make baskets, bows and arrows, tomahawks, and jewelry, which are sold at many of the homes or at roadside stands. An annual pow-wow is held each summer, featuring tribal dances, ceremonies, songs, Indian food, and Indian exhibits.

● **Traer Winding Stairs**
534 Second Street
Traer, Iowa

An iron spiral staircase, said to be the only one of its kind, located in a business district. The staircase was built in the 1890's by Burlington Iron Works for the *Traer Star-Clipper*. The newspaper had the outdoor, winding stairs built because there wasn't enough room inside the building for a stairway to the second floor office. This was the only public entrance to the newspaper office. The stairs start at the curb edge of the sidewalk and wind up to a 20-foot catwalk into the second floor of the building. The newspaper offices moved in 1953 to another location, but the staircase has been preserved and placed on the National Register of Historic Places. The bottom 5 steps of the staircase were accidentally torn away from the center pole in January 1975 by snow removal equipment, but the damage has been repaired. The stairs provide the town with its motto: "Wind Up in Traer."

87 - TAYLOR

Bedford
I-4

Lake of Three Fires State Park
2 miles north of Bedford on
Iowa 49, and 2 miles east

State Conservation Commission
State Office Building
300 Fourth Street
Des Moines, Iowa 50319

According to legend, great Indian council meetings were held within the 642 acres included in the park. When the Indians roamed Iowa's prairies, this was one of their favorite hunting grounds. It is said that the exact location of their council meetings was announced by the smoke of 3 fires built on top of a high hill. The valley that is now the bed of the 125-acre Lake of Three Fires was the gathering place for many a pow-wow, council, or religious festival. The picturesque woodlands are used today by hikers, bird watchers, and photographers, and there are facilities for swimming, fishing, boating, picnicking, and camping. Part of the area is kept as a wildlife refuge.

State Boundary Marker
2½ miles west of
Athelstan, Iowa

The original cast iron marker that officially divides Iowa and Missouri, located in the SE ¼ of Section 25 of Jackson Township. The marker is located in the middle of the state line road, which divides around the post. It was placed in the ground in 1816, and was one of a series of markers located every 10 miles along the Iowa-Missouri state line, on east of the original marker. This particular marker was once the official northwest corner of Missouri. All land west of here and east of the Missouri River was considered waste land and unfit for habitation.

The Honey War (see Van Buren County) evolved from a dispute between Iowa and Missouri over the official state line. The U. S. Supreme Court settled the matter when it declared at the January term in 1849 that the boundary should be determined by the original survey made in 1816 by John C. Sullivan, principal surveyor, and Samuel K. Caldwell, assistant surveyor. Their survey went eastward from the iron monument to the middle of the Des Moines River.

Taylor County Genealogical Society

Mrs. E. J. (Helen) Janson, President
Gravity, Iowa 50848

or

Mrs. Patti Combs O'Dell, Researcher
R.R. 1, Box 79
New Market, Iowa 51646

Organized: 1968
Meetings: As announced
Number of Members: 50
Dues: $3.00 annual

Does geneological research on Taylor County residents. Tombstone records have been compiled. A bulletin is published on basic county records, such as deeds, tax lists, and marriages. In 1975, the Society sponsored the reprinting of the 1881 *Taylor County, Iowa History* by Lymon Evans.

88 - UNION

Creston
H-5

McKinley Park
West part of
Creston, Iowa

Schoolhouse Open: Sunday and holidays during June and July, 2:00-4:00 p.m.; other times by appointment

The historical section, located at the south side of the city park, is being developed with the cooperation of Union County Historical Society (see below). This area contains an old blacksmith shop, a replica of an old country store, the last rural schoolhouse used in Union County, a small rural depot, the watchpost or "crows nest" in use until 1974, and a Burlington Northern Railroad caboose of 1900

8 - UNION
(continued)

McKinley Park
(continued)

vintage. The old Spaulding Methodist Church has been moved from north of Creston to the city park and will house a museum of historical items and antiques from the area. A brick sidewalk was built by the Boy Scouts.

● **Mount Pisgah**
5 miles southwest of Lorimor, Iowa, off U.S. 169

Union County Conservation Board
Jerry Mikkelsen, Executive Officer
704 West Montgomery
Creston, Iowa 50801

This is the site of the first white settlement in Union County, and one of 8 camps or stations established by the Mormons on their trek from Nauvoo, Illinois to Utah in 1846. These Camps of Israel were conceived as rest camps for those unable to continue the journey, and as supply stations for later groups headed west. Located on high hills overlooking the Grand River Valley, Mount Pisgah reached a population of about 3,000 at its peak, and was occupied until 1852. The first post office in the county was established here in 1851. All that remains today is a burial ground and a limestone obelisk erected in 1888 in memory of the 800 Mormons who died here in 1846, 1847, and 1848. The names of some 64 persons buried here during the 3-year period are listed on the 4 sides of the tall monument, located in the center of the burial ground. Included are the names of 2 elders and a "Stranger not in the Church." Individual grave markers were not used, as it was feared these would attract Indians who might disturb the burials. A parking lot and picnic area are maintained in Mount Pisgah Park, an 8-acre area adjacent to the 1-acre cemetery.

● **Site of the Blue Grass Palace**
Old Union County Fairgrounds
Creston, Iowa

The idea to create a Blue Grass Palace originated with the Blue Grass League of Southwest Iowa, whose headquarters were in Creston, "bluegrass center of the world." In the opinion of one writer, "Never before had art and nature been manipulated with so great genius and skill as was demonstrated in the blue grass palaces of 1889 and 1890." The primary purpose of the palaces was to exhibit products of the soil and provide people with a place to meet together after the harvest was past. Eighteen counties cooperated to build the elaborate structures and exhibit fruits, vegetables, grasses, grains, dairy products, wood, coal, sandstone, marble, and other products of the region. The palace-like buildings were completely covered with a variety of native grasses, flowers, and novel decorations. The first palace opened to the public on August 26, 1889 and was so successful that the idea was repeated the following year, but on a much larger scale. The 1890 palace was three times the size of the earlier one, with a total length of 265 feet and a width of 132 feet. The main tower was 120 feet high. The 1890 exposition and industrial exhibit was opened by Governor

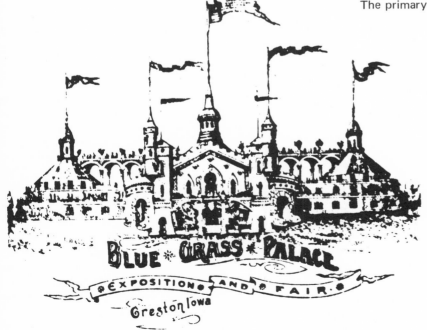

88 - UNION
(continued)

Site of the Blue Grass Palace
(continued)

Horace Boies, and the Iowa State Band provided music for the occasion. An enthusiastic audience of 4,000 persons filled the elaborately decorated auditorium, a scene described as "grand beyond description."

● **Talmadge Hill Park**
2 miles west of Thayer, Iowa

Union County Conservation Board
Jerry Mikkelsen, Executive Officer
704 West Montgomery
Creston, Iowa 50801

An undeveloped, natural area of 18 acres consisting of a high ridge covered with a variety of native trees, shrubs, and wild flowers. The park is used for picnicking, primitive group camping, and as an outdoor classroom for nature study.

● **Union County Historical Society**
210 South Elm Street
Creston, Iowa 50801

P. E. Applegate, President
508 West Montgomery
Creston, Iowa 50801

Organized: October 25, 1966
Meetings: As called; annual meeting in May
Number of Members: 132
Dues: $1.00 annual; $25.00 life

The Society is developing a historical section, including buildings of bygone days, in McKinley Park in Creston (see above). In October 1966, Lincoln Township No. 5, a 1-room rural school built in 1872 was acquired and restored at the new location. Typical of the thousands of such schools that once dotted the Iowa countryside, this schoolhouse moved from about 6 miles northeast of Creston, was used for 94 years, until it closed in May 1966. The country schools were located so no pupil had to walk more than 2 miles to attend classes. Now, the old school is used for pupils to experience what it was like in the old days by attending classes there one day each year. The Society also arranged to acquire the white-frame United Methodist Church from Spaulding. The church serves as the Society's headquarters, with a county historical museum in the basement.

89 - VAN BUREN

Keosauqua
I-10

● **Amish Settlement**
Near Milton, Iowa

In 1968, an Old Order Amish settlement was started here by Amish families moving from Kalona and Hazelton in Iowa (see Washington and Buchanan Counties) and settlements in Illinois, Indiana, and Missouri.

● **Austin Park**
2 miles northeast of
Pittsburg, Iowa

Van Buren County Conservation Board
Norwood Teal, President
Keosauqua, Iowa 52565

An area of 6 acres located along the Des Moines River north of Keosauqua, within sight of the Phil Stong Birthplace (see below). The riverfront park provides facilities for picnicking, camping, boat launching, fishing, and hiking on nature trails. Part of the area is heavily wooded.

● **Bentonsport**
East of Keosauqua, Iowa

Once a bustling steamboat town of over 1,000 people, situated on the Des Moines River, Bentonsport is now referred to as "Iowa's liveliest ghost town" or the "Williamsburg of the Midwest." It is approached over a 1-lane iron bridge, one of the oldest still in use across the Des Moines River. Tree-covered hills hem in the town. The first paper mill in Iowa was located here; there were also grist, saw, linseed oil, and woolen mills. In addition, Bentonsport was a terminus of the Des Moines Valley Railroad. The remains of old foundations, cabins, mansions,

- VAN BUREN
(continued)

Bentonsport
(continued)

● **Bentonsport River Front Park**
Bentonsport, Iowa

Van Buren County Conservation Board
Norwood Teal, President
Keosauqua, Iowa 52565

and business houses, and the old river dam may be seen. Several homes have been restored.

After the townsite was platted and surveyed, it was called Port Benton and Benton's Port for the famous U.S. Senator from Missouri, 1820-50, Thomas Hart Benton (1782-1858), who was a granduncle of the artist of the same name, born in 1889. There is another version of the origin of the town's name. Shortly after the town was established, the settlers celebrated the Fourth of July with an old-fashioned barbecue. Some have declared that since everyone came **bent on sport** the town was so named.

Mason House (see below), a former hotel patronized by steamboat captains and railroaders, is now operated as a museum.

The Presbyterian Church, built in 1855, one of the 4 churches in the town, has been preserved. The Methodist Church continues in use.

The Odd Fellows (I.O.O.F.) Hall, built in the 1840's, was originally a furniture store. This was one of the first chapters of the lodge founded in Iowa. The brick building now houses a large collection of Indian artifacts and pioneer relics.

Vernon, or South Bentonsport, located on the Des Moines River opposite Bentonsport, was also a flourishing town with mills, stores, newspaper, church, and a clay pottery factory noted for its excellent jugs, crocks, and drain tile. The town's woolen mills manufactured blankets used by soldiers in the front lines during the Civil War. In 1837, a ferry was licensed to operate between Bentonsport and Vernon. It was to run every day from daylight until dark, and at night for mail and express, and in case of emergencies. The Vernon School, erected in 1867-68, is a classic brick building which served the area for over 90 years. A tower housing the bell that once called the children to school rises 80 feet above the ground. The old school is now privately owned and has been restored and furnished.

Established: 1969

A riverfront park of 5 acres located between the Des Moines River and the main street of Bentonsport (see above), on the Hiawatha-Pioneer Trail. Included in the park along Front Street are the remains of an old paper mill, and the former general store, bank, and Odd Fellows Hall--some of the 30 or so historic buildings still standing in the ghost town. The park is being developed for picnicking, boat launching, fishing, and limited camping.

89 - VAN BUREN
(continued)

● **Bonaparte Dam and Locks**
Bonaparte, Iowa

The lock walls and dam shoulder are the only ones remaining of the old Des Moines River Navigation Company system. There were to have been 28 dams and locks built to make the Des Moines River navigable from its mouth to Raccoon Forks (Des Moines), but these ambitious plans were never completed.

Bonaparte, another of the old steamboat towns, was named for the French Emperor. It was originally planned to establish another town across the river and name it Napoleon, but it was never built. Bonaparte was settled in 1837. In 1839, the Territorial Legislature of Iowa granted William Meek, founder of the town of Bonaparte, the right to build a dam and locks for a gristmill, completed 2 years later. Pioneers came from as far away as 100 miles to have their bags of grain ground. Before 1850, the Des Moines River Navigation Company had a contract with the government to improve the Des Moines River. In return, the company was ceded considerable land by the government. The locks at Bonaparte were 135 feet long, and the passageway was 35 feet wide. The old iron rings to which the boats tied up are also still in place. A flood in 1851 seriously damaged the structure, the company failed to complete its contract, and the improvements were auctioned off. The dam, locks, and gates at Bonaparte, which had cost about $80,000, were sold to Isaiah Meek (a son of William Meek) for $200. Disastrous floods in 1902 and 1903 washed most of the dam away, and the many mills (gristmills, sawmills, and woolen mills) that still line the river bank were forced to close. A flood in 1905 removed the last remnants of the old dam. (See Lock Tender's House, Davis County, also.)

● **Burg Building**
Farmington, Iowa

An attractive, native limestone building relating to the 1860's and 1870's when the town of Farmington (laid out in 1839) was an important manufacturing center. Interesting architectural details include metal window lintels and heavy cornices. Lewis Burg came to Farmington from Bavaria and established the Wagon and Carriage Works. Here, his woodworkers, blacksmiths, painters, and leather workers reached an annual production of 250 wagons and 100 carriages.

● **Grave of Mary Ann Rutledge**
Bethel Cemetery,
near Bethel Church
5½ miles northwest of
Birmingham, Iowa

The grave of Mrs. Mary Ann (Miller) Rutledge, mother of Ann Rutledge who, according to legend, was the sweetheart of Abraham Lincoln. Ann's father owned the tavern or inn at New Salem, Illinois and Lincoln boarded here during his first months in the village. Ann died August 25, 1835, after a brief illness, at the age of 22. Mrs. Rutledge died December 26, 1878 at the age of 91. Her grave is marked by a tall shaft monument. The Rutledge homestead was a mile east of Bethel Cemetery.

Bethel Church had its beginnings in 1838, when D. G. Cartwright, a Methodist circuit rider organized the first congregation at Birmingham. The first church building was a log structure, built in 1844, and used for 25 years, when the present church was started.

- VAN BUREN
(continued)

● **Indian Lake Park**
½ mile southwest of
Farmington, Iowa

Van Buren County Conservation Board
Norwood Teal, President
Keosauqua, Iowa 52565

A 122-acre park of natural timberland with a 44-acre lake. There are facilities for picnicking, camping, swimming, fishing, boating, horseback riding, and hiking. Formerly a state park, it is now operated under a lease agreement by the Town of Farmington and Van Buren County Conservation Board.

Indian Creek empties into the Des Moines River. The creek is said to have received its name from the early days of settlement when pioneers saw a small band of Indians camped near the mouth of the stream. Many mills were built and operated in the area as early as the 1830's, and some of the old pioneer trails crossed through the Indian Creek Watershed.

● **Iowaville**
West of Selma, Iowa, near the
junction of Davis, Jefferson,
Van Buren, and Wapello Counties

The Iowa Indians established their principle village here along the Des Moines River. (See Davis County, also.) Never a large tribe, the Iowas were constantly at war with the Sac and Fox, and often with the Sioux and Osage Indians. According to some accounts, the village was burned and most of the Iowas were killed in 1823 or 1824 by a huge war party of Sac and Fox warriors led by Pashepaho, "The Stabber." Black Hawk, then a young warrior chief, also took part in the battle. Both Black Hawk and Keokuk spent much time in the area, and Black Hawk was buried near here, at his dying request, on the farm of James H. Jordan, Indian Agent and trader. On July 3, 1839, Chief Black Hawk's body was taken from the grave. About a year later the bones were recovered from a dentist in Quincy, Illinois, who had received them from St. Louis. Black Hawk's widow then left the remains in the care of "good old man," Governor Lucas. The bones were placed in the museum of the Burlington Geological and Historical Society and lost when the building burned in 1855.

Iowaville Cemetery, one of the oldest west of the Mississippi, may be seen along highway 16. There are many graves of persons born in the 1700's. A memorial cross has been erected here for Chief Black Hawk (1767-1838).

● **Lacey-Keosauqua State Park**
near Keosauqua, Iowa, off Iowa 1

State Conservation Commission
State Office Building
300 Fourth Street
Des Moines, Iowa 50319

Established: 1921

Iowa's largest park--2,260 acres of flower-and shrub-covered woods--extends for 2 miles along the great horseshoe bend of the Des Moines River. The park was named for Major John Fletcher Lacey, eminent lawyer, statesman, soldier, and conservationist, known for his work in establishing many parks. This area was the site of an ancient Indian village and a series of Indian mounds are located near the river. The mounds have been excavated and their contents removed to museums. Ely's Ford, on the north side of the park, was the river crossing for the Mormon Trail and the pioneers, before bridges were built. Woodsmen lived on the southern slopes of one of the ridges in the park. These pioneers made their entire living by cutting and selling timber. The ruins of some of the old cabins may still be seen.

89 - VAN BUREN
(continued)

Lacey-Keosauqua State Park
(continued)

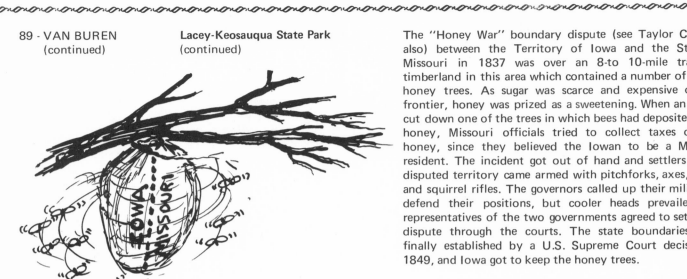

The "Honey War" boundary dispute (see Taylor County, also) between the Territory of Iowa and the State of Missouri in 1837 was over an 8-to 10-mile tract of timberland in this area which contained a number of bee or honey trees. As sugar was scarce and expensive on the frontier, honey was prized as a sweetening. When an Iowan cut down one of the trees in which bees had deposited their honey, Missouri officials tried to collect taxes on the honey, since they believed the Iowan to be a Missouri resident. The incident got out of hand and settlers in the disputed territory came armed with pitchforks, axes, clubs, and squirrel rifles. The governors called up their militias to defend their positions, but cooler heads prevailed and representatives of the two governments agreed to settle the dispute through the courts. The state boundaries were finally established by a U.S. Supreme Court decision in 1849, and Iowa got to keep the honey trees.

Many trees in the park are over 200 years old. A wide variety of ferns and wild animals abound in the area, and a species of cottony prairie grass, found nowhere else in Iowa, grows on one part of the park's golf course. Overlooks provide panoramic views of the park area, nature trails rim the river, and a 30-acre lake is within the park.

● **Limestone Mine**
Douds, Iowa

Douds Stone, Inc.
Douds, Iowa 52551

An operating limestone mine, claimed to be Iowa's largest underground mine. The limestone quarry was started in 1926 as a surface operation in a creek bed. A small pulverizer was powered by a steam engine while other work was done by horses and hand labor. With the increased demand for agricultural lime and crushed rock for roads, the company decided to go underground about 1930 in order to increase production and get a better quality stone. A total of about 80 acres has now been mined out. Streets in the mine are 40 feet wide and ceilings are 25 feet high. To support the overburden, consisting of 65 feet of rock and 48 feet of dirt, 40-foot square pillars are left standing. The floor of the mine is 140 feet below the surface at the deepest part. The year-round temperature in the mine is 54 degrees. Privately owned and operated, visitors may see the mining operation with permission.

Limestone is produced in 64 of Iowa's 99 counties. It is used in concrete aggregate, cement manufacturing, for road surfacing, and for building stone, and as agricultural lime to condition soil. Over 70 percent of the total value of all mineral production in Iowa is accounted for by limestone.

The main street of the village of Douds follows the old territorial road from Memphis, Missouri to Fairfield, Iowa. A number of coal mines formerly operated adjacent to the town. When steamboats came up the Des Moines River, Douds was a refueling point.

COUNTY AND COUNTY SEAT; LOCATION ON MAP	NAME AND LOCATION	DESCRIPTION

- VAN BUREN
(continued)

● **Mason House**
Front Street
Bentonsport, Iowa

Herbert K. Redhead
Mason House Museum
Bentonsport, Iowa

● **Milton Depot**
Milton, Iowa

Admission: $0.50; children $0.25
Open: April 1 through October, 9:30 a.m.-6:00 p.m.

A 3-story brick and stone structure of modified Georgian design operated by Mr. and Mrs. L. J. Mason as a hotel from 1857 until their death. Mason House, built in the late 1840's by Billie Robinson, was originally called Ashland House. The hotel became known up and down the Des Moines River during the period when boats stopped regularly at Bentonsport (see above)--one of Iowa's largest towns and also an important railroad terminus. All river traffic ceased around 1872 and Bentonsport began to decline.

The old landmark has been restored and serves as a museum with lavish Victorian furnishings of over a century ago. A country store, stocked with merchandise from the past, and an 1852 Steamboat Gothic white-frame building are next door. Built of black walnut, the latter building was once Iowa's seventh post office.

The former C.B. & K.C. Railroad Depot, purchased by the town of Milton after train service was discontinued in 1969. The railroad came to Milton in 1871-72, when the rails were laid with the help of many volunteers interested in having the railroad reach the town. The depot was built soon after. It has been restored and is now used as a community building. Arts and crafts are displayed here during the annual Van Buren County Summer Arts Festival, held during the last full weekend in June.

Eggs, cream, and livestock were shipped out of Milton by the carload. Two carloads of eggs was the usual weekly shipment. Around 150 carloads of livestock were shipped each year by the Snodgrass Brothers, and a stockyard track was laid to their farm to serve them and other shippers. The Snodgrass switch was removed May 7, 1941, but freight was handled at this point until November 15, 1961.

A large pond formerly at the west edge of Milton provided water for the steam locomotives. The pond also served as

89 - VAN BUREN
(continued)

Milton Depot
(continued)

the town's swimming hole in the summer and as a place to ice skate in the winter. The pond was drained when trains converted to diesel power in 1951.

With 2 passenger trains a day for many years, the depot served as the town's news and social center. Milton boasted 2 hotels at one time, both near the depot. A large livery stable just south of the depot provided transportation for salesmen and other passengers after they arrived on the train.

● **Milton Heritage Society**
Milton, Iowa 52570

Mrs. Clark (Mavis) Stokesberry, President
P. O. Box 37
Milton, Iowa 52570

Incorporated: January 1, 1975
Meetings: Monthly
Number of Members: 250
Dues: $1.00 annual; $50 life

Organized to acquire a church which is being restored as a meeting place for senior citizens.

The brick church was built in 1900 as a Presbyterian church and continued as such until 1947. The original stained glass windows are still intact. Articles of historic interest in the community are being collected and placed on display.

● **Morris Memorial Park**
Stockport, Iowa

Museum Exhibits Open: During summer; other times by appointment

A memorial to members of the Morris family, pioneer settlers in this area. The memorial log cabin, a replica of the original built by Henry and Jane Morris at this site in 1838, is located in a grove of hardwood trees. The cabin and other buildings house relics of the Midwest--pioneer tools, agricultural equipment, and domestic items. A 1-room rural schoolhouse, a replica of a water-powered gristmill and of a sawmill, and a small lake are also in the park. Facilities for picnicking, hiking, fishing, and camping are available. Nature and bridle trails pass through the most scenic part of the 30-acre park. Wildlife, trees, wild flowers, and rocks may be viewed in natural surroundings.

● **Pearson House**
Pittsburg Road
2 blocks northwest of
Van Buren County Courthouse
Keosauqua, Iowa

Open: Guided tours available

Built in the 1840's by Franklin Pearson, the brick and stone house has been restored and is owned and operated by Van Buren County Historical Society. The house is of modified Georgian style with double-end chimneys, and once served as a religious meeting place. A trapdoor in one of the rooms leads to a small secret cellar used as a hideout for escaping slaves traveling on the Underground Railroad during Civil War times. The house was extensively damaged during the tornado of April 16, 1967. Bricks from the old Negro Methodist church, which was demolished by this tornado, were used to rebuild Pearson House. Keosauqua had 2 Negro churches, built in the 1870's for the more than 200 Negroes who lived here. An Afro- Masonic Lodge was also established in Keosauqua.

9 - VAN BUREN
(continued)

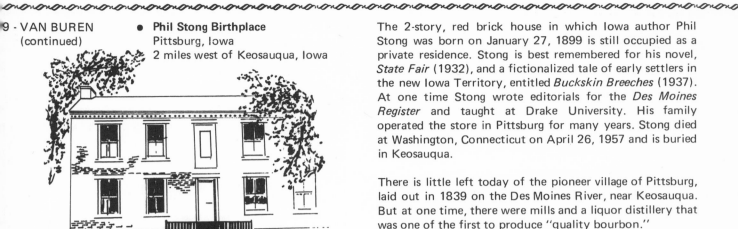

● **Phil Stong Birthplace**
Pittsburg, Iowa
2 miles west of Keosauqua, Iowa

The 2-story, red brick house in which Iowa author Phil Stong was born on January 27, 1899 is still occupied as a private residence. Stong is best remembered for his novel, *State Fair* (1932), and a fictionalized tale of early settlers in the new Iowa Territory, entitled *Buckskin Breeches* (1937). At one time Stong wrote editorials for the *Des Moines Register* and taught at Drake University. His family operated the store in Pittsburg for many years. Stong died at Washington, Connecticut on April 26, 1957 and is buried in Keosauqua.

There is little left today of the pioneer village of Pittsburg, laid out in 1839 on the Des Moines River, near Keosauqua. But at one time, there were mills and a liquor distillery that was one of the first to produce "quality bourbon."

● **Pioneer Historical Society**
Farmington, Iowa

Forrest Moreland, President
Farmington, Iowa 52626
or
Mrs. Verna Olson, Secretary
Farmington, Iowa 52626

Organized: February 27, 1966
Incorporated: April 4, 1966
Meetings: Last Monday of each month except December, 7:30 p.m.
Number of Members: 184
Dues: $1.00 annual; $10.00 sustaining; $25.00 endowment; $50.00 benefactor; $100.00 life

Organized to locate, preserve, and mark historic landmarks, sites, and points of interest. The old Congregational Church (1847) in Farmington is being restored to be maintained as a museum. It was the second church of that denomination to be established west of the Mississippi and is now the oldest still standing. The building was patterned after the little white country churches of New England.

● **Shimek State Forest**
East of Farmington, off
Iowa 2

State Conservation Commission
State Office Building
300 Fourth Street
Des Moines, Iowa 50319

Approximately 7,600 acres of forest, located in Van Buren and Lee Counties, offers a chance to return to a wilderness area, with hunting, fishing in numerous stocked ponds, hiking on fine trails, picnicking, and primitive camping. Since 1937, approximately 2,000 acres have been planted to various species of conifers, including red, white, Austrian, Scotch, and jack pine.

Named for Iowa naturalist and early conservationist Bohumil Shimek (see Lee County), the State Forest has been established by many purchases of depleted farm land. Deer and other small game and wild turkeys are abundant.

● **Site of Salubria**
Located in cultivated fields,
2 miles south of Farmington, Iowa

The site of Iowa's only so-called "infidel colony." In 1839, Abner Kneeland (April 7, 1774-August 27, 1844), a controversial figure from New England, and one of the most widely known intellectuals of his day, established a settlement here with the hope that he could obtain "freedom of inquiry." Kneeland, who was of Scotch ancestry, worked as a carpenter for a time (his father's trade), taught school, and then took up preaching--first as a Baptist, then as a Universalist. A free thinker, Kneeland spent some time in prison for frankly expressing his blasphemous religious beliefs. He considered himself a

89 - VAN BUREN
(continued)

Site of Salubria
(continued)

pantheist, not an atheist. After his release from prison, Kneeland, at the age of 65, established the colony of "The First Society of Free Enquirers" and the community of Salubria in Iowa Territory. The cluster of roughly built houses and cabins making up the colony was in the heart of a forest, on bottomland, bordered by the Des Moines River to the south, and by deep ravines. No buildings remain today to indicate where the town was located. For the remainder of his life, Kneeland lived in his home, the "Mansion of Salubria." During this period, he wrote, lectured, and engaged in politics. He was married 4 times, and his wives bore him 12 children.

Salubria, intended to become the capital of free thinkers, never really took root. Apparently the Iowa pioneers found pantheism too abstract, too impersonal, and too cold. Following Kneeland's death in 1844, at the age of 70 years, the little settlement of Salubria gradually disappeared and his followers joined other churches in the neighborhood. Kneeland was first buried on his own farm, but his body was later moved to the northwest corner of the old section of Farmington Cemetery. His wife, Dolly, died November 5, 1871 at the age of 71, and is buried beside her husband. The graves are marked by simple marble slabs.

● **State Line House**
½ mile east of Farmington, Iowa
on Iowa 2

A brick and stone structure built in the late 1830's, which formerly served as a wayside inn or tavern. It was called State Line House because of its proximity to the Iowa-Missouri border line. Architectural features include wide windows and doors, and hand-hewn oak and walnut log beams inside. The old house is now a private residence.

● **Van Buren County Historical Society**
Keosauqua, Iowa

James McGrath, Sr., President
Keosauqua, Iowa 52565

Organized: 1960
Meetings: Third Friday of month
Number of Members: 125
Dues: $1.00 annual; $10.00 life

Pearson House (see above) is owned and operated by the Society. An annual tour of historic homes in various towns of the county has been held since 1965. Two books on Van Buren County and its part in the Civil War have been written by Theo M. Cook, former Van Buren County Superintendent of Schools. A museum is housed in the old stone post office, located in downtown Keosauqua. An old log cabin has been relocated and restored along highway 16 in Selma, and has articles on display. The Society cooperates with the Van Buren County Development Association on the Summer Arts Festival.

Van Buren County Courthouse, constructed from 1840-43, is the oldest courthouse in continuous use in Iowa, the second oldest to be completed (Lee County was finished the year before), and was the scene of the state's first murder trial. The first legal hanging in Iowa took place in Hangman's Hollow, just north of the courthouse. The gallows used in this hanging of William McCauley are

) - VAN BUREN
(continued)

Van Buren County Historical Society
(continued)

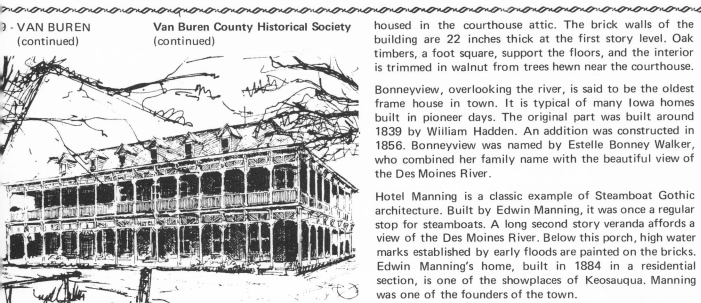

) - WAPELLO

Ottumwa
H-9

● **Airpower Museum, Inc.**
Ottumwa Airport
Ottumwa, Iowa 52501

George Utterback, Museum Director

housed in the courthouse attic. The brick walls of the building are 22 inches thick at the first story level. Oak timbers, a foot square, support the floors, and the interior is trimmed in walnut from trees hewn near the courthouse.

Bonneyview, overlooking the river, is said to be the oldest frame house in town. It is typical of many Iowa homes built in pioneer days. The original part was built around 1839 by William Hadden. An addition was constructed in 1856. Bonneyview was named by Estelle Bonney Walker, who combined her family name with the beautiful view of the Des Moines River.

Hotel Manning is a classic example of Steamboat Gothic architecture. Built by Edwin Manning, it was once a regular stop for steamboats. A long second story veranda affords a view of the Des Moines River. Below this porch, high water marks established by early floods are painted on the bricks. Edwin Manning's home, built in 1884 in a residential section, is one of the showplaces of Keosauqua. Manning was one of the founders of the town.

Chartered: 1965
Admission: Donations accepted
Open: Monday through Friday, 9:00 a.m.-5:00 p.m.; other times by appointment

A "living air museum" displays bits and pieces of the saga of man's conquest of air and space, which really started back on December 17, 1903 at Kill Devil Hill, near Kitty Hawk, North Carolina when the Wright Brothers, Orville and Wilbur, made their first flight.

During World War II, Navy fliers trained here. The museum is housed in the former instrument (Link) trainer building. Among the items to be seen are 25 aircraft engines, dating from a 1912 LeRhone rotary; 200 model planes; scrap books; and artifacts from the early days of aviation. A library houses over 600 volumes. There are 22 airplanes, some of which can still be flown, including a 1924 Anderson biplane with an OX-5 engine, a 1930 New Standard D-25, and a 1933 Lockheed Vega (valued at $35,000).

A complex of several additional buildings and old-style hangars takes visitors back to an era when flying was "by the seat of one's pants." A 1917 fire engine and early cars and vehicles will be displayed.

90 - WAPELLO
(continued)

● **American Gothic House**
Northeast edge of Eldon, Iowa
at corner of Burton
and Hearn (or Gothic) Streets

The frame house with its 2 large Gothic windows, front and back, used as a model by Iowa artist Grant Wood (1892-1942) for his painting "American Gothic." This painting (owned by The Art Institute of Chicago), done in 1930, brought him immediate fame. The 1½-story house caught Wood's eye one day when he happened to be driving by. From a photograph of the house, he did the background for his painting, and used his sister, Nan (then 28), and his dentist, Dr. B. H. McKeeby of Cedar Rapids, as the models. "American Gothic" became one of the most reproduced and satirized paintings by an American artist. When it was first shown, many Iowans felt the picture was an insult to the Iowa farmer.

Grant Wood, together with Thomas Hart Benton and John Steuart Curry, was associated with the school of "regional painters," which depicted the American scene of the 1930's.

The cottage is located on a lot W. H. Jacques owned in 1881, and it is believed by old-timers that he may have built the house soon after. It was owned by Gideon Jones when discovered by Grant Wood in 1929. The house, listed in 1974 on the National Register of Historic Places, is still privately owned and unoccupied (1975).

● **American Gothic Trail**
Along the Des Moines River
between Eldon and
Selma, Iowa

American Gothic Trail Committee
P.O. Box 84
Eldon, Iowa 52554

A 10-to 20-mile hiking trail and a 22-mile auto trail covering a number of points of historic interest. The trail, sponsored by Boy Scout Troop 22, starts at Lion's Park at the southwest edge of Eldon, off Iowa 16. To be seen along the way are American Gothic House (see above), Sioc Cemetery and Indian mounds (3 miles southeast of Eldon), Soap Creek Cable Bridge, a restored log cabin at Selma, Iowaville (see Van Buren County), site of the James Jordan house, and the Lock Tender's House (see Davis County).

● **Antique Airplane Association**
Antique Airfield
P. O. Box H
Ottumwa, Iowa 52501

Robert L. Taylor, Founder

Organized: 1953
Number of Members: 6,000
Dues: $20.00 annual; $10.00, associate members

Organized to preserve, restore, and fly old aircraft. The Association publishes *The News*, conducts an annual fly-in of antique airplanes for members and guests, and operates the Airpower Museum (see above). This international organization has local chapters throughout the world, with 2 in Iowa (Des Moines and Iowa City).

● **Ballingall Park**
West Main Street
Ottumwa, Iowa

It was on a plot of ground owned by Peter G. Ballingall, located near the Burlington Railroad depot, that the famed Ottumwa Coal Palace stood, (1890-91) fronting Main Street. It was Ballingall, a pioneer innkeeper, who conceived the idea of building a palace of coal, emblematic of the then important coal mining industry. To finance the project, $5 shares of Coal Palace stock were sold. The 230-by 130-foot structure was partly Gothic and partly Byzantine architecture. The tallest of its 3 towers was 200 feet high. The entire building, completed on September 15,

) - WAPELLO
(continued)

Ballingall Park
(continued)

1890, was veneered with coal and imitation coal made of paper mache, worked into attractive designs. The interior was decorated at an estimated cost of $10,000. Corn, oats, wheat, rye, hemp, wool, coal, and other agricultural and mineral products were worked into the designs. Pictures and other decorations were added. On the opening day, an estimated 6,000 people were on hand to hear Governor Horace Boies (1890-94) give the dedicatory address.

A feature of the Coal Palace was a replica of a coal mine, built underneath the structure. A mule named Maud pulled spectators through the tunnel to a sunken garden, lush with decorative greenery, flowers, and a waterfall. There were displays of natural products from neighboring counties and other parts of Iowa. Among the distinguished visitors to the exposition was U.S. President Benjamin Harrison.

After his death, while on a trip to Japan in 1891, Ballingall's body was brought back to Ottumwa and services were held in the fantastic structure he had conceived. According to historians, Ottumwa had never before--and perhaps since--witnessed a funeral to equal that given for "P. G."

● **Grave of Chief Wapello**
Near Agency, Iowa

Four important Indian chiefs lived in the area around present-day Ottumwa. Iowa counties and cities have been named for them——Wapello, Mahaska, Keokuk, and Poweshiek. Chief Wapello is buried, at his request, in a plot with General Joseph M. Street and his family at the site of the old (1838) Indian Agency. Street was the Indian Agent and a close friend of Wapello, who was considered a wise counselor and able leader, farsighted in his thinking. He did much to further peaceful relations with the white man. Street died in 1840——Wapello, 2 years later. The graves are along the C.B. & Q. Railroad right-of-way, and a number of historical markers have been erected at the site. Atop the Wapello County Courthouse and directly over the Fourth Street entrance stands a statue of Chief Wapello, dedicated in 1894.

● **Mars Hill Baptist Church**
4 miles west and north of
Floris, Iowa, just north of
the Wapello-Davis County line

Harry W. Thomas, Chairman
Box 531
Eldon, Iowa 52554
or
Mrs. Harley (Maria) Hartwig,
Senior Trustee
R.R. 1
Eldon, Iowa 52554

One of the largest single room log buildings ever constructed in Iowa, measuring 28' by 26' by 10'. The pioneer church was built in the 1850's, and completed in 1856, when the first regular services were held. Hand-hewn oak logs were used to construct the church. Some of the logs are 28' long. About 3 acres of land was donated for a burial ground and church site by Mrs. Barbara Clark, whose husband was the minister. The property was deeded to the trustees of Missionary Baptist Church on May 16, 1857 and filed on May 22. The

90 - WAPELLO
(continued)

Mars Hill Baptist Church
(continued)

oldest grave, that of a son of the Clarks, dates back to 1846. Oak, hickory, and evergreen trees surround the rural cemetery. The church is reputedly the Mother Baptist Church of all Baptist faiths west of the Mississippi River. It has been restored as a historic landmark and contains some of the old furnishings. Annual church services are held on the third Sunday in July, and the old log church is still used for weddings, funerals, and group meetings.

● **Ottumwa Memorial Park**
North Jefferson Street
Ottumwa, Iowa

A small zoo, containing bison (buffalo), deer, llamas, and smaller animals in cages, are the chief feature. Wooded ravines, a rustic foot bridge, and picnic facilities are included in the park.

● **Ottumwa Public Library**
129 N. Court Street
Ottumwa, Iowa 52501

Open: Weekdays, 9:00 a.m.-9:00 p.m.

The lobby and dome of the building were decorated with murals by the German artist, Johannes Scheiwe, but the 4 murals in the main lobby are all that remain of the work. The library has a collection of small Babylonian tablets dating back to 2300 B.C. These specimens, made of soft clay, include merchandise receipts and contracts and a small votive cone made by the priest of the Temple of the Goddess of Ishtar and sold to visiting pilgrims. In the Children's Department is an unusual display of dolls collected from around the world by Alberta Powell Graham, author of numerous children's books.

● **Site of the Coal Palace**
Ottumwa, Iowa

Built before the turn of the century to tell the world of the important coal mining industry. See Ballingall Park, above.

● **Southeast Chapter,**
Iowa Archeological Society
c/o Wapello County Historical Society
402 Chester Street
Ottumwa, Iowa 52501

George Baker, President
R. R., Eldon, Iowa 52554
        or
Don Spears
536 South Davis Street
Ottumwa, Iowa 52501

Organized: February 1965
Meetings: Second Friday of month, 7:30 p.m., in Iowa-
           Illinois Gas Company Auditorium, 225½ East
           Main Street, Ottumwa, Iowa
Number of Members: 40

A regional chapter of the Iowa Archeological Society (see Cherokee County). Aboriginal materials from southeast Iowa are displayed at the Wapello County Historical Museum (see below).

- WAPELLO
(continued)

● **Wapello County Genealogical Society**

Mrs. Miles E. Bacon,
Corresponding Secretary
R. R. 1
Ottumwa, Iowa 52501

Founded: November 6, 1970
Meetings: Fourth Wednesday of month, 7:00 p.m., in Ottumwa Public Library
Number of Members: 42

A chapter of the Iowa Genealogical Society (see Polk County). Activities include the canvassing of cemeteries, copying obituaries, and adult classes in genealogy.

● **Wapello County Historical Museum**
402 Chester Street
Ottumwa, Iowa 52501

Dedicated: September 25, 1971
Admission: Free
Open: Daily, 2:00-4:30 p.m.; other times by appointment

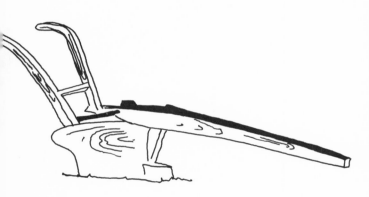

A museum, originally opened in 1966 in the Ottumwa City Hall, where it was housed in the main lobby and on the third floor. In 1970, the former John Wormhoudt home was purchased to use as a museum and headquarters of Wapello County Historical Society (see below). Wormhoudt (1869-1954) was the founder of Wormhoudt Lumber Company in Ottumwa and the builder of this house. On display in the basement are stonemason and blacksmith tools; a sausage mill; farm implements, including a 16-inch wooden-beam ground plow; and an early 1900 doctor's office. On the first floor are items associated with Ottumwa and Wapello County, such as the terra cotta ornaments from the Grand Opera House, torn down in 1941, and from the old City Hall, torn down in 1965; a railroad car coupler; war mementoes; a Swedish Bible; old pictures and maps; and a star bolt or masonry bolt from an old building at the site of Fort Sanford. Fort Sanford, a temporary military establishment, was located on the Des Moines River between Ottumwa and Agency. It was from Fort Sanford (Garrison Rock) that Captain James Allen and a small detachment of Dragoons left by river steamer in 1842 to visit Raccoon Forks where Fort Des Moines No. 2 (see Polk County Historical Society) was constructed the following year. A small cemetery on the Des Moines River bluffs at the site of old Fort Sanford contains the unmarked graves of several soldiers.

● **Wapello County Historical Society**
402 Chester Street
Ottumwa, Iowa 52501

Russell Harper, President
101 Vogel Avenue
Ottumwa, Iowa 52501
or
W. Sinclair Venables, Curator
165 West Alta Vista
Ottumwa, Iowa 52501

Incorporated: October 14, 1959
Meetings: Second Wednesday in February, March, April, October and November, or as called
Number of Members: 321
Dues: $2.00 annual; $50.00 life

Organized to discover, collect, and preserve items and documents related to Wapello County. The Society owns and operates Wapello County Historical Museum (see above), and conducts tours to historic sites.

91 - WARREN

Indianola
G-6

- **Berry Woods**
  5 miles northwest of
  Indianola, Iowa

  Donald G. DeLisle
  Department of Botany
  Simpson College
  Indianola, Iowa 50125

A 42-acre timber tract located on the bluffs of Middle River, containing many old trees (white oak 100-250 years old, and hickory), wild flowers, and fungi. In the spring, bloodroot, violets, Dutchman's breeches, and spring beauties are abundant, and Indian pipe may be found later in the year. Donated by newspaper publisher Don L. Berry to the Iowa Chapter of The Nature Conservancy, the tract is used for nature study.

- **Bundy's Mill Historical Marker**
  Along Iowa 92
  Ackworth, Iowa

A marker containing the original burrs used in Bundy's Mill, which was erected 1½ miles east of Ackworth in 1855. John Bundy bought the sawmill and gristmill from the Haworth family in 1873. The mill ceased to operate in 1905.

- **Carver Hall**
  Simpson College campus
  Indianola, Iowa

Dedicated: October 6, 1956

The science building at Simpson College, named for George Washington Carver (1864-1943). He attended classes in the old science building, now the Henry A. Wallace Hall of Science. Before enrolling at Simpson College, Carver lived in Winterset, Iowa where he worked as a cook in the C. C. Schultz Hotel, did laundry, and took on all sorts of odd jobs to earn money. He also sang in the Methodist Church choir, walked the woods and studied nature, and gained a reputation with garden lovers in Winterset as the "plant doctor." When he decided to go to college, he walked the 25 miles to Indianola to enter Simpson College. He later (in 1894) graduated from Iowa State College of Agriculture and Mechanic Arts (now Iowa State University) in Ames (see Carver Hall, Story County). Carver, who was born of slave parents on a plantation near Diamond, Missouri, became an eminent teacher, botanist, and agriculture research chemist. His efforts to improve the economy of the South while at Tuskegee Institute (1894-1943) included diversification of crops and soil improvement. He discovered hundreds of new uses for the peanut, pecan, soybean, and sweet potato.

- **Lake Ahquabi State Park**
  5½ miles southwest of Indianola, Iowa,
  off U.S. 65-69 on Iowa 349

  State Conservation Commission
  State Office Building
  300 Fourth Street
  Des Moines, Iowa 50319

A 775-acre wooded area including a 130-acre artificial lake. Ahquabi is an Indian word said to mean "The Resting Place." The park contains many old white oak trees, survivors of the original forest that covered this valley when it was one of the favorite areas frequented by Indians. Activities include fishing, boating, swimming, picnicking, camping, hiking, and nature study.

- **Nature Trail**
  East from North 9th Street
  along the city limits of Indianola,
  Iowa

  Mrs. Eugene Smith
  Indianola Park Board
  Indianola, Iowa 50125

Established: January 1966

A 3/4-mile stretch of abandoned railroad right-of-way, formerly part of a branch line of the Chicago, Burlington, and Quincy Railroad from Chariton to Indianola (1881-1961), preserved in its wild state as a walking nature trail and refuge for birds, animals, and insects. The trail is used by botany classes for study of native plants.

- WARREN
(continued)

● **Warren County Genealogical Society**
Indianola, Iowa

Mrs. Helen Schooler,
Corresponding Secretary
307 North 10th
Indianola, Iowa 50125

A local chapter of the Iowa Genealogical Society (see Polk County). A facsimile reprint of the 1887 *Atlas of Warren County* was sponsored.

● *Warren County Historical Society*
Indianola, Iowa

Charles Beam, President
310 West Boston
Indianola, Iowa 50125

Organized: 1933
Incorporated: 1965
Meetings: Fourth Tuesday of each month, except July and August
Number of Members: 425
Dues: $2.00 annual; $20.00 life

The Society has an information booth during the Warren County Fair. The Mount Hope School House has been moved to the fairgrounds, restored, and furnished as of the 1910 period. A log cabin, built in the 1850's, was donated to the Society by the Wallace McKee family and is now located next to the school house. Log Cabin Days is held in September. Both the school and log cabin are open Sunday afternoons during the summer. The Sandyville Christian Church (Pioneer Christian Church) is also owned by the Society and is being preserved as a historic landmark. The original bell remains in the steeple and most of the original stained glass windows are intact. The wooden frame church building is unaltered, for the most part, and contains the original pulpit, chancel furniture, and pews, and an old coal and wood burning stove. The property was deeded to the church in 1874 by James M. Sandy for $75. The building was constructed in 1874, but was destroyed in a severe windstorm on July 23, 1884. The present church was built 10 years later and dedicated Christmas Eve, 1893. The church was last used for regular services in 1964 and for Sunday School in 1968, and was presented to Warren County Historical Society in 1970.

In preparation are county maps to show old stage routes, Indian camps, mills, mines, rural schools, railroads, and cemeteries. Plans include marking of historic sites and establishing a county museum. A newsletter "The Jam Jar" is published regularly, the 1879 *History of Warren County* has been reprinted, and historical tours are sponsored.

- WASHINGTON

shington
G-10

● **Amish Settlement**
Near Kalona, Iowa

The first Amish settlers, or "plain people," came to this area in 1846. The strictest of 4 distinct groups are the Old Order Amish, characterized by their simple way of life and their resistance to change. Horse-drawn buggies are used for transportation rather than automobiles, and most modern conveniences are rejected. Homes are usually large, sometimes with "grandpa" houses or smaller homes attached for use of succeeding generations. The settlement may be seen along Iowa 1, where motorists are warned to "watch for horse-drawn vehicles" which use the surfaced shoulders of the highway.

92 - WASHINGTON
(continued)

● **Brinton Forest Area**
3 miles northwest of
Brighton, Iowa

Washington County Conservation
Board
John L. Davis, Executive Officer
Ainsworth, Iowa 52201

A 310-acre tract of hardwood timber adjacent to the Skunk River. The area is maintained in its natural state as a timber and wildlife preserve for nature study.

● **D A R Log Cabin**
(Alexander Young Log House)
Sunset Park
Washington, Iowa

Mrs. Stephen Viggers, Regent
Washington Chapter, D A R
R.R. 3
Washington, Iowa 52353

Open: Second and fourth Thursday afternoons during July and August, or by appointment for groups

The Alexander Young log house was built in 1840 on a 320-acre tract 4½ miles northwest of Washington in Cedar Township. The house was moved to the southwest corner of Sunset Park in 1912 and restored by the D A R as a relic of pioneer days. This was the home of the Alexander Young family (which included 8 children, an aunt and an uncle) until 1876. The log building also served as a schoolhouse, polling place, meeting house, and social center.

The 2-story house with its paned glass windows, rough stone fireplace, and walls of hand-hewn logs, has been furnished with over 200 antiques appropriate to the period when it was built. A Civil War flag, presented to the old Washington Township School No. 5, over 100 years ago is one of the historical items on display. Made sometime between 1861-63, the 12-x 6-foot flag has 34 stars, and was made of home-spun wool and sewed by hand with white thread.

The ancestors of Alexander Young came from England to settle in America in 1634. Alexander, born in Fleming County, Kentucky on April 20, 1792, was the eldest of 10 children born to James and Nancy Young. Alexander Young later served in the War of 1812, was married in 1815, and lived with his wife and family in Kentucky and Indiana until 1839 when they migrated to Iowa in covered wagons.

For 36 years the 4-room log house served as the family home and a rest stop for tired travelers. Church services were often held in the home and at least one term of school was conducted in the kitchen of the house. The first marriage in Cedar Township took place here on December 30, 1841, when Alexander Young's oldest daughter Nancy was wed to Newton Smith. During the Civil War, the Young cabin was a gathering place to hear the latest news from the "front," and to receive mail.

To move the cabin to its present location, it was dismantled, log by log, and each piece was marked so that the house could be rebuilt just as it was originally. A bronze tablet has been placed above the doorway. In 1973, the cabin was named to the National Register of Historic Places.

Another log cabin, also built about 1840, was moved next to the D A R log cabin in 1974. Originally located on a farm northwest of what is now Washington, it has been restored by Washington County Historical Society.

- WASHINGTON
(continued)

● **Dublin Store**
7 miles west of Washington, Iowa

William Robertson, Owner

Established: 1845
Open: By request

All that remains of a flourishing settlement that boasted a brick kiln, wagon factory, blacksmith shop, cheese processing plant, and a lively tavern during the peak of its existence. A total of 6 doctors practiced here through the years. Torchlight parades took place on the village streets. The first white settlers came here in 1835 and lived among the Sac and Fox Indians. The general store was opened in 1845 by John D. Robertson. The building was restored in 1967 and is now a museum and community center. Old dishes, cooking utensils, tools, patent medicines, posters, and other "store" items are on display.

● **Fern Cliff Park**
12 miles southeast of
Washington, Iowa

Washington County Conservation
Board
John L. Davis, Executive Officer
Ainsworth, Iowa 52201

A well-timbered bluff——considered the highest elevation in the county——along Main Crooked Creek where 2 branches join. The 40-acre area features scenic views, picnicking, camping, hiking, horseback riding, fishing, and winter sports, and is used as an outdoor classroom and game and wilderness preserve. All kinds of native trees and plants abound in the park. Sockum Ridge (see below) may be seen from the cliff.

● **Foster Woods**
1½ miles southwest of
Wellman, Iowa

Washington County Conservation
Board
John L. Davis, Executive Officer
Ainsworth, Iowa 52201

Seventeen acres of rolling-to-rugged terrain covered with an excellent stand of hardwood timber, including most species native to southern Iowa, as well as native shrubs and wild flowers. The woods is named for the family who had previously owned about 14 acres of the land since 1890, and who presented it to the county. An additional 3 acres were donated by Maplecrest Turkey Farms. There are hiking trails and facilities for fishing and picnicking. The tract is also used as a timber preserve and an outdoor classroom for nature study.

● **Grace Hill Moravian Church**
Grace Hill, Iowa

Eugene Engle
Brighton, Iowa 52540
or
Mrs. Max Waterhouse
R.R. 1, Washington, Iowa 52353

Established: 1866

One of possibly 10 Moravian Churches established in Iowa. The white-frame, steepled church, located in Franklin Township, is reminiscent of rural churches in New England. The first settlers came here in 1854 to make their homes along the Burlington-Sigourney trail. The village of Grace Hill at one time had, in addition to the church, a post office, general store, greenhouse, stone quarry, tailor, upholsterer, cabinetmaker, stonemason, wagon maker, and blacksmith, and in 1875, Dr. G. C. Wallace hung out his shingle. The church is maintained and is still used on special occasions. Grace Hill Cemetery, nearby, dates back to 1867. Originally, the choir system of burial was followed; men were buried in one group, women in another, and children in a third row. But, by 1890, family plots were in use. There are many fine old evergreens in the cemetery and a patch of native Iowa prairie.

92 - WASHINGTON
(continued)

● **Hayes Timber**
½ mile west of
Washington, Iowa

Washington County Conservation Board
John L. Davis, Executive Officer
Ainsworth, Iowa 52201

A 34-acre tract deeded to Washington County in the 1920's by Caroline M. Hayes to be held as a memorial timber preserve. Native trees, some of large size, cover the area. There are hiking trails and limited picnic areas. The natural outdoor classroom is used primarily for nature study.

● **Iowa Mennonite Historical Society**
Kalona, Iowa

Clarence Bender, President
R.R. 1
Kalona, Iowa 52247

Organized: 1948
Number of Members: 41

The Society maintains a collection of historical records and objects from Washington and Johnson Counties in the Mennonite Museum, built in 1971-72. The brick building is a part of the Kalona Historical Villege complex developed and operated by Kalona Historical Society (see below).

● **Jonathan Clark Conger House**
903 East Washington Street
Washington, Iowa

Washington County Historical Society
P. O. Box 89
Washington, Iowa 52353

Stephen Viggers, President
Historic Conger House, Inc.
903 East Washington Street
Washington, Iowa 52353

Admission: $1.00
Open: June through October, 2:00-5:00 p.m.; other times by appointment

A 23-room brick house, once the social and political center of Washington County, acquired by Washington County Historical Society and restored in 1973 as a county museum and meeting place. An old-fashioned Christmas is observed the first 2 weekends in December. The house is on the National Register of Historic Places.

Jonathan Clark Conger started work as an apprentice shoemaker at the age of 15 and ended up as one of the wealthier men in the community. His fortune came from land speculation, money lending, and purchase of county warrants. The property was purchased by Conger on June 6, 1848 from the heirs of Thomas Ritchey, and consisted of 77 acres and a small house. This became the southeast wing of the present house, built just after the Civil War. The original brick exterior was covered with cement soon after 1900 for easier maintenance. There are 5 fireplaces, and the interior woodwork includes a walnut stairway.

The Conger's daughter, Clara, was married to Colonel C. J. Wilson, a lawyer, and the Wilsons inherited the property following Conger's death in 1904. Mrs. Conger had died in 1896. Colonel Wilson was curator of the original Washington County Historical Society, organized June 6, 1906. It was in the den of the house that the extensive collection of Civil War mementoes and Indian relics was kept by the Society.

Prior to acquisition of the house by Washington County Historical Society, it was used for a restaurant and a nursing home at different times, after which it stood vacant for a number of years.

- WASHINGTON
(continued)

Jonathan Clark Conger House
(continued)

The mansion is restored to depict the major periods in its history -- 1850, 1870, and 1900. Featured are a pioneer kitchen, loom room, front and back parlors, and den. Old-fashioned gardens will be replanted to include peonies, iris, poppies, moss rose, and tuberoses for which Colonel Wilson was well known.

● Kalona Historical Society
South side of Iowa 22, west of Ninth Street, Kalona, Iowa

H. E. Peterseim
Kalona, Iowa 52247

Organized: 1970
Meetings: Board, first Thursday of month; Annual, as called
Admission to Historical Village: $1.00

The old Rock Island Railroad depot, acquired by the Society as a gift was moved to its new location, to become the first building on the site of the Historical Village. A pioneer log cabin was later acquired from a farm near Kalona. The Kempftown Store has also been moved to the village and refurbished. This general store served the Amish community from about 1890-95, and was run by Menno and Milo Kempf, twin brothers. Also included in the village is one of the area's first 1-room schools ("Straw College"), a "Grandpa" house, outdoor brick oven, antique machinery building, the Iowa Mennonite Historical Society Museum (see above), the Wahl Museum (named for the donor of several hundred artifacts and a parcel of land included in the village site), a gift shop, and an information center. During the Fall Harvest Festival, homemade goods and foods may be sampled, old time entertainment and craft demonstrations are featured, and art works displayed.

● Lake Darling State Park
3 miles west of Brighton, Iowa

State Conservation Commission
State Office Building
300 Fourth Street
Des Moines, Iowa 50319

Dedicated: September 17, 1950

A 1,417-acre park, with a 2½-mile long, 400-acre artificial lake which is fed by Honey Creek and several small branches and has a maximum depth of 31 feet. Lake Darling is named for Jay Norwood (Ding) Darling (1876-1962), Pulitzer Prize-winning cartoonist with the *Des Moines Register.* Ding was a nationally known conservationist who served on many committees and in organizations concerned with preservation of lands waters, and wildlife. Lake Jay Darling, a waterfowl nesting restoration in Saskatchewan, Canada, supported by Ducks Unlimited, Inc., was also named in his honor.

● Norman Chipman Grave
Woodlawn Cemetery
Washington, Iowa

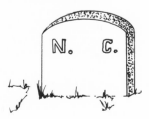

A small gravestone bearing the initials "N. C." marks the final resting place of Norman Chipman, the father of Norton Parker Chipman (1834 or 1836-1924). A companion stone marked "S.P.C." is that of his mother Sara P. Chipman. The younger Chipman was one of the persons who took the necessary action to designate Memorial Day as a national holiday in the United States, first observed May 30, 1868. At that time, Chipman, who claimed Washington, Iowa as his home, was adjutant general of the G.A.R. in Washington, D. C. The idea of Memorial Day belongs to an unknown soldier whose native Germany followed this custom, but it was Chipman who wrote the order creating the holiday.

92 - WASHINGTON
(continued)

Norman Chipman Grave
(continued)

Chipman fought with distinction in the Civil War, and was severely wounded in the thigh on February 15, 1862, during the siege and capture of Fort Donnellson in Tennessee. During the summer of 1863, while home on furlough, Colonel Chipman (later brigadier general) was called to South English to subdue an uprising--the Tally War or Skunk River War (see Keokuk County). A mob of 600 gathered on the river bottoms during this Civil War incident.

Chipman served as judge advocate during the Andersonville Trials and later (in 1911) published a book, "The Tragedy of Andersonville." He was also in the War Department under Secretary Stanton and was with President Abraham Lincoln when the Gettysburg Address was delivered. Chipman died in San Francisco, California.

● **Sockum Ridge Park**
5 miles southeast of
Washington, Iowa

Washington County Conservation Board
John L. Davis, Executive Officer
Ainsworth, Iowa 52201

An 80-acre tract, mostly covered with timber native to Iowa——oak, hickory, walnut, and elm——located near Main Creek where the pioneers first settled in Washington County. Birds and game are numerous. The area is used as an outdoor classroom, and there are scenic views from the ridge, bridle and hiking trails, and facilities for picnicking, fishing, and camping.

● **Timothy Brown Memorial**
Elm Grove Cemetery
Washington, Iowa

A monument erected to the memory of Timothy Brown by the State of Iowa and the citizens of Washington, Iowa. Brown, a Revolutionary War soldier, served under General George Washington and died in Washington County, Iowa on May 30, 1852 at the age of 90.

● **Walnut School**
Between Washington and Brighton, Iowa
on Iowa 1

An early 1-room schoolhouse preserved in its original state. It was formerly known as Memorial Miller School.

● **Washington County Historical Society**
P. O. Box 89
Washington, Iowa 52353

Charles Hotle, President
839 South Avenue B
Washington, Iowa 52353

Organized: June 6, 1906
Incorporated: November 13, 1959
Meetings: February, June, and September
Number of Members: 110
Dues: $1.00 annual

The Society sponsors annual summer tours to points of historic interest within Washington County. A room in the City Library contains written material of historic interest. A log cabin (c. 1840) has been moved to a site near the D A R Log Cabin (see above) in Sunset Park.

Also of historic interest is Washington County Hospital, dedicated July 15, 1912, the first tax supported county hospital in the United States. There have been several additions to the original building.

● **Wassonville Mill Site**
1 mile north of Wellman, Iowa

The site of the old town of Wassonville and the mill, located along the English River, has been preserved as a picnic area. According to legend, John Brown stayed in the village and left boxes of clothing, never claimed. A peaceful old cemetery and an old quarry site are nearby. There are Indian campsites and mounds along the river.

- WAYNE

rydon
-7

● **Corydon Lake County Park**
1 mile west of Corydon, Iowa

Wayne County Conservation Board
Charles Humeston, Jr.
Humeston, Iowa 50123

A multi-use park of 78 acres of heavily timbered land surrounding Corydon Reservoir (51 acres), the source of water for Corydon. An abundance of wildlife, many varieties of trees and shrubs, and a wildlife management area are within the park. There are hiking trails, nature study areas (wild flowers, shrubs, and wildlife), and facilities for picnicking, fishing, and camping.

● **Harry's Dog House**
Next to Dial Telephone Building
Humeston, Iowa

H. W. Marks
P. O. Box 215
Humeston, Iowa 50123

Established: Early 1920's
Admission: Free

A collection of over 10,000 ornamental dogs, claimed to be the world's largest, is on dispaly in 4 separate rooms. The figures are made of all kinds of materials——metal, wood, glass, ceramics, plaster of Paris, and cement——and over 100 are animated. There are dogs with wagging tails, others whose mouths open and close, dogs on a teeter-totter, and dogs riding on a merry-go-round and a ferris wheel.

● **Little Red School House**
1 mile north of Lineville, Iowa
on U.S. 65

Owned by Wayne County Historical Society, this old school building is equipped with desks, pot-bellied stoves, classroom equipment, and manikins of the teacher and pupils in the dress of their day.

● **Wayne County Historical Museum**
On Iowa 2
Corydon, Iowa

Mrs. Harry (Ann) Hibbs, Curator
Corydon, Iowa 50060
or
Mrs. Beecher (Edith) Crawford,
Assistant Curator
Corydon, Iowa 50060

Erected: 1964; new addition completed 1971
Admission: $0.50; children (5-14 years) $0.25
Open: Daily during summer, 1:00-5:00 p.m., except Monday; Sunday only, during winter; other times by appointment

A museum containing 20,000 square feet of floor space and over 26,000 items related to Wayne County history. The Colonial-style brick building includes exhibits of general merchandise; the cage and safe from the original Ocobock Bank of Corydon, robbed of $10,000 by Jesse James in 1871; dentist's office; doctor's office; an early kitchen, dining room, parlor, living room, period room, and bedroom; general store; drugstore; post office; barber shop; toy shop; music room; church; jail; and the furniture and railings from the courtroom where Clell Miller, a member of the Jesse James gang, was tried for murder. There are also collections of early tools, telephones, textiles, and over 300 varieties of birds and animals from Wayne County. Many of the 1,200 items formerly housed in the Dickey Museum (Shantytown) are now on display here. A Historical Memorial honoring the Mormon trek was formally opened July 14, 1973 at the museum.

According to *William Clayton's Journal* (published by Clayton Family Association, Salt Lake City, 1921, Deseret News), Clayton composed the Mormon hymn "All Is Well" (also called "Come, Come Ye Saints") on the morning of April 15, 1846 while the pioneers were camped along Locust Creek, south of present-day Corydon. Clayton had just received word that his wife had safely delivered "a fine fat boy" back in Nauvoo, Illinois, and all was well. The

93 - WAYNE
(continued)

Wayne County Historical Museum
(continued)

song caught on and became the grand marching song of all Mormons who trudged across the plains.

The D A R Log Cabin formerly located in Corydon's Walden Park was given to Wayne County Historical Society, and was moved in 1969 to Dotts Park, near the museum. This cabin was built from logs used in an original pioneer home of the early 1850's, one of the first log cabins to be built in Wayne County. The cabin has been furnished with items brought into Wayne County in "mover wagons."

● **Wayne County Historical Society**
Corydon, Iowa

Amy Robertson, President
Promise City, Iowa 52583

Organized: August 7, 1942
Meetings: Monthly
Number of Members: 1,425
Dues: $1.00 annual; $10.00 life

Sponsors exhibits and workshops. Owns and operates Wayne County Historical Museum at Corydon (see above) and the Little Red School House at Lineville (see above).

94 - WEBSTER

Fort Dodge
D-5

● **Blanden Art Gallery**
920 Third Avenue South
Fort Dodge, Iowa 50501

Stephen L. Rhodes, Director

Opened to Public: 1931
Dedicated: June 5, 1932
Dues for Blanden Gallery Federation of Arts, Inc.: $5.00
    annual; $10.00 family; $2.50 student
Admission to Art Gallery: Free
Gallery Open: Tuesday through Friday, 1:30-4:30 p.m.;
    Saturday, 9:00 a.m.-noon; Sunday, 1:30-
    5:00 p.m.; closed Monday

A yellow brick building of classic design, presented to the citizens of Fort Dodge by Charles Granger Blanden in memory of his wife, Elizabeth Mills Blanden. Mr. Blanden was only 30 years old when elected mayor of Fort Dodge. Mrs. Blanden was a teacher in the Fort Dodge public school system. Outstanding examples of contemporary art are on display, including the work of Calder, Chagall, Kandinsky, Klee, Lipchitz, and Miro. Special events are sponsored, art classes offered, and a children's classic film series shown. Group tours are available. A number of local clubs hold regular meetings at the gallery.

● **Carlson Recreation Area**
Southwest of Stratford, Iowa

Webster County Conservation Board
Robert Heun, Executive Officer
R.R. 2
Fort Dodge, Iowa 50501

A 94-acre wooded tract, adjacent to the Des Moines River, set aside for wildlife habitat and recreation. The small 1-room, Anderson log cabin, built about 1857 is in the area. Across the road, toward the river, is a meadow of native grasses and wild flowers. The area is used for hiking, birdwatching, and nature study.

The grave of Mrs. Joseph (Jane) Hardin, who died in 1855, is also located in Hardin Township, which was named for her husband.

- WEBSTER
(continued)

● **Central Chapter,**
Iowa Archeological Society
Fort Dodge, Iowa

David Carlson, President
R. R.
Otho, Iowa 50569
or
Mrs. Ray Mittelstadt,
Secretary-Treasurer
1425 North 10th Street
Fort Dodge, Iowa 50501

Organized: 1969
Meetings: Second Monday of month, 7:30 p.m., September through May
Number of Members: 27
Dues: $3.00 annual; $5.00 family; $2.00 student (16 and over); $10.00 sustaining; $50.00 life; nonvoting institutional $3.00; nonvoting junior $1.00

A regional chapter of the Iowa Archeological Society (see Cherokee County). Permanent displays of artifacts may be seen at Iowa Central Community College. Work is done at archeological sites during the summer. Speakers on archeology and early man in Iowa are featured at meetings, some of which are held jointly with Webster County Historical Society (see below).

● **Deception Hollow**
3 miles southeast of
Lehigh, Iowa

State Conservation Commission
State Office Building
300 Fourth Street
Des Moines, Iowa 50319

Forty acres of climax timber which suddenly appears in an area of flat land along the Des Moines River. The large basswood and oak trees provide homes for wildlife. Along the river edge and the creek, water life may be seen. Wild flowers and birds are abundant.

● **Dolliver Memorial State Park**
4 miles northwest of Lehigh, Iowa
off Iowa 50

State Conservation Commission
State Office Building
300 Fourth Street
Des Moines, Iowa 50319

Dedicated: June 28, 1925

This area of about 600 acres is one of 5 large parks located on the Des Moines River, and is a memorial to Jonathan P. Dolliver, orator, statesman (U.S. Senator from Iowa, 1900-1910), and conservationist who once lived and worked in these hills and valleys. A bronze likeness of Dolliver has been placed on a sandstone ledge, above a spring, located in the center of the park. The plaque is the work of Lorado Taft (1860-1936), noted American sculptor.

Of interest in the park are the deep ravines and slopes of over 1,000 feet, massive sandstone cliffs 150 feet high, caves, and wooded hills covered with almost every variety of tree, shrub, wild flower, and fern native to central Iowa. Indian mounds are located atop one of the highest points in the state. Boneyard Hollow, a narrow, rocky ravine running back from the river, was named for the wagon loads of bones of buffalo (bison), elk, and deer supposedly unearthed there by early settlers. It has been said that Indians used this dead-end valley as a trap for the animals, and many ancient Indian relics have been found in the area.

Flakes Riffle, located on the Des Moines River at the south edge of the park, is believed to be a dam constructed by Indians of rocks, and was used for fish drives.

Copperas beds, located in sandstone bluffs which are also impregnated with iron and coal, are the park's most unusual geological feature. These deposits lie along the banks of

94 - WEBSTER
(continued)

Dolliver Memorial State Park
(continued)

Prairie Creek and were used by Indians for paint and dyes. Dolliver is also a paradise for birds. There are facilities for picnicking, fishing, and camping, and there are 5 miles of hiking trails.

Just outside the park is Woodman Hollow (named for A. S. Woodman), which has been designated a State Preserve. These areas are intended for such passive activities as nature study and observation, photography, hiking, and bird watching, and not for recreational purposes. A deep gorge cuts into sandstone slopes, famous for ferns, wild flowers, and rare plants. A forested ridge overlooks the Des Moines River.

Lehigh, southeast of the park, was settled in the 1850's and was first called Slabtown, then Tyson's Mill and Vesper, before the change to its present name. For many years coal mining was the chief industry. Lehigh is now one of the largest clay producing towns in the area.

● **Fort Dodge Historical Foundation, Inc.**
Museum Road and U.S. 20
Fort Dodge, Iowa 50501

James Maurer, President
540 A Street
Fort Dodge, Iowa 50501
or
Mrs. Jay (Betty) Smith, Curator
1404 North 9th Street
Fort Dodge, Iowa 50501

Established: 1962; replica of fort dedicated in May 1964
Number of Members: 750
Admission: $0.50; children, $0.25; under age 5, free
Open: Daily, 9:00 a.m.-7:00 p.m., Memorial Day through Labor Day; 9:00 a.m.-5:00 p.m., after Labor Day to October 15; closed October 15-May 15; other times by appointment

Owns and operates the Fort Dodge Historical Museum, Stockade and Fort. A government fort, built in 1850 as quarters for the U. S. Sixth Infantry, was established at Fort Dodge to protect the early settlers against hostile Sioux Indians. The completed fort contained 21 buildings. When the post was abandoned in July 1853 it was the most northerly fort in Iowa. Later events would indicate that Fort Dodge was abandoned too soon. Indian raids during subsequent years increased in ferocity, culminating in the Spirit Lake Massacre (see Dickinson County).

The post's sutler was Major William Williams, who subsequently purchased the abandoned fort site and barracks in 1854, and later became the first mayor of the City of Fort Dodge. The grave of Major Williams is in Oakland Cemetery. The original fort was located about a mile from the present site, between Lizard Creek and Soldiers Creek, along the Des Moines River (see Site of Fort Dodge, below).

Two original log cabins--one the first hotel and the other the first post office in Fort Dodge--were used in recreating the old fort. It was from the settlement of Fort Dodge that Major Williams led the Spirit Lake Massacre Relief Expedition in 1857. The post is a replica of Fort Schuyler (also called Fort Williams), which was built at Chain Lakes (now Iowa Lake) on the Iowa-Minnesota border, during the Indian uprisings in Minnesota in 1864, by members of the Northern Border Brigade under Major William Williams. The Northern Border Brigade was organized by northern Iowans

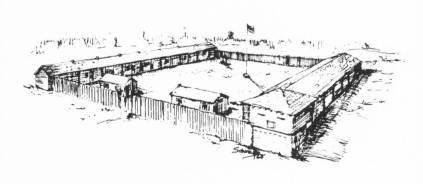

- WEBSTER
(continued)

Fort Dodge Historical Foundation, Inc.
(continued)

during the Civil War. They built and manned forts to protect residents in this part of the state from Indian attacks.

Collections of the old Webster County Historical Society (organized in 1931) are included in the museum displays, consisting of Indian artifacts, pioneer articles related to the community, a reproduction of Fort Schuyler (built at Iowa Lake by men of the Northern Border Brigade in 1862), leg irons used on the assassin of President William McKinley, century-old furniture and home furnishings, old wooden carpenter's tools (plane, brace and bit, router, and shaver-plane), fossils and rocks, stuffed birds, World War I and II articles, and Chinese and Alaskan art. The fort is surrounded by a stockade. Outside the palisade is the first school built in Webster County, at Border Plains, and "Arts Art," a collection of wood and concrete figures of bison, deer, elk, polar bear, camel, rhino, and other life-size animals carved and formed by the late Art Caffrey on his farm near Jolley and moved here in 1966.

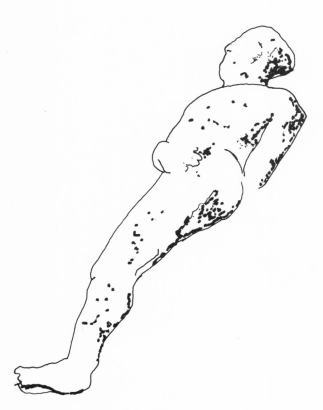

A replica of the Cardiff Giant is being carved from a 12-foot-long, 8-foot-wide, 5-foot-thick block of gypsum, weighing about 24-tons, obtained from the National Gypsum Company quarry near Fort Dodge. The replica will be exhibited at the Fort Dodge Historical Museum, Stockade and Fort. Wesley, Iowa sculptor Clif Carlson was hired to create the replica. The original Cardiff Giant was one of America's most famous hoaxes, which began in 1866. At that time, George Hull, a cigar maker from Binghamton, New York, whose sister lived in Ackley, Iowa, decided to perpetrate the hoax to prove the existence of Biblical giants. A 5-ton block of gypsum was located in a mine at Shady Oaks, 5 miles southeast of Fort Dodge, loaded on a wagon drawn by 6 teams of oxen, and hauled to Boone, Iowa, the nearest railhead. The trip took 3 weeks. From Boone, the gypsum block went to Chicago, where stonecutter Edward Burkhardt carved the fake man. The figure was 10 feet 4½ inches tall and weighed about 1½ tons. The completed giant was shipped to Union, New York as "machinery," late in the fall of 1868. From there it was taken to Cardiff, New York and buried under cover of darkness. It was then "discovered" in 1869, and soon the entire country was jumping with excitement over the incident. Thousands of persons paid an admission fee to see the remarkable object, and there were arguments among the scientists as to whether the figure was a petrified giant or a statue left by an earlier civilization. The experts were baffled by the pores in the gypsum (made with needles) and the antique appearance (produced by sulphuric acid). After the hoax was finally exposed, the giant was returned to Iowa in 1913 when Joseph R. Mulroney of Fort Dodge purchased it for $10,000. In the late 1920's, the figure was bought and displayed at the Hawkeye Fair Grounds by the Cardiff Giant Association. Then, in 1935, Gardner Cowles, Jr. (at that time vice-president of the Des Moines Register and

94 - WEBSTER
(continued)

Fort Dodge Historical Foundation, Inc.
(continued)

Tribune Company) obtained the Cardiff Giant and displayed it at the Iowa State Fair. Cowles sold the giant in 1948 to the New York State Historical Association, operators of the Farmers' Museum in Cooperstown, New York, where "Old Hoaxie" has remained.

● **Hardscrabble (Linnburg, Iowa)**
1 mile north of Iowa 175, along the Des Moines River (about 6 miles east of Dayton, Iowa)

The coal mining town of Linnburg, in southeast Webster County, was nicknamed "Hardscrabble" from the fact that residents had a difficult time to eke out an existence. Once a thriving community in the 1890's, it has long since become a ghost town. One building (now a farm home) remains to mark the townsite, located in a beautiful valley known as Hungry Hollow, through which Skillet Creek runs. Rotting remains of several old buildings can be seen. Other buildings were moved to new localities after Hardscrabble passed out of existence. An old stagecoach trail is still visible in places. At its peak, the community boasted 3 producing coal mines, a hotel, grocery, meat market, cafe, tool shop, post office (July 25, 1894 - April 30, 1914), and 40 to 50 homes, and as many as a dozen trains a day served the settlement. The Des Moines River is unique in the area, running between precipitous bluffs only a mile apart. There are Indian mounds on top of the hills.

● **Lake Ole Park**
Dayton, Iowa

Webster County Conservation Board
Robert Heun, Executive Officer
R. R. 2
Fort Dodge, Iowa 50501

A 29-acre tract, characterized by moderately heavy tree cover and a valley through which Skillet Creek flows. Around 1910, a dam was built on Skillet Creek, impounding about 2½ acres of clear water which became known as Lake Ole. The pond was used for swimming and fishing in the summer and ice skating in the winter. At one time, ice was cut from the lake and stored in a large icehouse nearby to be shipped by railroad during the warmer months. The lake gradually silted in, sloughs and wetlands in the area were drained, and the dam deteriorated until the lake became very small. In the early 1940's the remaining portion of the dam was dynamited out. The construction of a new impounding dam and concrete spillway will form a new 3½-acre lake about 20 feet deep.

● **Liska-Straneck Prairie**
6 miles southwest of
Fort Dodge, Iowa

Webster County Conservation Board
Robert Heun, Executive Officer
R. R. 2
Fort Dodge, Iowa 50501

A 20-acre tract of prairie covered with big bluestem grass. This is primarily upland prairie--never plowed or grazed--but includes some marshland. Native plants include compass plant, prairie clover, purple coneflower, wild strawberry, prairie aster, water hemlock, rattlesnake master, blazing star, goldenrod, and Indian grass. The prairie is being preserved as an outdoor classroom and wildlife area.

● **Lorenzo S. Coffin Farm (Willow Edge) and Burial Plot**
Northwest of Fort Dodge, Iowa;
1 mile west of Junction of U.S. 169 and Iowa 7, then 1 mile north on gravel road

The one-time 1000-acre showplace farm of Lorenzo S. Coffin (April 10, 1823-January 17, 1915), teacher, reformer, philanthropist, and prominent pioneer farmer. A native of New Hampshire, Coffin settled in Iowa in 1854. One of his friends was James A. Garfield, a friendship that began during college days. Coffin was a lay preacher and for many years was a circuit rider. He served in the Civil War. In 1883, Coffin was appointed by Governor Sherman to the Iowa State Railroad Commission, and continued in that

4 - WEBSTER
(continued)

Lorenzo S. Coffin Farm (Willow Edge) and Burial Plot
(continued)

office until 1888. During this time, he attained national recognition for his railroad safety legislation, passed by Iowa and, 4 years later, by the United States Congress. This required automatic brakes and coupler equipment on all railroad cars. He was forever concerned with the welfare of railroad men.

In 1891, he built Hope Hall on the farm, for the benefit of convicts recently released from prison, a project abandoned when Anamosa became a reformatory. The home was then transferred to the W.C.T.U. and used as a home for wayward girls until it burned. In 1906, Coffin was a candidate for Governor of Iowa on the Prohibition ticket, and in 1908 he was the Christian Unity Candidate for vice president. His wife and daughter were active in the Iowa women's rights movement.

The house has been altered considerably and reduced in size from when Coffin lived there. An 8-sided barn, built in 1869, stood for 90 years, but finally collapsed.

Coffin is buried with other members of his family in a cemetery plot on the farm. The cemetery is fenced and is maintained by the Railroad Brotherhoods as a memorial.

● **Lost Grove**
Southeast of Harcourt, Iowa ½ mile, in N.E. ¼ of Section 24, Lost Grove Township, on the Orville Anderson farm

A grove of trees that has attracted attention since pioneer times, named for the fact that when this area was first settled it was the only clump of trees for miles around and there seemed to be no explanation for its existence——a misplaced or lost grove of trees. Discovery of the grove in 1863 is generally credited to Reverend Father Youker, an early settler near Gowrie. The grove was originally on an island in a shallow lake which protected the trees from prairie fires. The lake has since disappeared and the trees are now in the center of a pasture.

94 - WEBSTER
(continued)

Lost Grove
(continued)

There are many stories associated with the grove. According to legend, this was a favorite camping ground for Indians, a place of refuge for the stagecoach and passengers during sudden winter blizzards, and a place where a thief fleeing from justice buried his loot. The grove undoubtedly served as a landmark for early settlers and many lost travelers. When Lost Grove Township was organized October 12, 1869, it took its name from this clump of trees. Many of the trees are now dead or dying and, since no new ones are taking their place, the old landmark may eventually disappear.

● **Pioneer Museum**
Main Street
Harcourt, Iowa

Francis Carlson, Sr., Owner
R. R. 1
Harcourt, Iowa 50544

Established: 1965
Admission: $0.35
Open: Daily, 1:00-5:00 p.m., May 1 to September 1; other times by appointment

Features a collection of antique tools, furnishings, utensils, and family belongings brought to Iowa from Sweden. Model "rooms" include a children's room, with toys and small furniture; a living room, complete with parlor organ, Edison phonograph with cylinder-shaped records, iron heating stove, and rocking chair; a bedroom with antique furnishings; and a kitchen with iron range, cupboard, kettles, and dishes. There are also over 125 old irons, from charcoal irons and flatirons to electric irons; a top buggy; an 1856 Wheeler and Wilson sewing machine; sleigh bells; a 1925 Model T roadster; early spark plugs; antique greeting cards; grindstone; wooden pump; the sign and pot-bellied stove from the old Harcourt depot; cider press; churns; jugs and kegs; bee smokers; a magazine and newspaper collection; and an old Swedish family Bible.

● **Powers Crossing Stagecoach House**
South of Tara, Iowa, southwest of Fort Dodge, Iowa

Privately owned, but the house may be viewed from the road

A brick house with 5 chimneys, constructed around 1858 at the ford on Lizard Creek. This was a stagecoach stop and inn on the road from Fort Dodge to Sioux City until the stagecoach was replaced by the railroad in the 1870's.

In the limestone ledges along Lizard Creek, small brachiopods, crinoid fragments, and other fossils may be found. Limestone with ripple marks is also present.

● **Richey Log Cabin**
Harcourt, Iowa

Mrs. Laurel Bittle Carlson, Owner
Harcourt, Iowa 50544

Admission: Donation
Open: By appointment

A pioneer home, originally built in 1855 in Dayton Township, Webster County, by Gasper T. Richey, who came to Iowa from Ohio. The log house, 20 by 24 feet in size, was built of hewed native oak logs, pegged together, and was originally 2 stories in height. Floors were of walnut. Water came from a spring in the hillside. The log house, located high above the Des Moines River, had been covered with siding. In 1967, the building was moved 12 miles to Harcourt, converted to a 1½-story log cabin, and restored to its original condition as nearly as possible. The cabin has been furnished and is maintained as a relic of bygone days.

- WEBSTER
(continued)

● **Rossow Prairie**
5 miles north of Duncombe, Iowa

Webster County Conservation Board
Robert Heun, Executive Officer
R.R. 2
Fort Dodge, Iowa 50501

Approved for Acquisition: November 16, 1971

Forty acres of virgin prairie slough, including a 12-acre prairie marsh, preserved in its natural state for nature study and use as an outdoor classroom. The land, owned by the Rossow family since pioneer days, has never been plowed. Because of the variety of native prairie vegetation, the area is especially attractive to botanists and nature photographers.

● **Site of Fort Dodge (military post)**
Northwest corner of 1st Avenue North
and North 4th Street
Fort Dodge, Iowa

On the grounds of the Fort Dodge Community School Administration Building, formerly Wahkonsa Elementary School, a 5-foot boulder and bronze tablet mark the site of the old military post established in 1850 to protect early settlers from the Indians. The fort was first called Fort Clarke, after Brevet Major Newman S. Clarke. Since other posts in this territory had the same name, it was renamed Fort Dodge on June 25, 1851. This was to honor Henry Dodge (1782-1867), Governor of the Territory of Wisconsin (1836-41 and 1845-48) and U.S. Senator from Wisconsin (1848-57), who fought in the War of 1812, the Black Hawk War of 1832, and other Indian wars. The post buildings extended from 3rd Street east, along 1st Avenue North (originally named Williams Street). The fort was abandoned in 1853 and became the nucleus of the present City of Fort Dodge.

● **Swede Bend Church**
Southwest of Stratford, Iowa,
in Hardin Township

A pioneer church dating back to the 1860's, considered to be the mother church of the Mission Covenant denomination. Many of the original fixtures are contained in the church, which is still used on special occasions.

● **The Diggings**
North edge of Fort Dodge, Iowa

Howard Jensen
2501 North 7th Street
Fort Dodge, Iowa 50501

A 7-acre woods near the Des Moines River, containing black oak, red oak, white oak, hickory, black maple, ash, and basswood. A hogback hill runs through the property, providing slopes facing north, west, and south. The timber has been protected for many years.

The property was acquired by the Iowa Chapter of The Nature Conservancy in 1968 as a gift from Mrs. Susan Atwell, who resided adjacent to the woods.

● **Vegors Cemetery**
North of Stratford, Iowa

This 1849 cemetery, overlooking the valley of the Boone and Des Moines Rivers, was also the burial site of Indians (500 B.C. to 500 A.D.) before the white man came. It is estimated that over 250 Indian mounds exist along the Des

94 - WEBSTER
(continued)

Vegors Cemetery
(continued)

Moines River between Ledges and Dolliver Memorial State Parks. Over 100 of these are located in the Stratford area. Five conical Indian mounds are located within Vegors Cemetery, 4 of which contain graves of white persons.

A monument in the cemetery marks the grave of "Mrs. Jno. H. Lott," wife of the Henry Lott credited with being responsible for the Indian uprisings that led to the Spirit Lake Massacre. (See Dickinson County.) Lott was described by Major Williams, founder of Fort Dodge, as a bootlegger, scoundrel, cut-throat, horse thief, murderer, and all-round shady character. Mrs. Lott was driven from her cabin during an Indian raid in 1846. She became ill from shock and exposure, died a short time afterwards, and was the first white woman to be buried in the area. (See Bloody Run and Lotts Creek Park, Humboldt County.) A 12-year old son, Milton Lott, froze to death while running for help after escaping from the Sioux Indians who were led by Sidominadotah or "Two Fingers." The boy's body was found December 18, 1846. He was the first white person to die in Boone County, and was later buried along the river bank. The site of the grave was lost as years went by, but was rediscovered in 1903 by 2 men who were present and assisted in the original burial, and members of the Madrid Historical Society. On December 18, 1905, some 59 years after the body was found, a monument and marker were placed within a few feet of the final resting place of young Milton Lott.

A Revolutionary War soldier, Benjamin Bell (1751-1853), is also buried here (see Bell's Mill Park, above). He lived to the age of 102 and is believed to be the only veteran of the American Revolution buried in central Iowa.

● **Vincent Home**
824 Third Avenue South
Fort Dodge, Iowa

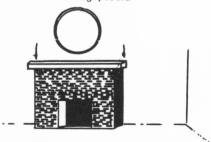

A 3-story, soft red brick house on which construction was begun in 1871 by James Swain. The house was sold to Webb Vincent in 1879. The original design has been essentially preserved through the years. The sturdy exterior walls are 30 inches thick. The house features slender, 11-foot-high windows with an unusual type of wooden shutters; parquet flooring in the dining room; high ceilings; fireplaces——one with nursery rhyme ceramic tiles; and a huge ballroom on the third floor. The roof is of mansard style. The home was occupied by the Vincent family until the recent death of Mrs. Donald Vincent, who willed the property to the Fort Dodge Y.W.C.A.

● **Webster County Historical Society**
Fort Dodge, Iowa

Mrs. Mildred Jones, President
716 North Second Street
Fort Dodge, Iowa 50501
or
Roger Natte
Iowa Central Community College
330 Avenue M
Fort Dodge, Iowa 50501

Reorganized: January 1970
Meetings: Second Monday of month
Number of Members: 100
Dues: $3.00 annual; $5.00 contributing; $100.00 life; $0.50 student

Organized to collect and reproduce historical materials, present programs on Iowa and local history, and publish a newsletter.

- WINNEBAGO

Forest City
A-6

● **Hogsback Area**
3 miles northwest of
Lake Mills, Iowa

Winnebago County Conservation Board
Jim Amelsberg, Executive Officer
R. R. 2, Thorpe Park
Forest City, Iowa 50436

A 149-acre recreation area featuring a narrow, defined hill, covered with oak and hickory trees, and surrounded on 3 sides by a marsh. The entire hogsback formation extends for a distance of approximately 10 miles, is 60 to 80 feet high, and is from 200 to 400 feet wide. An ancient glacier left this formation in an area made up, for the most part, of flat prairie land. In pioneer times, early settlers used the hogsback for a wagon trail from their homes to the town of Lake Mills. The hogsback comprises about 50 acres of the total area; the balance is marshland kept in its natural state as a wildlife preserve. This marsh area is heavily covered with aquatic vegetation. The Winnebago River (formerly called Lime Creek) is near the west edge of the property. Today the area is used for nature study, picnicking, camping, archery, hunting, and winter sports.

● **Lime Creek Genealogical Society**
Forest City, Iowa

Frank D. Myers,
Corresponding Secretary
236 North 11th
Forest City, Iowa 50436

Organized: January 1974

A local chapter of the Iowa Genealogical Society (see Polk County).

● **North Central Iowa Museum
and Historical Society**
Forest City, Iowa

Mrs. Roy (Amy) Belsaas, President
148 Woodland Drive
Forest City, Iowa 50436

Incorporated: August 31, 1964

Renamed Winnebago Historical Society September 10, 1974 (see below).

● **Pilot Knob State Park**
4 miles east and 1 mile south of
Forest City, Iowa

State Conservation Commission
State Office Building
300 Fourth Street
Des Moines, Iowa 50319

See Hancock County for information

● **Site of First Consolidated
School in Iowa**
Southeast corner of grounds
of Buffalo Center Community
School
Buffalo Center, Iowa

A monument marks the site of the first consolidated school west of the Mississippi River, and one of the first 4 or 5 in the United States. A commemorative bell is supported by a gray granite monument, dedicated August 27, 1972 at the 75th anniversary of the founding of the school.

The people of Buffalo Township pioneered in the creation of a rural consolidated school in 1897. This Township, including the town of Buffalo Center, was one of the last parts of Winnebago County to be settled. Buffalo Center was not founded until 1892, and was located on a branch of the Rock Island Railroad. When the settlement was incorporated in 1894 it had a population of 350.

The first school in Buffalo Center was conducted on the upper floor of a private home. These quarters also served

95 - WINNEBAGO
(continued)

**Site of First Consolidated
School in Iowa**
(continued)

temporarily for a Sunday School for the Congregational Church and City Hall. In February 1894, a frame school building opened with 2 teachers instructing 50 pupils. A brick schoolhouse was built in 1895, at a cost of $15,000. There were additions to this building before it was torn down in 1922. A new school was constructed on the site south of the old building. Bricks salvaged from the old building were later used in the construction of the Buffalo Center City Hall.

In 1895, the National Education Association appointed a committee of 12 educators to study the rural school system, which was under criticism. Heading the committee was Iowa's State Superintendent of Public Instruction (1888-92, 1894-98) Henry Sabin. Another Iowan serving on this committee was Henry Wallace. The committee's report was for many years the standard on the rural school problem.

Consolidated schools first became possible with the authorization to use public funds for the transportation of pupils to a central school. Massachusetts was the first state to do this (1879). The first state in the Midwest to transport pupils at public expense was Indiana (1889).

The consolidated school movement began officially in Iowa in 1897 when the *Code of Iowa* first stipulated ". . . when there will be a saving of expense, and the children will also thereby secure increased advantages, (to) arrange with any person outside the board for the transportation of any child to and from school in the same or another corporation, and such expense shall be paid from the contingent fund." This addition to the school laws was the key which opened the door to consolidation.

At the beginning, many farm people were reluctant or unwilling to take their children from the little one-room rural school and send them to Buffalo Center. Some mothers cried when they heard of the proposal and refused to send their children to school in town. However, the patrons of one sub-district (No. 3) asked the school board to furnish transportation for their pupils to Buffalo Center. This was on August 23, 1897, so this date marks the beginning of consolidatation in Iowa. A week later, 2 more rural schools were closed and, by 1899, all but 2 rural schools in the township were included in the consolidation. The last rural school in the centralized district closed in 1921.

Enrollment at Buffalo Center rose from 170 to 350 in the first 5 years of the school's existence. Average daily attendance was 93 percent of the total enrolled. Educational costs in the township dropped from $5.04 per pupil per month to $1.80 at the central school. Among other advantages mentioned were "the stimulating influences of large classes, giving a long time for recitations and individual work and placing of pupils in classes of equal ability."

Teams pulling hacks or, in the winter months, bobsleds, transported rural students to the schools.

- WINNEBAGO
(continued)

● Winnebago Historical Society

Mrs. Helen Brown, Secretary
436 North 11th
Forest City, Iowa   50436

Renamed: September 10, 1974
Dues: $1.00 annual; $20.00 life

Formerly North Central Iowa Museum and Historical Society.

- WINNESHIEK

corah
A-10

● Baker Park
2½ miles northwest of
Bluffton, Iowa

Winneshiek County Conservation Board
Charles J. Ohlert, Executive Officer
P. O. Box 25
Calmar, Iowa 52132

A 12-acre recreational and scenic area with nature trails, river access, and facilities for picnicking, camping, and fishing, also used as an outdoor classroom. A flat plateau, adjacent to the Upper Iowa River, and a high bluff support both bottomland and upland timber, birds, and wild animals. Nature trails along the perimeter of the plateau afford a good view of Chimney Rock, approximately 3,000 feet away to the northeast. The scenic Upper Iowa River through this area is popular with canoeists. The park is named for the former owner, C. P. Baker.

● Bily Clock Exhibit
Dvorak House
Spillville, Iowa

Chamber of Commerce
Spillville, Iowa 52168

Admission: $1.00; children, 7-12 years, $0.35; special rates to schools and large groups
Open: Daily, 8:30 a.m.-5:30 p.m., May through October; 10:00 a.m.-4:00 p.m. during April; weekends during March and November; closed during December, January, and February

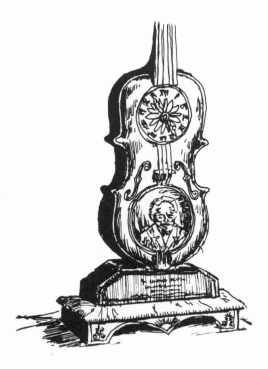

Hand-carved clocks of unique design, with mechanical figures, created by the Bily (pronounced Beelee) brothers——Frank L. (1884-1965) and Joseph C. (1880-1964). Of Czech descent, the brothers' main occupations were farming and carpentry; wood carving was their hobby. Woods from around the world were used to carve the Apostles' Parade Clock, American Pioneer History Clock, Statuary Clock, Lindbergh Clock, Little Brown Church Clock, Paradise Clock, Village Blacksmith Clock, Parade of Nations Clock, and many others. The first of the clocks was carved in 1913. The collection is housed in the building occupied by the composer Antonin Dvorak during his stay in Spillville in 1893. Guides describe the various features of the clocks and demonstrate the mechanical features, chimes, and music boxes.

A museum is located on the second floor of the building. Unusual items of pioneer times, wood-carving tools used by the Bily brothers, and old coins are displayed. A separate room is dedicated to Dvorak and contains memorabilia related to the famous composer of "New World Symphony," "Humoresque," and "American Quartette," including the organ he used in Spillville.

The Antonin Dvorak Memorial is located in Riverside Park, at Spillville.

96 - WINNESHIEK
(continued)

● **Bloomfield Township
Historical Society**
Castalia, Iowa

W. F. Buddenberg, President
Castalia, Iowa 52133

Organized: 1962
Meetings: Second Sunday of month, except August and
December
Number of Members: 59
Dues: $1.00 annual

Organized to preserve an old stone school building at
Frankville, Iowa, the Society has also erected historical
markers and sponsors tours and programs on local history.

● **Bluffton Fir Stand**
Across Upper Iowa River
opposite Bluffton, Iowa

State Conservation Commission
State Office Building
300 Fourth Street
Des Moines, Iowa 50319

A scenic, forested area containing a rare natural stand of
balsam fir, which has been designated a State Preserve.
Picnicking is permitted on the north side of the Upper Iowa
River.

Bluffton is an early pioneer village along the Upper Iowa
River. Limestone bluffs rise high above the water. The river
is a favorite of canoeists. Cold Water Creek, an outstanding
trout stream, joins the Upper Iowa River about 2 miles
above Bluffton.

● **Cold Water Cave**
4 miles east of Kendallville, Iowa, or
about 10 miles north and
east of Cresco, Iowa

State Conservation Commission
State Office Building
300 Fourth Street
Des Moines, Iowa 50319

Cave Discovered: 1967 (by University of Iowa geology
students David Jagnow and Stephen Barnett)

A forested area with a spring-fed creek (fishing permitted)
is the site of the only known entrance to Cold Water Cave.
Although not open to the public, this wet or living cave is
the longest and by far the most spectacular in Iowa. It is
located in the Driftless Area, which was covered by glaciers
a million years ago. The cave has been formed out of the
ancient limestone deposits by a tributary of the clear trout
stream, Clear Water Creek, which flows year-round. The
passageways, dome-pits, and rooms could originally be
reached only by an underwater entrance at the base of a
100-foot cliff. The constant air temperature is 48 degrees,
while the water temperature remains at about 47 degrees.
There had been no circulation of the air inside the cave
with the outside atmosphere, since the cave's only known
natural entrance was under water. This kept the cave
hidden through the centuries, and the extremely moist,
humid conditions inside the cave made possible the
spectacular formations it contains.

Drop by drop, through untold millions of years, fantastic
formations of living stone have been forming——lacy
curtains of dripstone, frozen waterfalls, rippled pillars,
shelves of flowstone, stalactites hanging from the ceiling,
and stalagmites growing up from the floor. Some stalactites
are hollow tubes of stone, like soda straws. The color of the
various formations depends upon the amounts and
composition of the minerals contained in the water that
forms them. There are brilliant reds, browns, grays, and
whites.

A number of mudbanks, some covered by flowstone
deposits, are also in the cave. Fresh raccoon tracks were
found in mud by the discoverers of the cave, and small fish

6 - WINNESHIEK
(continued)

Cold Water Cave
(continued)

(slimy sculpins) which have adapted to life in total darkness, small trout, salamanders, earthworms, amphipods, tiny insects, and plant seedlings washed in from the surface, have also been observed. The creek flows through the cave in a series of crystal clear pools, tumbling rapids, and a waterfall that fill the passages with the sound of rushing water. Rimstone dams have formed, cutting off aquatic life from above and below. In places, huge blocks of limestone have fallen from the ceiling, sometimes partially blocking the passageway. Many side passages branch off from the main cave. Some 3 miles back from the natural entrance is a series of vast rooms; beyond here is a narrow crawlway. Much of the cave remains unexplored.

At the time of discovery, the uncontaminated environment of the cave was practically untouched by the hand of man. The State Preserves Advisory Board recommended that Cold Water Cave be preserved as a unique scientific laboratory for a period of at least 5 years. A dry entrance with several air locks was planned to provide easier access to the cave and preserve the centuries-old atmosphere. Meanwhile, a steel gate was placed across the cave's under water entrance, to bar unauthorized entry.

On February 22, 1972, after previous test drills, geologists penetrated into the cave from the surface, breaking through into an open part of the main cave. The 6-inch, 94-foot-deep hole was then enlarged to 10 inches. A 30-inch hole was then drilled as an offset to it, so men and equipment could enter and do additional scientific exploration, mapping, and study of the cavern during the next 3 years. This work completed, an 80-page report was then presented to Governor Robert D. Ray on February 12, 1975.

With the expiration early in 1975 of the State's 3-year lease, control of the cave and access to it reverted back to the Kenneth Flatland family, who own the land surrounding the man-made entrance. The development of Cold Water Cave as a public recreation facility by the State of Iowa is estimated to cost a minimum of $1 million, exclusive of land acquisition.

● **Dunning's Spring**
Decorah, Iowa

Just outside a large cave eroded into the side of a rock bluff, the gurgling waters of a cool spring tumble down the 60-foot cliffside. There are a number of other springs at about the same level along this side of the Upper Iowa River. This is where William Painter, first white settler in Decorah, set up a grist mill in 1849, using millstones brought from Ohio.

96 - WINNESHIEK
(continued)

● **Fort Atkinson State Park**
Northwest edge of Fort
Atkinson, Iowa

State Conservation Commission
State Office Building
300 Fourth Street
Des Moines, Iowa 50319

Dedicated: May 20, 1962
Admission: Free
Open: Mid-May through mid-October, 1:00-5:00 p.m., Tuesday through Friday; 10:00 a.m.-5:00 p.m.,Saturday and Sunday; closed on Monday and during winter

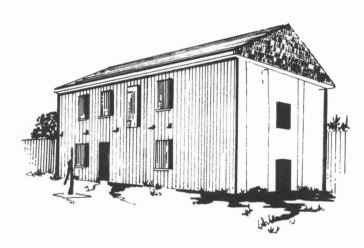

This federal military post was established along the Turkey River in 1840 to protect the peaceful Winnebago Indians against the hostile Sioux, Sac, and Fox Indians. The fort was named to honor General Henry Atkinson, commander of Jefferson Barracks in St. Louis. The earliest forts were usually made of logs, but Fort Atkinson was built mainly of limestone, quarried nearby. It took 2 years to complete, and cost the Army about $90,000. Located in the 40-mile-wide Neutral Ground, the original layout of the fort included 2 stone and 2 log barracks enclosing a parade ground. The 2-story stone buildings were occupied by commissioned officers and their families. Soldiers occupied the other buildings. Approaches were guarded by cannon houses at the northeast and southeast corners. A powder magazine, quartermaster storehouse, sutlers store, and guard house were also built. An Indian Agency was established near the post, as well as a grist and saw mill, and a schoolhouse, where classes were conducted for children of the officers. Although the fort was heavily armed, there is no record of its ever having been attacked.

In 1848, the Winnebagos were moved from the Neutral Ground to a new reservation at Fort Snelling, by treaty. As civilization advanced across Iowa, there was no longer a need for Fort Atkinson. The last troops left on February 24, 1849. Supplies were sold and, although a caretaker was appointed, travelers and settlers found the old fort a wonderful source of firewood, glass, lumber, and hardware. Finally, the buildings were sold for $3,521 in 1855 and the land made available to settlers for $1.25 per acre. The only buildings to survive destruction were the southwest blockhouse, the powder magazine, and part of the north stone barracks. The fort was acquired by the State of Iowa in 1921; reconstruction began in 1958.

The historical museum is located in an old barracks, which also included the hospital and chapel. Artifacts and information pertaining to the fort and the military forces who served there are on display, including rosters, maps, drawings, photographs, old letters, implements, tools, weapons, and uniforms. Many artifacts were recovered by archeologists in 1966 from the original outhouses within the fort. The latrines were evidently used as a dump by military personnel and such things as broken plates, cups, mugs, pitchers, bottles, uniform buttons and buckles, spurs, parts of old muskets, pieces of window glass, gaily decorated chamber pots with matching lids, and a fancy carved ivory cane head were recovered.

6 - WINNESHIEK
(continued)

- **Frankville Historical Museum**
  Frankville, Iowa

Acquired: 1963

A local historical museum operated by Winneshiek County Historical Society (see below). The museum contains approximately 900 items related to the early history of Winneshiek County——photographs, maps, books, old records, tools, 19th Century weapons, clothing, and the equipment used by frontier photographer, Leighton Hoffman, who was born near Frankville. Hoffman lived in Miles City, Montana during the days of Indian fighting and buffalo killings. A pioneer log cabin, over 100 years old, has been moved to the site from Springfield Township and restored. The 2-story cabin is appropriately furnished.

- **Green's Sugar Bush**
  4 miles northeast of Castalia, Iowa or southwest of Frankville, Iowa

  Dale Green, Owner
  Castalia, Iowa 52133

Established: 1851
Open: During syrup season

One of Winneshiek County's oldest and most unique industries is the processing of maple syrup and sugar each spring when "sap's running." Nights are still crisp and cold and the ground is still frozen hard, but days are warm and sunny when life begins to stir in the sugar maples and sap begins to rise. The maple forest——or Bush——in the area was first tapped in the 1850's by Gideon Green, although it is said that Winnebago Indians used the same maple trees before the white man arrived on the scene. Over the years the operation has been carried on by various families. More than 2,000 taps are made in the Bush. In the last days of February and the first few days of March, holes are bored in the maple trees and the spiles or spigots inserted. Only trees that are at least 10 inches in diameter, or 50 to 60 years old, can be tapped. Many of these trees are over 200 years old. Whereas the Indians used hollowed-out butternut or basswood logs, galvanized pails or plastic containers are now used to collect the rich maple sap which begins to flow as temperatures rise. The sap is emptied into a large gathering tank pulled through the woods by tractor, then poured into 1,250 gallon underground, glass-lined storage tanks or cisterns until it is ready for processing. Prior to 1960, the gathering tank was pulled on a wooden sled through the timber by horses. Since the sap is 97 percent water, it takes nearly 40 gallons of the raw sap to cook down to 1 gallon of finished syrup, which weighs 11 pounds and is 62½ percent sugar. Still further cooking is required to make sugar of the syrup. The season runs through mid-April, or until the trees begin to bud, at which time the sap acquires a bitter taste. At the end of the season, the spile is removed and the wound in the tree heals over. Some of the trees that were first tapped well over 100 years ago are still producing.

96 - WINNESHIEK
(continued)

● **House of Clocks**
Spillville, Iowa 52168

Admission Charge
Open: May through October, 8:00 a.m.-6:00 p.m.

A collection of over 300 clocks, from miniature clocks to a grandfather clock 10 feet high, all in running condition. Included are a clock made in 1692, a pocket watch dating back to 1708, a clock made entirely of wood, and a French clock made in 1878 for an Egyptian Emperor. Also on display are an 1875 typewriter, an 1889 kerosene picture projector, and a 100-year-old music box.

● **Ice Cave**
Ice Cave Road, north of
business district,
Decorah, Iowa

Located on a high rocky bluff overlooking the Upper Iowa River, the cave is over 200 feet deep. It was formed when a large stone slab broke away from the face of the cliff and slid toward the river on the underlying shale, leaving the hole exposed. Ice forms year-round from condensed moisture in the cave.

● **Kendallville Park**
Along Iowa 139, ½ mile north of
Kendallville, Iowa

Winneshiek County Conservation Board
Charles J. Ohlert, Executive Officer
P. O. Box 25
Calmar, Iowa 52132

An area of 15 acres including a timbered limestone bluff and flats along 1,000 feet of the Upper Iowa River, which is approximately 100 feet wide at this point. The park includes an old 4-foot-high dam, located about 1 mile below a large spring, and impounds a large body of cold water, providing fine trout habitat. Local sportsmen built the dam of logs cabled together and large rocks covered with cement. The river bottom is limestone. A number of birch and white pine trees grow nearby, in an area of scenic beauty. There are facilities for boating, fishing, swimming, picnicking, and camping.

● **Laura Ingalls Wilder Park**
Burr Oak, Iowa

Laura Ingalls Wilder Park, Inc.
David De Cou, President
Box 43
Burr Oak, Iowa 52131

A 1-acre memorial park and museum honoring Laura Ingalls Wilder (1867-1957), author of pioneer tales for children. The television series, "Little House on the Prairie," was based on her "Little House" books. The Charles Ingalls family lived in Burr Oak from 1876 to 1878. During one of these years they lived and worked at the Masters Hotel, which was built in 1857. The old boarding house hotel is being restored to its 1875 appearance.

● **Merlin Moe Memorial Park**
8 miles southeast of
Decorah, Iowa

Winneshiek County
Conservation Board
Charles J. Ohlert, Executive Officer
P. O. Box 25
Calmar, Iowa 52132

A 10-acre recreational area on privately-owned land until it was donated to Winneshiek County following the death of the owner, Merlin Moe. Within the park is a high bluff covered with hardwood timber and filled with birds and wild animals——an area for hiking, nature study, and wildlife habitat. There are also picnicking and camping facilities.

● **Meyer Lake Park**
(Calmar Park)
2½ miles southwest of
Calmar, Iowa

Winneshiek County Conservation Board
Charles J. Ohlert, Executive Office
P. O. Box 25
Calmar, Iowa 52132

A multiple-use outdoor recreational area of 126 acres, including a 38-acre artificial lake. The land is covered with hardwood timber. The park is used by picnickers, boaters, swimmers, fishermen, and campers, and as an outdoor classroom, nature study area, and wildlife habitat.

6 - WINNESHIEK
(continued)

● **Northeast Chapter, Iowa Archeological Society**
Decorah, Iowa

R. Clark Mallam, President
Sociology Department
Luther College
Decorah, Iowa 52101

Organized: May 1970
Meetings: Four times annually, as announced
Number of Members: 25
Dues: $2.00 annual; $0.50 students

A regional chapter of the Iowa Archeological Society (see Cherokee County). Organized to preserve the cultural heritage of northeastern Iowa through systematic and controlled study of prehistoric Indian sites.

● **Norwegian-American Museum**
520 West Water Street
Decorah, Iowa 52101

Marion Nelson, Museum Director

Darrell Henning, Curator

Established: February 16, 1877
Admission: Museum and Stone Mill, $1.00; children $0.50; adults in groups $0.50; children in groups $0.35; children under 6 years free
Open: Daily, 9:00 a.m.-5:00 p.m., June, July, and August; 10:00 a.m.-4:00 p.m., May, September, and October; closed November to April

The museum building was originally Arlington House, an early luxury hotel. The building was later used as a dormitory for students attending Decorah Institute, then became the Lutheran Publishing House, which continued at this location until 1932. The building has been used since then to house the museum collection begun in 1877 by Luther College. The Norwegian-American Museum, a non-profit corporation, was organized to preserve and expand the collection. An extensive renovation of the museum building was begun in 1974.

Two additional buildings in the Decorah business district have been acquired by the museum. One is Stone Mill (Painter-Bernatz Mill) which has been restored and converted to the Gallery of Pioneer Industry. The interpretive exhibits relate to early industries engaged in by the Norwegian settlers, including agriculture, lumbering, carpentry, and smithing. A study collection of related and duplicate materials is available for research. The second building, an early 3-story machine shop and mill, houses offices, library, classrooms, and temporary exhibitions.

Stone Mill, built by William Painter in 1851-52 of native stone from Winneshiek County quarries, is now the oldest remaining structure in Decorah. Painter's Mill was the first one constructed on the Upper Iowa River. On February 28, 1890, Anthony and George Bernatz, who had operated a mill in Fort Atkinson, Iowa, bought the mill in Decorah. For nearly a century this mill was run by power furnished by the Upper Iowa River. Built as a flour mill, it had a central place in the economy of the town during the pioneer period when Norwegian immigrants populated the rich farm land surrounding Decorah. The massive stone walls are 6 feet thick at the base, tapering to 2½ feet at the first floor. It is generally regarded as the last of Iowa's truly great mills to have operated with full water power. In 1947, a levee was built which blocked the flow of water through

96 - WINNESHIEK
(continued)

Norwegian-American Museum
(continued)

the old millrace, so a switch was made to diesel power until the mill ceased operations in 1966. Threatened with destruction in 1967, local historians took steps to preserve the distinctive old stone building. The mill was donated to the Norwegian-American Museum in 1968 for restoration as an exhibition hall.

Located at the Stone Mill site is a small log blacksmith shop built by Mikkel Mikkelson Sinnes who emigrated with his wife, Hage, from Telemark, Norway to Houston County, Minnesota in 1849 and, in 1856, built the shop. It is a good example of a home craft shop, serving the farm community, where tools were made, minor repairs were made to metal tools and implements, and blacksmithing and horseshoeing were carried on. The farm was sold in 1894 to a nephew, Gunder O. Skree, but Mikkel and Hage continued to live on the place until their deaths. The blacksmith shop was acquired from the Anton Skrea family, descendents of Gunder O. Skree, and moved to the Stone Mill site in Decorah during 1971. The pioneer shop has been restored to operating condition, and contains original furnishings, including the old leather bellows.

Washington Prairie Norwegian Methodist Church, 6 miles southeast of Decorah, was acquired by the Norwegian-American Museum in 1971. The simple 1-room, 1-story stone church has been restored and contains original furnishings. Organized in 1852 as the first among Norwegians west of the Mississippi, construction on the church building was begun in 1862. The church dedicated in 1868, was built of fine-grained, yellowish-brown native limestone. The last regular church services were held in 1888, but special services were held in the church until 1930. Ole Peter Peterson founded the Methodist congregation among the Norwegians in the area. He returned to Norway before Washington Prairie Norwegian Methodist Church was completed, and established the first Methodist congregation in Norway.

Workshops in Scandinavian crafts are conducted by the museum during the spring and summer. On Sundays, special activities include demonstrations of pioneer crafts, folk music (occasionally), and hostesses in costume. Guided tours are given twice daily, and to groups by reservation. A quarterly newsletter and other publications are issued.

The Decorah Nordic Fest, initiated by the Norwegian-American Museum and the Decorah Junior Chamber of Commerce in 1966, attracts large crowds in late July (last full weekend of month). Norse crafts are demonstrated, Norse specialty foods served, and folk music and dancing are enjoyed. There are special Norwegian sports events (rock throw and log throw), costume parades, and exhibits of paintings, drawings, and antiques.

6 - WINNESHIEK
(continued)

Norwegian-American Museum
(continued)

Norwegian immigrants, attracted by the wooded bluffs, scenic spring-fed streams, and rugged beauty of the area, settled here around 1850. Decorah is the largest Norwegian settlement in Iowa, and a Norwegian-language newspaper, *Decorah Posten*, started publication here in 1874. At one time its circulation exceeded 45,000, but the weekly publication ceased to exist after 98 years, in December 1972.

Luther College, established in 1861 at Halfway Creek, Wisconsin, was moved to Decorah the following year. It was the first Norwegian-American institution to offer an academic degree. From Main Tower, situated on a high bluff, there is an entrancing view of Decorah and the scenic Upper Iowa River Valley. A Planetarium is in the Science Building.

A group of typical pioneer buildings may be seen on Luther College campus (near Brandt Hill), a part of the Norwegian-American Museum. The 5 early log buildings nestled in a grove of trees, have been moved from their original sites, restored, and furnished. Included are 2 pioneer homes, a parochial schoolhouse (1879) from near Nordness, Iowa, a tasa drying house for grain and malt, and a small millhouse. One of the log dwellings was built by Erik Egge in 1851-52, shortly after the Norwegian colony was founded in Winneshiek County. Built of squared logs, it measures 16 by 14 feet. This cabin was used by Rev. and Mrs. U. V. Koren, who spent their first American winter here in 1853-54. It is believed to be the first Norwegian-American Lutheran parsonage west of the Mississippi River.

Adjacent to the campus and back from the Upper Iowa River is the Sherman A. Hoslett Memorial Field Study Area, established by the biology department of Luther College. The 15-acre tract includes 2 ponds. It was named for a 1930 graduate and faculty member who died in 1971.

Acquired: July 12, 1966
Admission charge
Open: Saturday and Sunday, 1:00-4:00 p.m., May through October

● **Porter House Museum**
401 West Broadway
Decorah, Iowa 52101

Adelbert Field (Bert) Porter, widely-known collector-naturalist-artist of Decorah, deeded his home and contents to Winneshiek County Historical Society (see below) to be used as a museum operated by a board of trustees. The stately Victorian home was built of local brick in 1867 by D. B. Ellsworth of New York, who came to Decorah in 1855. Collections of rare butterflies, moths, and insects from all over the world; stamps; coins; shells; Indian relics; and other articles are in the old Porter mansion. The rock wall, which surrounds the property on 3 sides, was designed and built by Mr. Porter and includes agate, jasper, rose quartz, onyx, amethyst, petrified wood, and crystal. On the grounds are miniature waterfalls, pools, and secluded gardens. Mr. Porter died on March 10, 1968 (at the age of 89) in the home where he had lived for 64 years.

96 - WINNESHIEK (continued)	● **St. Anthony of Padua Chapel** Festina, Iowa	*Dedicated:* 1886 Said to be "the smallest cathedral in the world," this little chapel seats 8 people. It was built in 1885 on the south bank of the Turkey River by Johann Gaertner (1793-1887), who had served as a soldier under Napoleon. Gaertner came to Iowa in 1846 and later dedicated the 12- x 16-foot chapel to his safe return from the disastrous winter retreat of Napoleon's army from Moscow. He and his wife and sister-in-law are buried behind the chapel in the Old Mission Cemetery. The 40-foot belfry was added in 1888, and the miniature alter and stained glass windows were installed in 1903. On June 13 each year, the feast of St. Anthony is celebrated.
	● **St. James Lutheran Church** Northwest edge of Fort Atkinson, Iowa	A church built in the mid-1800's, partially restored by the congregation of St. Peter Lutheran Church of Eldorado. There is also a small cemetery. The property is a State Preserve.
	● **St. Wenceslaus Church** Spillville, Iowa	An impressive stone church, reminiscent of the Old World, built in 1860 by artisans trained in their native Bohemia. Antonin Dvorak was guest organist in the church during his stay in Spillville in the summer of 1893. In the cemetery nearby is the grave of Joseph Spielman (Spillman), immigrant miller who founded the town of Spillville in 1854.
	● **Silver Springs Park** South edge of Ossian, Iowa Winneshiek County Conservation Board Charles J. Ohlert, Executive Officer P. O. Box 25 Calmar, Iowa 52132	An area of approximately 10 acres, used for picnicking, fishing, camping, and winter sports, and formerly the site of a privately-owned creamery. Stone for the building was quarried on this tract of land. An old 1-acre, spring-fed ice pond in the center of the park was used to furnish ice for the creamery. After the creamery ceased operations, the buildings were used for a slaughter house, and then closed and abandoned.
	● **Spillville Mill** Spillville, Iowa	The rushing sound of water pouring over the dam at the Spillville Mill on the Turkey River is said to have inspired composer Antonin Dvorak to write his famous "Humoresque." He spent the summer of 1893 in this quiet Bohemian town. The pioneer stone mill still grinds feed, but electric power is now used. The old water wheel went long ago, and much of the dam has been broken out by ice.
	● **Stone Mill (Bernatz Mill)** Decorah, Iowa	*Opened to Public:* July 4, 1971 A part of the Division of Pioneer Industry, Norwegian-American Museum (see above). The Bernatz family operated the mill until 1966. The grist mill was built in 1851, by a Mr. Painter, but ownership changed several times through the years.
	● **Trout Run Mill** 1 mile southeast of Decorah, Iowa, along Iowa 9	Made of native limestone, this relic of bygone days has switched from water to electric power and is now a meat processing plant (Reardon's).

6 - WINNESHIEK
(continued)

● **Vesterheim**
Downtown Decorah, Iowa

A complex of historic buildings, referred to as Vesterheim, is being restored in downtown Decorah by the Norwegian-American Museum (see above). Most of the buildings in this city block were built in the 1850's and 1860's; included are the Stone Mill and the Museum building. Vesterheim is a term used by emigrants from Norway when referring to their home in the western world.

● **Wiest Mill**
North of Fort Atkinson, Iowa

Built in 1857 on the Turkey River as a flour mill, it is still in operation, grinding livestock and poultry feeds. The millpond below the dam is a popular spot with fishermen. Painted a bright red, with white trim and stone foundation, the mill makes a charming picture.

● **Winneshiek County Historical Society**
Decorah, Iowa

E. J. Weigle, President
R. R. 2
Decorah, Iowa 52101

Historical markers have been installed in the county, and abandoned graves and cemeteries located and restored. Locust School, which was in operation for 106 years (1854-1960), has been renovated at Locust, Iowa and is open on Sunday during the summer. A museum, located in a former 2-story stone school building, is maintained at Frankville, Iowa. (See Frankville Historical Museum, above.) The Society also operates Porter House Museum (see above) in Decorah.

● **Wonder Cave**
2 miles northeast of
Decorah, Iowa

John Matter
R. R. 2
Decorah, Iowa 52101

Opened to Public: 1936
Admission charge: group rates and family rates are available
Open: Daily, 8:00 a.m.-6:00 p.m., June 1-August 30; week-ends only during May, September, and October

A natural cave 200 feet below the surface, with multicolored formations, including an 87-foot stalactite. One of the rooms (opened in 1969) has a ceiling 150 feet high. The cave occurs in Galena limestone which had its origin some 350 million years ago.

Forty-minute tours of the cave are given. Picnic facilities are available on the grounds. A 1-room rural school has been moved to the site and furnished with old desks and other equipment.

7 - WOODBURY

oux City
D-1

● **Bigelow Park**
Near Salix, Iowa,
off Iowa 141

Woodbury County Conservation Board
Rick Schneider, Executive Officer
Courthouse, 7th and Douglas
Sioux City, Iowa 51101

A 24-acre, heavily-wooded tract, bordering Brown's Lake of approximately 640 acres. The lake is one of several oxbows formed by earlier meanderings of the Missouri River. The park, operated under a management agreement between Woodbury County Conservation Board and the State Conservation Commission, is used for hiking, picnicking, sight-seeing, fishing, boating, swimming, bird watching, camping, and winter sports, and some of the natural woodland is preserved as a game refuge.

● **Cathedral of the Epiphany**
1011 Douglas Street
Sioux City, Iowa 51105

Built in 1904, the cathedral contains beautiful examples of art glass work. Its brilliantly-colored stained glass windows, which are insured for approximately $300,000, were made by the Franz Mayer Studios of Munich, Germany.

97 - WOODBURY
(continued)

● **Council Oak**
Riverside Park
Sioux City, Iowa

The tall, gnarled stump of an ancient burr oak tree, located at the junction of the Missouri and Big Sioux Rivers. Under the branches of the more than a century-old oak, legend has it that many councils of war and of peace were held between the white men and the Indians in early days. A monument has been erected by the Sioux City Garden Club in recognition of the contributions of the pioneers of western Iowa.

● **Floyd Monument**
South of Sioux City, Iowa
near Interstate 29

A stone obelisk rising 100 feet above the summit of Floyd's Bluff marks the burial place of Sergeant Charles Floyd. He was the only person to die on the Lewis and Clark Expedition of 1804-06, and the first U.S. soldier to die west of the Mississippi River in the area included in the Louisiana Purchase of 1803. The entry of August 19-20, 1804 in the journal kept by Lewis and Clark indicates that Sergeant Floyd died from a "stomach disorder" (probably acute appendicitis). His original grave was marked with a cedar post which long served as a landmark for navigators on the Missouri River. By 1857, a considerable portion of the bluff had washed away, exposing the bones of Sergeant Floyd. In late May of that year, the remains were reinterred, with appropriate ceremony, in a grave about 200 yards back from the bluff. The new grave was not marked and its exact location was all but forgotten by 1895. The grave was located and opened again, and Sergeant Floyd's remains were reburied at the present site on August 20, 1895, the 91st anniversary of his death. It was several more years after this ceremony before arrangements were completed for a suitable marker. Construction on the towering shaft was begun in 1900 and it was dedicated May 30, 1901. The remains of the Sergeant were placed in the concrete foundation. The grave site and monument was the first registered National Historic Landmark in the United States, possessing, as the plaque reads, "exceptional value in commemorating and illustrating the history of the United States of America." In 1956, the monument was struck by lightning, following which it was repaired, cleaned, and pointed. From the base of the monument may be seen a sweeping panorama of the Missouri River and its valley and a view of the 3 states of Iowa, Nebraska, and South Dakota.

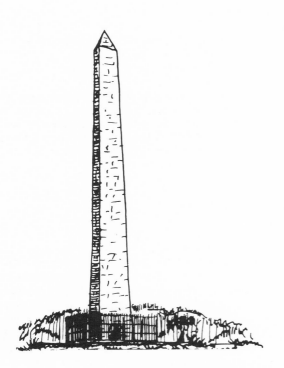

● **Lewis and Clark Historical Association**
P. O. Box 1804
Sioux City, Iowa 51102

Dr. V. Strode Hinds
President
3121 Grandview Boulevard
Sioux City, Iowa 51104

Organized: 1950
Meetings: As called
Number of Members: 90
Dues: $5.00 annual

The Society is mainly concerned with promoting the Sergeant Charles Floyd National Historic Landmark, located in Floyd Park (picnic facilities), and the Lewis and Clark Trail. A limited edition of a Sergeant Charles Floyd Monument Medallion, dedicated to the first American soldier to die west of the Mississippi River in the service of his country, was released in 1974. Funds from the sale are being used to develop a visitor center at the Monument.

7 - WOODBURY
(continued)

● **Little Sioux Park**
2 miles southwest of
Correctionville, Iowa,
off Iowa 31

Woodbury County Conservation Board
Rick Schneider, Executive Officer
Courthouse, 7th and Douglas
Sioux City, Iowa 51101

Dedicated: August 27, 1967

A 448-acre tract, including the old Bellamy Gravel Pit, developed as a multiple-use recreational area. There is fishing in the Little Sioux River and several gravel pits, and facilities are provided for horseback riding, hiking, picnicking, swimming, and camping. Portions of the park are suited to bird watching and nature study.

A replica of Fort Correctionville (1862), one of 6 military forts that once existed in the Northern Border Brigade, has been built. A rural schoolhouse, one of the last in the county, has also been moved to the park. The school is furnished with desks, pot-bellied stove, bell, and other equipment. A museum building has been completed and contains pioneer implements.

● **Sioux City Art Center**
513 Nebraska Street
Sioux City, Iowa 51101

David West, Director

Dedicated: 1938
Admission: Free
Open: Tuesday through Saturday, 10:00 a.m.-5:00 p.m.;
Sunday, 1:00-5:00 p.m.; closed Monday
Membership Dues: $15.00 family; $5.00 student

The art gallery features over 300 works including those of contemporary American and Midwestern artists——paintings, prints, drawings, sculpture, and ceramics. Traveling exhibits, a foreign film series, children's films, art classes, lectures, programs, and tours are also sponsored.

● **Sioux City Museum and Historical Association**
2901 Jackson Street
Sioux City, Iowa 51104

William Felton, President

Organized: 1961
Number of Members: 300
Dues: $5.00 annual

A nonprofit organization formed to assist in the operation of the Sioux City Public Museum (see below). The Association administers the Rumsey Fund, a bequest set up to acquire items of local historical interest, and sponsors 8-week museum classes for children and adults, 4 times during the year. These classes cover such subjects as rocks, minerals, fossils, model crafts, natural science, gem cutting, antique glass, and stitchery. The Association also operates a sales desk and gift shop in the museum, and sponsors a volunteer work program at the museum, a lecture series, and tours.

● **Sioux City Public Museum**
2901 Jackson Street
Sioux City, Iowa 51104

B. R. Diamond, Director

Founded: 1858 (as Sioux City Lyceum; located in the
Peirce Mansion since 1961)
Admission: Free
Open: Tuesday through Saturday, 9:00 a.m.-5:00 p.m.;
Sunday, 2:00-5:00 p.m.; closed Monday and on
national holidays

Located in the Peirce Mansion, built in 1889-90 by John Peirce, an early-day realtor and developer. There are displays on anthropology, archeology, natural history,

97 - WOODBURY
(continued)

Sioux City Public Museum
(continued)

science, and history. Articles related to the Plains and Eastern Woodland Indians (dugouts, ceremonial trappings, and artifacts), pioneer objects and clothing, glassware, birds and animals, minerals and fossils, Civil War articles (weapons, uniforms, and equipment), and a model of the steamboat *Omaha* (built in the 1850's), and circulating exhibits are included. Guided tours, lectures, films, classes, and formally organized school tours are also offered by the museum. Schools, youth organizations, and civic groups participate in program presentations (see Sioux City Museum Association, above). An activity center is available for meetings.

● **Sites of Sioux City Corn Palaces**
Northwest corner of Fifth and Jackson Streets (1887); Sixth and Pierce Streets (1888); and other locations in downtown Sioux City, Iowa

Beginning in 1887, and continuing until 1891, the people of Sioux City built a total of 5 colorful corn palaces to show their appreciation of agriculture. Those in the Sioux City area contributed large amounts of produce for decorating materials —— corn and grain, vegetables, and fruits.

The first Corn Palace Festival officially opened on October 3, 1887 and closed on October 10. Parades, speeches, concerts, dances, and fireworks highlighted the activities. This event attracted an estimated 130,000 visitors, including such notables as President Grover Cleveland, Cornelius Vanderbilt, and Chauncey Depew.

In succeeding years, even more elaborate edifices were erected and larger crowds were attracted as Sioux City proclaimed itself the "Corn Palace City of the World." The fifth and last of the corn palaces closed its doors on October 25, 1891. Although it was intended that the tradition be continued, a destructive flood in 1892, followed by the unforeseen financial panic that swept the country, prevented the building of another palace. Meanwhile, the citizens of Mitchell, South Dakota, recognizing a promising venture, opened the Mitchell Corn Palace in the fall of 1892, and it has continued there ever since.

● **Sloan Historical Society**
Sloan, Iowa

Ralph Juneman, President
Sloan, Iowa 51055

Incorporated: April 15, 1969
Number of Members: 100
Museum Open: By appointment

Operates a museum containing farm machinery, clothing, furniture, and several furnished pioneer rooms.

● **Smithland Forest Preserve**
½ mile west of Smithland, Iowa

Woodbury County Conservation Board
Rick Schneider, Executive Officer
Courthouse, 7th and Douglas
Sioux City, Iowa 51101

A natural woodland (oak, ash, ironwood, basswood, locust, cottonwood, and elm) of 50 acres, preserved for hiking, picnicking, nature study, and limited camping. Trails to the upper ridges afford distant views over the valley.

97 - WOODBURY
(continued)

● **Smithland Historical Society**
Smithland, Iowa

Mrs. Dorothy Aldrich, President
Hornick, Iowa 51026
or
Miss Lavina Nanson
Smithland, Iowa 51056

Admission to Museum: Free
Museum Open: On special occasions, or by appointment

The Society is largely inactive, but maintains a reconstructed log cabin (built by the National Youth Administration) which is used as a museum. The cabin contains historical records, pictures, old guns, tools, and pioneer relics.

● **Snyder Bend Park**
3 miles southwest of Salix, Iowa

Woodbury County Conservation Board
Rick Schneider, Executive Officer
Courthouse, 7th and Douglas
Sioux City, Iowa 51101

A 35-acre area along a lake formed by a change in the channel of the Missouri River. The lake is about 3 miles long and from 3 to 20 feet deep, and is located about 2 miles from Brown's Lake in Bigelow Park (see above). Willows and cottonwoods cover part of the area. The land is comparatively flat except for sand dunes near the lakeshore to the north. The park is used for fishing, boating, swimming, picnicking, and camping.

● **Stone State Park**
R. R. 3
Sioux City, Iowa 51103

State Conservation Commission
State Office Building
300 Fourth Street
Des Moines, Iowa 50319

Acquired: 1935

Named for Thomas Jefferson Stone, whose family donated a 365-acre tract to Sioux City for a park, which now includes about 900 acres. The land was originally purchased by Hector Talbot from the earliest settlers, and has been under 3 flags——those of Spain, France, and the United States. Talbot experimented with the hybridization of animals on the huge farmstead, and collected and mounted bird specimens.

This area, at the junction of the Missouri and Big Sioux Rivers, was a feeding ground for many kinds of wild animals in the old days. The last wild buffalo (bison) in Iowa is said to have been killed within the park boundaries. Many of the old, worn trails through the park are believed to have been originally formed by buffalo.

The rugged, wooded ridges and loess hills abound in wild flowers. More than 70 species have been identified and recorded here. Most unusual of these are the yucca and prickly pear cactus. Tall grama oats, one of the principal foods of the buffalo, thrive on the tops of the hills.

The loess soil, a fine, buff-colored silt between sand and clay, was deposited by dust storms. Such deposits are found in only 2 or 3 places in the world. Fine views may be had from Dakota Point, Stony Point, Mt. Lucia (1,410 feet above sea level), and other ridges. The miles of bridle trails within the park make it a popular place for horseback riding, while winter sports enthusiasts like its facilities for skiing and tobogganing. There are also foot trails for hikers, picnic areas, and a modern campground.

● **Theophile Bruguier Log Cabin**
Riverside Park
Riverside Boulevard
Sioux City, Iowa

Located in Sioux City's oldest recreational park is an old log cabin, originally built in 1849 by the Frenchman, Theophile Bruguier (1813-95), who married 2 daughters of Chief War Eagle (see below). Bruguier was the first white

97 - WOODBURY
(continued)

Theophile Bruguier Log Cabin
(continued)

settler in what is now Sioux City. The cabin, which has been relocated, was not only a home, but served as an Indian trading post. As many as 200 Indians camped around the log building while trading their beaver pelts. In more recent years, a house had been built around the cabin at its original location, and the log building was then "discovered" when the house was razed in the 1930's. The 29-x 32-foot cabin, built of square hewn logs, is said to be the second dwelling built within the boundaries of present-day Sioux City. It is now used by the "Girls of '68" (1868).

- **War Eagle Park**
  End of War Eagle Drive
  Sioux City, Iowa

  Woodbury County Conservation Board
  Rick Schneider, Executive Officer
  Courthouse, 7th and Douglas
  Sioux City, Iowa 51101

Chief War Eagle's grave is here on a high bluff overlooking the Missouri and Big Sioux Rivers, and is marked by a cast concrete block, erected in 1922. The bronze tablets on the monument were subsequently removed by vandals. War Eagle, who died in 1851, was always a friend of the white man. He is said to have spent much time in the hills and valleys within the park, and took part in religious ceremonies. From this bluff he could watch the approach of friends or enemies. A story was circulated that Chief War Eagle was buried astride his horse, but this was later disproved when excavations were made for construction of the monument. This was sacred land to the Indians, and evidence of their many camps is found in "kitchen mounds" a few miles north of the park. The 25-acre park offers hiking on nature trails, and has picnic facilities. About half of the area is covered by hardwood timber, and the remainder is typical loess-type land. From the top of the bluffs, the states of Iowa, South Dakota, and Nebraska may be seen.

98 - WORTH

Northwood
A-7

- **Elk Creek Marsh**
  3 miles north of
  Joyce, Iowa

  State Conservation Commission
  State Office Building
  300 Fourth Street
  Des Moines, Iowa 50319

An area of 1,623 acres, bordering a stream, consisting of marsh and upland. The property is being developed as a wildlife refuge and public hunting area, supporting fur-bearing animals, waterfowl, pheasant, squirrel, rabbit, and deer.

- **Fertile Mill Park**
  South edge of Fertile, Iowa

  Worth County Conservation Board
  C. H. Mortenson, Secretary
  619 Central Avenue
  Northwood, Iowa 50459

A 10-acre park including a millpond and dam. In 1879, Iowa had 712 flour and grist mills. They were the center of commerce and industry. Wheat was an important crop. But the wheat frontier moved westward and, due to changes and improvements in marketing and transportation, new farming methods, the appearance of manufactured wheat products, and the arrival of steam power and electricity, the old mills disappeared into history. Many of the mills were damaged by high water, ice jams, fire, and vandals. Today, Iowa probably has no more than 18 of these vanishing landmarks, and none of those still operating are powered with water alone. William Rhodes, who founded the town of Fertile, built this mill more than a century ago. In those days it was basically a flour mill; today it is used for

B - WORTH
(continued)

Fertile Mill Park
(continued)

grinding feeds. The huge gears which once turned the mill are still intact. The 110-foot-long dam spanning the Winnebago River is part of the 10-acre park. This is now the only dam on any river in Worth County. Oaks and willows cover part of the area. A bass-rearing pond is located in the park. This is a popular spot to fish, boat, swim, and picnic.

● **Hartland Forest Area**
6 miles northwest of
Northwood, Iowa

Worth County Conservation Board
C. H. Mortenson, Secretary
619 Central Avenue
Northwood, Iowa 50459

A 40-acre tract consisting of timberland, with a variety of trees, used for picnicking and as an outdoor classroom for nature study.

● **Ochee Yahola Park**
(Dixon Timber)
4 miles northwest of
Northwood, Iowa

Worth County Conservation Board
C. H. Mortenson, Secretary
619 Central Avenue
Northwood, Iowa 50459

An area of 160 acres, much of which is covered with dense, old-growth hardwood timber, predominantly oak and hickory, bordering on the Shell Rock River. The park was named for an Indian warrior who was given this land by President James Buchanan for serving in the Creek War.

The source of the Shell Rock River is Albert Lea Lake in Minnesota. The stream enters Iowa 3 miles north of Northwood. First called the English River, the name was changed to Shell Rock because of the abundance of fossil shells and coral in its limestone cliffs. The ancient rock formations go back to a time when what is now Iowa was covered by a shallow sea. Before settlement by the white man, this area was covered with numerous potholes, swamps, and marshes, making it a paradise for birds and animals.

A 5-acre natural marsh within the park provides an excellent area for watching and studying the processes of nature, as there is still an abundance of wildlife. Hiking, horseback riding, and nature study trails are being developed, and there is opportunity for fishing, picnicking, camping, and outdoor recreation.

● **Silver Lake**
12 miles northwest of
Northwood, Iowa

State Conservation Commission
State Office Building
300 Fourth Street
Des Moines, Iowa 50319

A shallow lake, surrounded by scattered hardwood timber, primarily oak. The lake was formed some 14,000 years ago by glacial action. Waterfowl and fur-bearing animals may be seen here.

● **Stime Timber**
3 miles southwest of
Northwood, Iowa

Worth County Conservation Board
C. H. Mortenson, Secretary
619 Central Avenue
Northwood, Iowa 50459

A tract of 165 acres preserved for wildlife habitat and nature study. Over half the area is covered with hardwood timber, and 2 marshy ponds are located on the property.

98 - WORTH
(continued)

● **Turvold Woods**
6 miles southwest of
Northwood, Iowa

Worth County Conservation Board
C. H. Mortenson, Secretary
619 Central Avenue
Northwood, Iowa 50459

A game management and forest area comprising 32 acres. This virgin timber, predominantly oak, is frequented by deer, small game, and songbirds, and contains an excellent stand of bittersweet. The undeveloped area is made up of several old, established woodlots used by the previous owners when wood-burning stoves were in use. The timber and underbrush are being preserved as a wildlife habitat, nature study area, and public shooting ground in season.

● **Worth County Historical Society**
Northwood, Iowa

Arthur W. Holden, President
R. R. 1
Manly, Iowa 50456
or
Mrs. Harry M. (Norma) Thompto
R. R. 2
Northwood, Iowa 50459
or
Dorothy Holland
Northwood, Iowa 50459

Incorporated: November 6, 1970
Meetings: Monthly during summer; annual meeting, third Monday in September; board meetings monthly
Number of Members: 150
Dues: $2.00 annual; $20.00 or more, life

A Log Cabin Day Tour, held on June 20, 1971, launched the Society's first membership drive. Several log cabins located throughout the county, and a century-old native limestone home were included in the tour, which was open to the public. Sites included were the Pangburn (Gabriel) cabin, a furnished restoration located northwest of Northwood; the Swensrud cabin, attached to the Dale Johnson home northeast of Northwood, and used as a family room; the Leverson cabin, a replica, authentically furnished; the Loberg cabin, located in a park at Kensett; the Oswald (Sime) cabin, moved and reassembled, north of Fertile; the Douglas limestone house, located east of Manly; and the Tom Fretty Museum at Manly. The Society plans to make the tour of historic homes and landmarks an annual event. An antique show is also held for fund raising.

An old-fashioned, 1-room country schoolhouse, originally the Swensrude School, located northeast of Northwood, has been donated to the Society and restored. The building which once served as the Worth County Courthouse (1880-93) and later as the Northwood Public Library, has been acquired for use as a museum and repository for old books, pictures, records, and other historical materials.

99 - WRIGHT

Clarion
C-6

● **Bingham Park**
2 miles southeast of
Rowan, Iowa

Wright County Conservation Board
Willard Glade, Chairman
Dows, Iowa 50071

A 12-acre site, previously composed of woodlots used by the early pioneers for firewood and construction purposes. It was acquired as a gift from the Bingham estate. The park is heavily timbered with a wide variety of trees, including oak, walnut, maple, hackberry, box elder, elm, dogwood, and sumac, and there are many wild flowers. The area is used as an outdoor classroom for nature study, and for hiking, picnicking, and outdoor recreation.

● **Eldridge Park**
6 miles northeast of
Clarion, Iowa

Wright County Conservation Board
Willard Glade, Chairman
Dows, Iowa 50071

A wooded site of approximately 1 acre, located on the west side of Lake Cornelia, used for picnicking and recreation. The park is named in honor of the donor, William Eldridge.

9 - WRIGHT
(continued)

● **4-H Historical Building**
Central Avenue West
Clarion, Iowa

Wright County Extension Office
Post Office Building
Clarion, Iowa 50525

Restored: 1955, and opened June 1, 1956
Admission: Donations accepted
Open: June, July, and August, 1:00-5:00 p.m.; other times by appointment

The 1-room rural schoolhouse from Lake Township, District No. 6, credited as the birthplace of the 4-H emblem, has been moved to Clarion City Park. The building is now used as a museum of the early days of the 4-H Clubs and is dedicated to the memory of O. H. Benson (1875-1951), Wright County Superintendent of Schools, who originated the four-leaf clover emblem in this school. The 4-H program was designed to help young people grow mentally, physically, socially, and spiritually. The 4-H's stand for Head, Heart, Hands, and Health. The old school is furnished in the mode of the 1907-08 period. Many pictures pertaining to the school and the early rural social life of the community are included in the historical exhibits.

● **Oakdale Park**
2½ miles southeast of
Renwick, Iowa

Wright County Conservation Board
Willard Glade, Chairman
Dows, Iowa 50071

The park includes the original 1-acre site of Oakdale School. The first white child in Wright County attended this school, a white frame building. These country schools were usually spaced about 2 miles apart. The 20-acre park, next to the Boone River, is covered with natural vegetation——oak, walnut, locust, hawthorn, and elm trees; gooseberry and other shrubs; and wild flowers——and is used for picnicking, camping, hiking, and outdoor sports.

● **Pikes Timber**
8½ miles northeast of
Clarion, Iowa

Wright County Conservation Board
Willard Glade, Chairman
Dows, Iowa 50071

A 46-acre area covered with oak, hickory, linden, hackberry, hawthorn, walnut, maple, sycamore, cottonwood, willow, and elm trees. There are also many native shrubs and wild flowers. The Iowa River winds through the property, and Lake Cornelia is 2 miles west. A bird sanctuary and biological preserve are in one part of the area. Other uses are picnicking, hiking, fishing, and camping. The timber was used as a recreational area as early as 1856, when it was owned by Daniel and Eugene Pike.

● **Wright County Historical Society**

Mrs. Wesley Warner, President
R.R. 2
Goldfield, Iowa 50542

Incorporated: December 18, 1950

After a 20-year period of inactivity, the Society has reorganized.

CELEBRATIONS, FESTIVALS, AND HISTORIC EVENTS OBSERVED IN IOWA

EVENT	TIME	LOCATION
All Iowa Days	Late August	Okoboji
Antique Airmen, Inc. Fly-In	Labor Day Weekend	Ottumwa Airport
Antique Airplane Fly-In	10-day period ending on Labor Day	Antique Airfield near Blakesburg, Iowa
Arts and Music Festival	July	West Des Moines
Autumn Leaf Tours	October	Elkader, Fayette, Guttenberg, McGregor, and northeast Io
Beiderbecke Days (Bix Beiderbecke Memorial Jazz Festival)	Last weekend in July	Davenport
Bratwurst and Sauerkraut Days	July	Stacyville
Chuck Wagon Feed	September	St. Olaf
Civil War Days	1st weekend in June	Hopkinton
Cobblestone Theatre	June, July, August	Clear Lake
Corn Harvest Festival	Fall	Living History Farms, Des Moines
Covered Bridge Festival	October	Winterset
Dairy Cattle Congress	Late September	Waterloo
Dansk Fest (Danish)	June	Kimballton
Drake Relays	Last Friday and Saturday in April	Des Moines
Fall Harvest Festival	Last Friday and Saturday in September	Kalona
Farm Tours	July	West Branch
Frank Gotch Day	June	Humboldt
German Festival and Art and Craft Fair	October	Manchester
Governor's Days Celebration	Late July	Clear Lake
Grain Harvest Festival	Summer	Living History Farms, Des Moines
Grant Wood Art Festival	June	Anamosa-Stone City
Harvest Festival and Outdoor Art Show	September	Charles City
Hay Days	Early Spring	Rock Valley
Indian PowWow (Mesquakie)	Mid-August	Tama
International Folk Festival	June	Bettendorf
Iowa State Fair	August	Des Moines
Little Britches Rodeo	July	Massena
Midwest Old Settlers and Threshers Reunion	5 days starting Thursday before Labor Day	Mount Pleasant

Event	Time	Location
ss Iowa Pageant	3rd week in June	Davenport
tional Hobo Convention	Mid-August	Britt
tional Hot Air Balloon Races	Mid-August	Indianola
rdic Fest (Norwegian)	Last full weekend in July	Decorah
rth Iowa Band Festival	June	Mason City
oboji Summer Theatre	Nighly except Monday in July and August	Okoboji
toberfest (German)	October	Amana
d Settlers Reunion	August	Magnolia and Monroe
d-time Threshing Bee	Late July	2 miles south of Spencer
tdoor Art Show	June	Cresco
nt 'N Palette Club Art Show	July	Antioch School --- Grant Wood Memorial Park and Log Cabin Art Gallery 4 miles southeast of Anamosa
ncake Day	End of September	Centerville
ncake Day	Early March	Schaller
neer Craft Day Festival	Third Saturday in September	Nelson Pioneer Farm, Oskaloosa
lka Fest	September	Durant
pcorn Day	Early Fall	Ida Grove
pcorn Days	Late July	Schaller
pcorn Festival	September	Hamburg
verboat Days	1st week in July	Clinton
vercade	Late July	Sioux City
veresta	Summer	LeClaire
deo Championship	August	Sidney
se Festival	June	State Center
Patrick's Celebration (Irish)	3 days in March	Emmetsburg
uerkraut Day (German)	Summer	Ackley
uerkraut Days	Saturday and Sunday before Labor Day	Blairstown
andinavian Festival Days	June	Story City
owboat Theatre (Rhododendron)	Summer	Clinton
dewalk Antique Fair	September	Fort Dodge
ybean Days	August	Sheldon
eam and Antique Show	August	Ricketts
eamboat Days and Dixieland Jazz Festival	3rd week in June	Burlington
rawberry Days	June	Strawberry Point
mmer Arts Festival	Last full weekend in June	Van Buren County
eet Corn Days	August	Elkader
eet Corn Festival	August	West Point and West Union
-State Rodeo	September	Fort Madison
lip Festival (Dutch)	3rd week in May	Orange City
lip Time Festival (Dutch)	2nd week in May	Pella
ishea	1st week in May	Iowa State University, Ames
atermelon Day	3rd Saturday in July	Humeston
atermelon Days	Last Saturday and Sunday in August	Garrison
nter Sports Festival	Early February	Estherville
rld's Champion Goose Calling Contest	September	Missouri Valley

IOWA'S LITTLE COLONIES

(Nationality and Religious Groups)

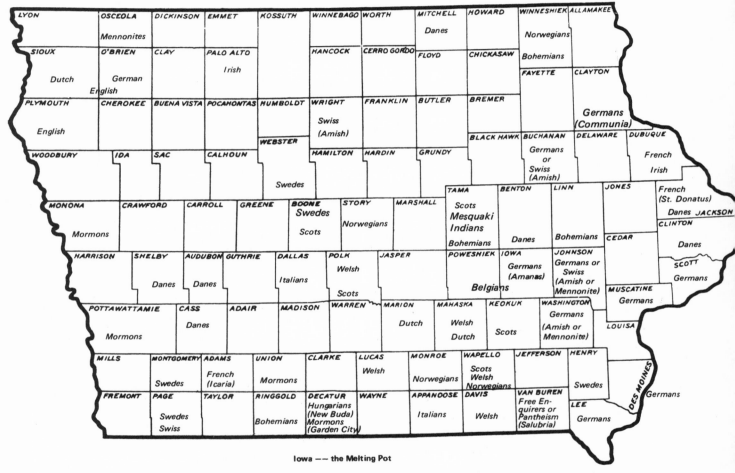

Iowa —— the Melting Pot

Iowans are a mixture of almost every nationality in the world. Many of these emigrants settled in colonies within the State. Other settlements were established by religious groups. The most important of these are shown on the above map.

IOWA'S RIVERS

Iowa

State Nickname: Hawkeye

State Motto: "Our Liberties We Prize and Our Rights We Will Maintain."

State Flower: Wild Rose

State Bird: Eastern Goldfinch (wild canary)

State Tree: Oak

State Rock: Geode

INDEX

NAME	COUNTY
First Gasoline Tractor Marker	Clayton
First Iowa State Fair, Site of	Jefferson
First Mississippi River Bridge	Scott
First Motor Vehicle Fatality in Iowa, Site of	Franklin
First Orchard in Iowa	Lee
First Public School in Des Moines, Site of	Polk
First Schoolhouse in Iowa, Site of (Galland School)	Lee
First Reinforced Concrete Bridge in the United States	Lyon
First Sod Turned in Madison Township, Site of	Jones
Fish Farm Mounds State Preserve	Allamakee
Fisher Creek	Fremont
Five Island Lake	Palo Alto
Flakes Riffle	Webster
Flint Creek	Des Moines
Flint Hills (Sho-quo-quon)	Des Moines
Flora Ellis Wildlife Sanctuary	Floyd
Flowing Well Park	Hardin
Floyd County Historical Society	Floyd
Floyd County Historical Society Museum	Floyd
Floyd Monument	Woodbury
Floyd Park	Woodbury
Floyd, Sergeant Charles	Woodbury
Floyd's Bluff	Woodbury
Flynn Mansion	Polk
Flynn, Martin	Polk
Follett Park	Clinton
Follett, William D.	Clinton
Forest Park and Museum	Dallas
Forney's Lake	Fremont
Fort Armstrong	Louisa, Scott
Fort Atkinson State Park	Winneshiek
Fort Benton, Montana Territory	Harrison
Fort Cherokee	Cherokee
Fort Clarke	Webster
Fort Correctionville	Woodbury
Fort Crawford	Clayton
Fort Defiance State Park	Emmet
Fort Des Moines No. 1	Lee, Palo Alto
Fort Des Moines No. 2	Palo Alto, Polk, Wapello
Fort Des Moines No. 3	Polk
Fort Dodge Historical Foundation, Inc.	Webster
Fort Dodge Historical Museum, Stockade and Fort	Webster
Fort Dodge (military post), Site of	Webster
Fort Donnellson (Tennessee)	Washington
Fort Gibson, Arkansas	Lee
Fort Leavenworth	Lee
Fort Madison	Lee, Polk
Fort Peterson	Clay
Fort Purdy, Site of	Crawford
Fort Sanford	Wapello
Fort Snelling	Winneshiek
Fort Sumter	Butler
Fort Sumter Rock	Butler
Fossil Crinoids	Marshall, Polk
Fossils	Cerro Gordo, Clayton, Johnson, Muscatine, Palo Also, Polk, Scott
Foster Woods	Washington
Foucault, Jean Leon	Polk
Foucault Pendulum	Polk
Fountain Spring Creek Park	Delaware
4-H Club	Page
4-H Historical Building	Wright
Fourth Street Elevator or Fenelon Place Inclined Railway	Dubuque
Frank A. Gotch State Park	Humboldt

NAME	COUNTY
Franklin County Historical Society	Franklin
Franklin Square	Polk
Frankville Historical Museum	Winneshiek
Freda Haffner Preserve (Arends' Kettlehole)	Dickinson
Frederic Knight Logan Home	Mahaska
Free Enquirers	Van Buren
Free Methodist Church	Palo Alto
Fremont County Historical Society	Fremont
Fremont, John Charles	Emmet
French, Daniel Chester	Pottawattamie
Fritz, Mathias	Jackson
Froelich, John	Clayton
F. W. Kent Park	Johnson
Gaertner, Johann	Winneshiek
Galland, Dr. Isaac	Lee
Galland School	Lee
Galland's Grove	Shelby
Garden Grove	Decatur
Gardner, Abigail (Abbe)	Dickinson
Gardner Log Cabin	Dickinson
Gardner, Rowland	Dickinson
Garfield, James A.	Webster
Garland, Hamlin	Mitchell
Garnavillo Historical Museum	Clayton
Garnavillo Historical Society	Clayton
Gass, Reverend Jacob	Louisa
Gehrke Wildlife Area	Hardin
General Curtis Home	Lee
General Dodge House	Pottawattamie
General John A. Logan	Delaware
General Joseph M. Street Grave	Wapello
General Sheridan	Polk, Pottawattamie
General Sherman	Polk, Pottawattamie
General William Tecumseh Sherman	Des Moines
General Winfield Scott	Scott
Geode State Park	Henry
George Davenport Home	Scott
George M. Verity Steamboat	Lee
Georgian Architecture	Pottawattamie
Georgetown Rest Area	Monroe
German Singing Society	Linn
Gettysburg Address	Washington
Gilbralter, Iowa	Lyon
Gifford Museum	Warren
Gitchie Manitou State Preserve	Lyon
Glacial Drift	Hardin, Johnson, Polk, Winnebago
Glacial Rock	Cherokee, Emmet, Floyd, Johnson, Linn, Osceola, Page, Pocahontas
Glenn Miller Home	Page
Gold Dome	Johnson, Polk
Gold Rush	Hardin
Golden Spike	Pottawattamie
Goldenrod School Museum	Page
Goodale Conservation Area	Chickasaw
Gotch, Frank A.	Humboldt
Governor's Mansion	Polk
Governor's Square	Polk
Grace Hill Cemetery	Washington
Grace Hill Moravian Church	Washington
Graham, Alberta Powell	Wapello
Grand Hotel	O'Brien
Grand River	Decatur, Union
Grandview Park	Polk
Granger, Barlow	Polk
Granger Homestead Project	Dallas
Grant City	Sac
Grant, Judge James	Scott
Grant Park	Sac
Grant, Ulysses S.	Jackson, Lee, Polk, Pottawattamie, Sac

NAME	COUNTY	NAME	COUNTY
Kettlehole	Dickinson	Lidtke Park and Mill	Howard
Kindlespire Park	Clay	Ligutti, Father L. G.	Dallas
King Park	Guthrie	Lilac Arboretum	Polk
Kingsley Historical Society	Plymouth	Lime Creek	Winnebago
Kinney Pioneer Museum	Cerro Gordo	Lime Creek Genealogical Society	Winnebago
Kirchner, J. A.	Clay	Limestone Mine	Van Buren
Kirkwood, James P.	Lyon	Lincoln, Abraham	Crawford, Harrison, Henry,
Kirkwood, Samuel J.	Jefferson, Johnson, Pottawattamie		Johnson, Lee, Polk, Pottawattamie, Scott,
Knapp, Seaman A.	Story		Van Buren, Washington
Kneeland, Abner	Van Buren	Lincoln Farm Marker	Crawford
Kneeland, Dolly	Van Buren	Lincoln Highway	Linn
Kopp Timber Tract		Lincoln Park	Fayette
(See Retz Memorial Forest)	Clayton	Lincoln Park and Monument	Pottawattamie
Kossuth Academy	Des Moines	Lincoln, Robert Todd	Crawford, Henry
Kossuth County Historical Society	Kossuth	Lincoln Statue	Cerro Gordo, Fayette, Greene
Kossuth County Historical Society Museum	Kossuth	Lincoln and Tad Statue	Polk
Kossuth, Iowa	Des Moines	Linn County Heritage Society	Linn
Kruger Mill	Lyon	Linn County Historical Museum Association	Linn
Ku Klux Klan	Jones	Linn County Historical Society	Linn
Kurio Kastle	Dickinson	Liska-Straneck Prairie	Webster
		Litchfield Company	Davis
Lacey, John Fletcher	Van Buren	Lithograph City (Devonia)	Floyd
Lacey-Keosauqua State Park	Van Buren	Litka Park	O'Brien
LaFollette, Senator Robert	Des Moines, Louisa	Little Bit O'Heaven, A	Scott
Lake Ahquabi State Park	Warren	Little Brown Church in the Vale	Chickasaw
Lake Cornelia	Wright	Little Cedar Creek Game Farm	Pocahontas
Lake Darling State Park	Washington	Little Clear Lake Park	Pocahontas
Lake Delhi	Delaware	Little Flock Chapel	Appanoose
Lake O'Delhi	Delaware	Little Maquoketa River	Dubuque
Lake of Three Fires State Park	Taylor	Little Ozarks of Iowa	Tama
Lake Ole Park	Webster	Little Red Schoolhouse	Wayne
Lake Pahoja Recreation Area	Lyon	Little Sioux Park	Woodbury
Lake View Historical Society	Sac	Little Sioux River	Cherokee, Clay, Dickinson,
Lakes Art Center	Dickinson		O'Brien, Plymouth, Woodbury
Langworthy, John	Clayton	Little Yellow Country Schoolhouse	Butler
Larrabee, William	Fayette, Howard	Littlefield Park	Audubon
Latter Day Saints	Fremont	Littlefield Wilderness	Audubon
Laura Ingalls Wilder Park	Winneshiek	Living History Farms	Polk
Laura Musser Art Gallery and Museum	Muscatine	Livingstone Cemetery	Delaware
Lea, Albert M.	Lee	Livingstone Home	Delaware
League of Women Voters	Floyd	Lizard Creek	Webster
LeClaire, Antoine	Scott	Lizard Lake Park	Pocahontas
LeClaire House	Scott	Loberg Cabin	Worth
LeClaire, Marguerite	Scott	Lock Tenders House	Davis, Wapello
Ledges State Park	Boone, Hamilton	Locust School	Winneshiek
Lee County Courthouse	Lee	Log Cabin Replica	Greene
Lee County Genealogical Society	Lee	Logan, Frederic Knight	Mahaska
Lee County Historic Center	Lee	Logan, General John A.	Delaware
Lee County Iowa Historical Society	Lee	Lone Rock	Kossuth
Lee, Captain Thomas J.	Allamakee	Lone Star (steamboat)	Scott
Lee de Forest Birthplace	Pottawattamie	Long Grove (Peterson)	Clay
Legel, John G., Jr.	Floyd	Long House	Poweshiek
Legel, John G., Sr.	Floyd	Long, Major Stephen H.	Pottawattamie
Lehigh, Iowa	Webster	Long Memorial Park	Hardin
Lenon Mills	Guthrie	Long's Landing	Pottawattamie
Lenox College	Delaware	Lookout Point	Pottawattamie
Leverson Cabin	Worth	Loomis Memorial Park	Franklin
Lewelling, Henderson	Henry	Lorenzo S. Coffin Farm (Willow Edge) and Burial Plot	Webster
Lewelling Quaker Shrine	Henry	Lost Grove	Webster
Lewis A. Jester County Park	Polk	Lott, Henry (John H.)	Humboldt, Webster
Lewis and Clark Expedition	Harrison, Monona	Lott, Milton	Webster
	Pottawattamie, Woodbury	Lott, Mrs. Jno. H.	Webster
Lewis and Clark Historical Association	Woodbury	Lotts Creek	Ringgold
Lewis and Clark Monument	Pottawattamie	Lotts Creek Park	Humboldt
Lewis and Clark State Park	Monona	Louisa County Historical Society	Louisa
Lewis and Clark Trail	Woodbury	Louisiana Purchase	Clayton, Monona, Woodbury
Lewis, John Llewellyn	Lucas	Love Log Cabin	Delaware
Lewis, Meriwether	Monona	Lover's Leap Park	Clayton
Lewis Town and Country Boosters	Cass	Lovilia Coal Mine No. 4	Monroe
Lewis Wildlife and Timber Preserve	Linn	Lowell Mills	Henry
Liberty Bell Replica	Polk	Lower Pine Lake	Hardin

NAME	COUNTY	NAME	COUNTY
Palo Marsh Wildlife Refuge	Linn	Plank Road	Des Moines
Pammel, Louis H.	Madison, Story	Plow in Oak Park	Audubon
Pammel State Park	Madison	Plum Creek	Delaware
Panama Canal	Page, Poweshiek	Plum Creek Park	Delaware
Pangburn (Gabriel) Cabin	Worth	Plum Grove	Johnson
Paradise	Jackson	Plymouth County Historical Museum	Plymouth
Parker Historical Society of		Plymouth County Historical Society	Plymouth
Clay County	Clay	Plymouth Rock Replica	Pottawattamie
Parkersburg Historical Society	Butler	Pocahontas County Historical Society	Pocahontas
Parkinson Musical Collection	Plymouth	Point Ann	Clayton
Parr, Charles H.	Floyd	Poisel Mounds	Des Moines
Parr, Elliott	Cedar	Polk County Historical Society	Polk
Parvin, Theodore S.	Linn	Polk, James Knox	Polk
Pashepaho (The Stabber)	Van Buren	Pony Creek Indian Site	Mills
Pearson, Franklin	Van Buren	Pony Creek Park	Mills
Pearson House	Van Buren	Popejoy Park	Franklin
Pearson Memorial Center	Jackson	Porter, Adelbert Field (Bert)	Winneshiek
Peary, Admiral Robert E.	Johnson	Porter House Museum	Winneshiek
Peddie, Alexander	Palo Alto	Pottawattamie County, Historical Society of	Pottawattamie
Pei, I. M.	Polk	Pottawattamie County Rotary Jail	Pottawattamie
Peirce, John	Woodbury	Pottawattamie Indians	Pottawattamie
Peirce Mansion	Woodbury	Potter, Captain Elbridge Gerry	Jackson
Pella Historical Site	Marion	Potter Mill (Dyas Mill)	Jackson
Pella Historical Society	Marion	Prairie Creek	Webster
Pembina Carts	Jones	Prairie Du Chien, Wisconsin	Clayton, Dubuque
P. E. O.	Henry	Pratt, W. H.	Louisa
Perkins, Charles Elliott	Des Moines	Preparation Canyon State Park	Monona
Perkins Park	Des Moines	President Abraham Lincoln	Crawford, Harrison
Perry, Bishop William Stevens	Cedar		Henry, Johnson, Lee, Polk, Pottawattamie, Washington
Peterson, Ole Peter	Winneshiek	President Benjamin Harrison	Muscatine
Petosa	Dubuque	President Grover Cleveland	Woodbury
Phebe W. Sudlow Marker	Scott	President Herbert Clark Hoover	Cedar
Phelps House	Des Moines	President James A. Garfield	Johnson
Phil Stong Birthplace	Van Buren	President James Buchanan	Worth
Phillips, William	Greene	President James Knox Polk	Polk
Phipps Site	Cherokee	President James Madison	Lee
Picture Rock	Clayton	President Martin Van Buren	Johnson
Pictured Rocks	Jones	President Theodore Roosevelt	Page, Pottawattamie
Pike, Zebulon M.	Clayton, Des Moines	President Thomas Jefferson	Monona
Pikes Hill	Clayton	President Ulysses S. Grant	Polk, Pottawattamie, Sac
Pikes Mountain	Clayton	President William McKinley	Pottawattamie, Webster
Pikes Peak	Clayton, Des Moines, Polk	Preston Niles Pioneer Village and Museum	Harrison
Pikes Peak State Park	Clayton	Prine School	Mahaska
Pikes Timber	Wright	Promontory Point	Pottawattamie
Pillsbury Point	Dickinson	Pushetonequa, Charles	Marshall
Pillsbury, Reverend Samuel	Dickinson	Putnam Museum	Scott
Pilot Creek Park	Pocahontas	Pyramid Coral (Goniophyllum)	Jones
Pilot Knob State Park	Hancock, Winnebago		
Pilot Rock	Butler, Cherokee	Quad City Area Archeological Society	Scott
Pin Oak Park	Delaware	Quaker Meeting House	Cedar
Pine Creek	Hardin, Muscatine	Quakers	Cedar, Henry, Johnson, Linn, Madison
Pine Creek Mill	Muscatine	Quartzite, Sioux	Lyon
Pine Lake State Park	Hardin	Queen, The	Dickinson
Pinicon Ridge Park	Linn	Quick, Herbert	Grundy, Hardin
Pinky's Glen	Fremont	Quorn	Plymouth
Pioneer Association of Lyon County	Lyon		
Pioneer Crafts	Mahaska, Polk	Raccoon Creek	Jackson
Pioneer Drug Store Museum	Kossuth	Raccoon River	Greene, Lee, Polk, Sac
Pioneer Hall	Polk	Rague, John Francis	Dubuque, Johnson
Pioneer Historical Society	Van Buren	Railroad Park	Polk
Pioneer Monument	Polk	Rainbow Point	Pottawattamie
Pioneer Museum	Webster	Rand Park and Chief Keokuk Monument	Lee
Pioneer Museum and Historical Society of		Rat Row	Lee
Northern Iowa	Cerro Gordo	Rathbun Lake	Appanoose
Pioneer Park	Page, Polk	Red River Carts	Jones
Pioneer Rock Church	Clayton	Red River of the North	Jones
Pioneer Separate Baptists	Keokuk	Red Rock	Marion
Piquenard, Alfred H.	Madison, Polk	Red Rock Dam	Marion
Pitts, Dr. William S.	Chickasaw	Red Rock Lake	Marion, Polk
Pittsburg, Iowa	Van Buren	Red Schoolhouse	Delaware, Marion, Wayne
Planetarium	Black Hawk, Cherokee, Polk, Winneshiek	Redhead Park	Polk

309

NAME	COUNTY	NAME	COUNTY
Sioux County Historical Society	Sioux	Steamboat Bertrand	Harrison
Sioux Indians	Webster	Steamboat Gothic	Van Buren
Sioux Quartzite	Lyon, Osceola	Steamboat Rock-Tower Rock- Fallen	
Sir Walter Scott	Ringgold	Rock Park	Hardin
Sites of Sioux City Corn Palaces	Woodbury	Stempel Bird Collection	Pottawattamie
Sitting Bull	Lyon	Stempel, Dr. Guido	Pottawattamie
Skillet Creek	Webster	Stephens State Forest	Lucas, Monroe
Skunk River	Des Moines, Henry, Jasper, Polk, Story, Washington	Stephens, T. C.	Lucas
Skunk River War	Keokuk, Washington	Stewart, Joseph Buffon	Polk
Slip Bluff Park	Decatur	Stiles School House Museum	Cherokee
Sloan Historical Society	Woodbury	Stime Timber	Worth
Smallpox Epidemic	Cedar	Stinson Prairie	Kossuth
Smallest Cathedral in the World	Winneshiek	Stone Barn	Black Hawk
Smith, Joseph, Jr.	Clarke	Stone City, Iowa	Jones
Smithland Forest Preserve	Woodbury	Stone City Quarry	Jones
Smithland Historical Society	Woodbury	Stone Mill (Painter-Bernatz Mill)	Winneshiek
Smithtown Church	Clinton	Stone School	Allamakee, Clayton
Snake Alley	Des Moines	Stone State Park	Woodbury
Snyder Bend Park	Woodbury	Stone, Thomas Jefferson	Woodbury
Soap Creek Cable Bridge	Wapello	Stong, Phil	Polk, Van Buren
Sockum Ridge Park	Washington	Story County Chapter, Iowa Genealogical Society	Story
Sod House	Polk	Story County Historical Society	Story
Solar Eclipse Marker	Des Moines	Straight, Halver R.	Polk
Soldiers and Sailors Monument	Polk	Straight Mineral Collection	Polk
Soldiers Creek	Webster	"Straw College"	Washington
Soper, T. K.	Story	Street, General Joseph M.	Davis, Wapello
Soper's Mill Area	Story	Stutsman's Mill	Pottawattamie
Sorghum Mill	Hamilton	Sudlow, Phebe (Phoebe) W.	Scott
South Central Chapter,		Sugar Bush	Winneshiek
Iowa Archeological Society	Ringgold	Sullivan Brothers	Black Hawk
South Raccoon River	Guthrie	Sullivan Park	Black Hawk
South Skunk River	Keokuk	Summit Cemetery	Scott
Southeast Chapter,		Summit Presbyterian Church	Scott
Iowa Archeological Society	Wapello	Sunday, Billy	Des Moines, Montgomery, Story
Southern Iowa Fair	Des Moines	Sunday, William Ashley (Billy)	Des Moines, Story
Sower, George	Marshall	Sunnyside Park	Cass
Sower, Susie	Marshall	Susie Sower Historical House	Marshall
Spaulding Methodist Church	Union	Swan Lake (Ghost Town)	Emmet
Spielman (Spillman), Joseph	Winneshiek	Swede Bend Church	Webster
Spillville Mill	Winneshiek	Swensrud Cabin	Worth
Spirit Lake	Dickinson	Swinging Bridge	Louisa
Spirit Lake Massacre	Clay, Dickinson, Hamilton, Humboldt, Kossuth, Webster	Swiss Valley Park	Dubuque
Spirit Lake Massacre Monument	Dickinson	Taber, Captain Benjamin P.	Lee
Spirit Lake Massacre Relief Expedition	Webster	Table Rock	Clayton
Spirit Lake State Fish Hatchery	Dickinson	Tabor City Park	Fremont
Split Rock Park	Chickasaw	Tabor College	Fremont
Spook Cave	Clayton	Tabor Historical Society	Fremont
Spring Branch Creamery Site	Delaware	Taft, Lorado	Webster
Spring Creek	Franklin	Talbot, Hector	Woodbury
Springbrook State Park	Guthrie	Tahiti	Jasper
Springfield, Illinois	Crawford	Tally War	Keokuk, Washington
Sprouse House	Lee	Talmadge Hill Park	Union
Sprouse, William	Lee	Tama Beach	Des Moines
Spruce Creek Chapel	Jackson	Tama County Courthouse	Tama
Squirrel Hollow Park	Greene	Tama County Historical Society	Tama
Staceyville	Monroe	Tama Indian Settlement	Tama
Stagecoach Trail	Delaware, Des Moines, Greene, Hamilton, Humboldt, Mills, Monroe, Polk, Shelby	Tama Town Prairie	Des Moines
Stainbrook, Merrill A.	Johnson	Taylor County Genealogical Society	Taylor
Stained Glass Windows	Van Buren, Woodbury	Taylor, Zachary	Scott
Standing Rock	Linn	Teachers Conservation Camp	Guthrie
Standpipe Hill	Jasper	Telephone Museum	Greene
Stanton, Elizabeth Cady	Floyd	Terrace Hill	Polk, Pottawattamie
Starr's Cave Park	Des Moines	Territorial Legislature	Des Moines, Johnson, Mahaska, Van Buren
Starrucca Viaduct (Pennsylvania)	Lyon	Territorial Road	Van Buren
State Boundary Marker	Allamakee, Taylor	Tesson, Louis Honore'	Lee
State Fair	Polk	Tetes des Morts (St. Donatus)	Jackson
State Historical Building	Boone, Polk	The Apple Trees	Des Moines
State Historical Society of Iowa	Johnson	The Diggings	Webster
State Line House	Van Buren	The Lily (magazine)	Pottawattamie
State Rock	Henry	The Market Place	Dubuque
Statue of Liberty Replica	Polk	The Nature Conservancy, Iowa Chapter	Clayton,

NAME	COUNTY
. . . . . .Dickinson, Henry, Johnson, Linn, Story, Warren, Webster	
The Police Gazette . . . . Linn	
The Sullivans . . . . Black Hawk	
Theophile Bruguier Log Cabin . . . . Woodbury	
Thietje, Walter . . . . Johnson	
Thomas Hart Benton, Jr. House . . . . Pottawattamie	
Thomas Mitchell Park . . . . Polk	
Thompson, Charles B. . . . . Monona	
Thorne, George . . . . .Clinton	
Three Bridges Park . . . . Marshall	
Thunder Woman Park . . . . Black Hawk	
Tilley, Edward . . . . .Pocahontas	
Timberland Museum . . . . Hancock	
Timmons Grove County Park . . . . Marshall	
Timothy Brown Memorial . . . . .Washington	
Tipton Union School . . . . .Cedar	
Tlapa, Professor Joseph . . . . Linn	
Todd House . . . . Fremont	
Todd, Reverend John . . . . Fremont	
Tom Fretty Museum . . . . Worth	
Toolesboro Indian Mounds . . . . Louisa	
Toronto, Iowa . . . . .Clinton	
Totem Acres Zoo . . . . Greene	
Tower Grove . . . . Linn	
Toy Museum . . . . Harrison	
Traer Winding Stairs . . . . .Tama	
Trailside Historical Park . . . . Decatur	
Trappist Monastery (New Melleray Abbey) . . . . .Dubuque	
Trayer, Robert . . . . Clayton	
Tree Claims . . . . .Osceola	
Tree Shakers Genealogical Society . . . . Polk	
Trout Haven . . . . Delaware	
Trout Run Mill . . . . .Winneshiek	
Tulip Time Festival . . . . Marion	
Turkey Creek . . . . .Guthrie	
Turkey River . . . . Clayton, Fayette, Winneshiek	
Turkey River Mounds . . . . Clayton	
Turkey River Park . . . . Clayton	
Turn of the Century Museum . . . . .Guthrie	
Turtle Creek Bay .Delaware	
Turtle Creek Recreation Area . . . . .Delaware	
Turvold Woods . . . . Worth	
Tuttle, Calvin . . . . Emmet	
Tuttle Creek . . . . Delaware	
Tuttle Lake . . . . Emmet	
Twain, Mark . . . . Lee	
Twin Bridges Park . . . . .Delaware	
Twin Ponds . . . . Chickasaw	
Uncle McIntosh . . . . Shelby	
Underground Railroad . . . . Cass, Cedar, Fremont,	
. . . . Henry, Mills, Poweshiek, Van Buren	
Union County Historical Society . . . . Union	
Union Pacific Railroad . . . . Pottawattamie	
Union Slough National Wildlife Refuge . . . . Kossuth	
United Mine Workers of America . . . . .Lucas	
United States Fur Factory . . . . .Des Moines	
Universalist Church . . . . Polk	
University of Northern Iowa . . . . Black Hawk	
University of Northern Iowa Museum . . . . . . Black Hawk	
Upper Iowa River . . . . .Winneshiek	
Upper Pine Lake . . . . Hardin	
Van Buren County Courthouse . . . . Van Buren	
Van Buren County Historical Society . . . . Van Buren	
Van Buren, Martin . . . . Johnson	
Vanderbilt, Cornelius . . . . Woodbury	
Van Spankeren Store . . . . Marion	
Vegors Cemetery . . . . Webster	
Ventura Marsh . . . . Cerro Gordo	
Vernon (South Bentonsport) . . . . Van Buren	
Vernon School . . . . Van Buren	
Vesterheim . . . . .Winneshiek	

NAME	COUNTY
Victorian Architecture . . . . Black Hawk, Des Moines,	
. . . . Dubuque, Fayette, Linn, Monroe, Polk,	
. . . . Pottawattamie, Poweshiek, Winneshiek	
Victorian House Museum . . . . .Des Moines	
Victory Park . . . . Lee	
Viking Lake State Park . . . . Montgomery	
Viking Mooring Stone . . . . .Pocahontas	
Vincent Home . . . . Webster	
Vincent, Webb . . . . Webster	
Volga River . . . . Clayton, Fayette	
Volga White Pine Forest Preserve . . . . Clayton	
Wagaman Mill (Lynnville Mill) . . . . Jasper	
Wahkonsa Elementary School . . . . Webster	
Wahl Museum . . . . .Washington	
Wakema Park . . . . Linn	
Wakpicada Area . . . . Linn	
Wallace, Henry .Winnebago	
Wallace, Henry A. or Henry Agard . . . . Adair,	
. . . . Story, Warren	
Walnut Creek . . . . Page	
Walnut Grove Park . . . . .Clinton	
Walnut Grove Village . . . . Scott	
Walnut Heritage House Museum . . . . Pottawattamie	
Walnut Hill Cemetery . . . . Pottawattamie	
Walnut Hill Farm . . . . Polk	
Walnut School .Washington	
Walnut Woods State Park . . . . Polk	
Wapello County Genealogical Society . . . . Wapello	
Wapello County Courthouse . . . . Wapello	
Wapello County Historical Museum . . . . Wapello	
Wapello County Historical Society . . . . Wapello	
Wapsi River Access . . . . Chickasaw	
Wapsie Mill . . . . Buchanan	
Wapsinonoc Creek . . . . .Cedar	
Wapsipinicon River . . . . Chickasaw, Clinton,	
. . . . .Jones, Linn	
Wapsipinicon State Park . . . . .Jones, Linn	
War Eagle Park . . . . Woodbury	
War of 1812 . . . . Lee, Scott, Washington, Webster	
Ware, Frederick .Des Moines	
Warren County Genealogical Society . . . . Warren	
Warren County Historical Society . . . . Warren	
Washington County Historical Society . . . . .Washington	
Washington County Hospital . . . . .Washington	
Washington, General George . . . . Des Moines, Washington	
Washington Prairie Norwegian	
Methodist Church . . . . .Winneshiek	
Wassonville Mill Site . . . . .Washington	
Waterfowl Migration . . . . Cerro Gordo, Fremont,	
. . . . Harrison, Linn, Marion,Pocahontas	
Water Works Park . . . . Polk	
Waterman Creek .O'Brien	
Watershed Divide Marker . . . . Adair, Guthrie	
Watertown, New York . . . . Jackson	
Waubeek, Iowa . . . . Linn	
Waubonsie State Park . . . . Fremont	
Waverly House . . . . .Bremer	
Wayne County Historical Museum . . . . Wayne	
Wayne County Historical Society . . . . Wayne	
Wayne, John . . . . Madison	
Weatherby Rural Schoolhouse	
(Taylor Township No. 4) . . . . Marshall	
Webster, Clement L. . . . . Floyd	
Webster County Historical Society . . . . Webster	
W. C. T. U. . . . . Webster	
Weed Park . . . . Muscatine	
Weldon River . . . . Decatur	
Werksplatt (carpenter shop) . . . . Marion	
West Bend Grotto . . . . .Palo Alto	
West Branch Heritage Foundation . . . . .Cedar	
West Des Moines Historical Society . . . . Polk	
West Fork Des Moines River . . . . Humboldt